Introduction to Maple

André Heck

Introduction to Maple

With 84 Illustrations

Springer-Verlag
New York Berlin Heidelberg London Paris
Tokyo Hong Kong Barcelona Budapest

André Heck
Expertise Center
  Computer Algebra Nederland (CAN)
Kruislaan 419
1098 VA Amsterdam
The Netherlands

Cover photograph courtesy of UNIPHOTO, Inc.

Maple is a registered trademark of Waterloo Maple Software.

Library of Congress Cataloging-in-Publication Data
Heck, A. (André)
    Introduction to Maple / André Heck
      p.   cm.
    Includes bibliographical references and index.
    ISBN 0-387-97662-0 (New York : acid-free). -- ISBN 3-540-97662-0
(Berlin : acid-free)
      1. Maple (Computer file) 2. Algebra --- Data processing. I. Title.
    QA155.7.E4H43 1993
    510´.285´53--dc20   93-8631

Printed on acid-free paper.

Production managed by Bill Imbornoni; manufacturing supervised by Vincent Scelta.
Photocomposed copy prepared from the author's TeX files.
Printed and bound by Hamilton Printing Co., Castleton, NY.
Printed in the United States of America.

9 8 7 6 5 4 3 2

ISBN 0-387-97662-0 Springer-Verlag New York Berlin Heidelberg
ISBN 3-540-97662-0 Springer-Verlag Berlin Heidelberg New York

Preface

In symbolic computation on computers, also known as computer algebra, keyboard and display replace the traditional pencil and paper in doing mathematical computations. Interactive computer programs, which are called computer algebra systems, allow their users to compute not only with numbers, but also with symbols, formulae, equations, and so on. Many mathematical computations such as differentiation, integration, and series expansion of functions, and inversion of matrices with symbolic entries, can be carried out quickly, with emphasis on exactness of results, and without much human effort.

Computer algebra systems are powerful tools for mathematicians, physicists, chemists, engineers, technicians, psychologists, sociologists,..., in short, for anybody who needs to do mathematical computations. Computer algebra systems are indispensable in modern pure and applied scientific research and education.

This book is a gentle introduction to one of the modern computer algebra systems, viz., Maple. Primary emphasis is on learning what can be done with Maple and how it can be used to solve (applied) mathematical problems. To this end, the book contains many examples and exercises, both elementary and more sophisticated. They stimulate you to use Maple and encourage you to find your way through the system. An advice: read this book in conjunction with the Maple system, try the examples, make variations of them, and try to solve the exercises.

In this book, emphasis is on understanding the basic principles and ideas of Maple so that you can use it effectively to solve your mathematical problems. Factual knowledge or information about every built-in Maple facility can be obtained from the on-line help system or from the Maple documentation that comes along with the software. This book does not teach mathematics; it is understood that you know the theory behind the examples. By chosing a variety of problems and showing how Maple can be used to solve them, you should get an idea of the capabilities of the system.

In this book, the usage of Maple as a programming language is not discussed at a higher level than that of defining simple procedures and using simple language constructs. However, the Maple data structures are discussed in great detail because good understanding of them is necessary for manipulating and simplifying expressions effectively. This also forms a good starting point to acquaint you further with Maple as a programming language.

About the Maple Version Used

It is assumed that you use Maple V Release 2; it is available on many computer platforms, ranging from mainframes and workstations to desktop computers such as Macintosh, NeXT, Amiga, IBM PC, and compatibles. Most of the book should be system independent.

About the Production of the Book

This book was produced with Maple V Release 2 on a Silicon Graphics Indigo Server. The Maple version was customized by Waterloo Maple Software to allow the capture in PostScript format of Maple output of separate commands. These PostScript results were embedded while typesetting the manuscript with TeX. In this way, "true Maple sessions" interleaved with comments, remarks, and explanations were produced. Therefore, you can be sure that you can reproduce the results on your terminal screen or on paper. Maple I/O has been typeset in Courier font so that you can easily distinguish it from other text fragments. Maple procedures have been typeset in bold face characters to distinguish them from ordinary words. The book was prepared in camera-ready format on the phototypesetter at CWI at a resolution of 1200 dots per inch.

About the Origin of the Book

In 1987 the author started to develop introductory Maple courses at the University of Nijmegen. Several revisions and updates of course material have appeared since then. The most important of these was the 1990 course book "Introductie in het gebruik van Maple", which was joint work of Ernic Kamerich from the University of Nijmegen and the author. In this course book, the existing material was restructured, updated, extended, and many parts were rewritten. The present book is based on the 1990 course book, but the appearance of Maple V Release 2 has made many alterations and extensions in the text inevitable. Furthermore, many examples of practical usage of Maple have been included. Nevertheless, Ernic Kamerich's collaboration should be regarded as one of the most important steps towards readability and usability of this book.

Acknowledgments

Many people have contributed to this book. First of all, I would like to thank my friends and colleagues of the Symbolic Computation Group at the University of Waterloo and of Waterloo Maple Software for their support, encouragement, and willingness to answer my questions throughout the past few years. I would like to thank Rüdiger Gebauer from Springer Verlag for his interest in this book and his patience with me. I am greatly indebted to Darren Redfern and Bruce Barber for their careful and thorough reading of the book, and for improving my English and my style of writing. Michael Monagan's comments, suggestions, and criticism were invaluable. I would like to thank Ron Sommeling for the many discussions we had about Maple and the course material. Nancy Blachman and Bert Ruitenburg commented on an earlier draft of book. Jan Schipper's help in getting the manuscript in camera-ready format is acknowledged. Marc van Leeuwen's advice on using TeX was indispensable. And last, but not least, I wish to thank my colleagues of the CAN Foundation and at the CAN Expertise Center, notably Arjeh Cohen, Jan Sanders, and Leendert van Gastel, for reminding me of the fact that books must be published and for handling CAN affairs while I was working on the book.

Despite all the help I got, I am sure that users of this book will come up with remarks, suggestions, corrections, etc. Please send them to

CAN Expertise Center
Attn. André Heck
Kruislaan 419
1098 VA Amsterdam
The Netherlands

or to the electronic mail address

heck@can.nl

Contents

1

Introduction to
Computer Algebra

The goal of this chapter is to briefly describe what computer algebra is about, present a little history of computer algebra systems, give some examples of computer algebra usage, and discuss some advantages and limitations of this new technological tool. We end with a sketch of the design of the Maple system.

The examples in this first chapter are sometimes of a rather advanced mathematical level. Starting with the second chapter, we give a detailed, step-by-step exposition of Maple as a symbolic calculator. The rest of the book does not depend much on this chapter. Thus, anyone who is so eager to learn Maple that he or she cannot wait any longer may skip this chapter and turn to it at any moment.

1.1 What is Computer Algebra?

Historically the verb "compute" has mostly been used in the sense of "computing with numbers." Numerical computation is not only involved with basic arithmetic operations such as addition and multiplication of numbers, but also with more sophisticated calculations like computing numerical values of mathematical functions, finding roots of polynomials, and computing numerical eigenvalues of matrices. It is essential in this type of computation that arithmetic operations are carried out on numbers and on numbers only. Furthermore, numeric computations are not in most cases not exact because in applications one is almost always dealing with floating-point numbers. Simple computations can be done with pencil and paper or with a pocket calculator; for large numerical computations, mainframes serve as "number crunchers." In the last fifty years numerical computation on computers flourished to such an extent that for many scientists mathematical computation on computers and numerical computation have become synonymous.

But mathematical computation has another important component, which we shall call *symbolic and algebraic computation*. In short, it can be defined as computation with symbols representing mathematical objects. These symbols may represent numbers like integers, rational numbers, real and complex numbers, and algebraic numbers, but they may also be used for mathematical objects like polynomials and rational functions, systems of equations, and even more abstractly for algebraic structures like groups, rings, and algebras, and elements thereof. Moreover, the adjective *symbolic* emphasizes that in many cases the ultimate goal of mathematical problem solving is expressing the answer in a closed formula or finding a symbolic approximation. By *algebraic* we mean that computations are carried out exactly, according to the rules of algebra, instead of using the approximate floating-point arithmetic. Examples of symbolic and algebraic computations are factorization of polynomials, differentiation, integration, and series expansion of functions, analytic solution of differential equations, exact solution of systems of equations, and simplification of mathematical expressions.

In the last twenty-five years great progress has been made regarding the theoretical background of symbolic and algebraic algorithms; moreover, tools have been developed to carry out mathematical computations on computers [15, 33, 56]. This has lead to a new discipline, which is referred to by various names: symbolic and algebraic computation, symbolic computation, symbolic manipulation, formula manipulation, and computer algebra, to name a few. Tools for mathematical computation on a computer are given as many names as the discipline itself: symbolic computation programs, symbol crunchers, symbolic manipulation programs, and computer algebra systems. Unfortunately, the term "symbolic computation" is used in many different contexts, like logic programming and artificial intelligence in its broadest sense, which have very little to do with mathematical computation. To avoid misunderstanding, we shall henceforth adopt the term *computer algebra* and we shall speak of *computer algebra systems.*

1.2 Computer Algebra Systems

In this section we shall give a very short, incomplete, and subjective overview of present-day computer algebra systems. They can be conveniently divided into two categories: *special purpose systems* and *general purpose systems.*

Special purpose systems are designed to solve problems in one specific branch of physics and mathematics. Some of the best-known special purpose systems used in physics are SCHOONSCHIP ([114] high-energy physics), CAMAL ([5] celestial mechanics), and SHEEP and STENSOR ([45, 71] general relativity). Examples of special purpose systems in the mathematical arena are Cayley and GAP ([20, 22, 106] group theory), PARI ([7] number theory), CoCoA ([54, 55] commutative algebra), Macaulay

([110] algebraic geometry), DELiA ([8] analysis of differential equations), and LiE([31] Lie theory). Our interest will be in the general purpose system Maple [24, 25], but the importance of special purpose systems should not be underestimated: they have played a crucial role in many scientific areas [15, 21, 73]. Often they are more handsome and efficient than general purpose systems because of their use of special notations and data structures, and because of their implementation of algorithms in a low-level programming language.

General purpose systems please their users with a great variety of data structures and mathematical functions, trying to cover as many different application areas as possible (q.v.,[66]). The oldest general purpose computer algebra systems still in use are MACSYMA [88] and REDUCE [68]. Both systems were born in the late sixties and were implemented in the programming language LISP, but this is practically all they have in common. MACSYMA is a powerful computer algebra system with a wide range of auxiliary packages, but because of its dependency on non-standard LISP and heavy demands on computer resources, MACSYMA can only be used on a small number of computers. The recent release of a PC version of MACSYMA may cause a revival of this system. REDUCE began as a special purpose program for use in high-energy physics, but gradually transformed into a general purpose system. Compared to MACSYMA the number of user-ready facilities in REDUCE is modest, but on the other hand it is a very open system (the complete source code is distributed!) making it easily extensible and modifiable. REDUCE is still under active development: REDUCE 3.4.1 was released in July 1992. It runs on a very wide range of computers and is well-documented.

In the eighties, MuMATH [123] and its successor DERIVE [112] were the first examples of compact non-programmable symbolic calculators, designed for use on PC-type computers. DERIVE has a friendly menu-driven interface with graphical and numerical features. Considering its compactness and the limitations of PC machines and hand-held calculators, DERIVE offers an amazing amount of user-ready facilities. Version 2.5 of September 1992 also has limited programming facilities.

Most modern computer algebra systems are implemented in the programming language C. This language allows developers to write efficient, portable computer programs, which really exploit the platforms for which they are designed. Many of these computer algebra systems work on a variety of computers, from supercomputers down to desktop computers.

In §1.6 we shall sketch the design of Maple [24, 25]. Another notable modern general purpose system is *Mathematica* [122]. *Mathematica* is the first system in which symbolics, numerics, and graphics are incorporated in such a way that it can serve as a user-friendly environment for doing mathematics. There exists on certain machines (such as Macintosh,

NeXT, PC running MS-Windows) the notebook interface, which is a tool to create a structured text in which ordinary text is interwoven with formulas, programs, computations, and graphics. Another feature of *Mathematica* is the well-structured user-level programming language. With the publicity and marketing strategy which went into the production of *Mathematica*, commerce has definitely made its entry into the field of computer algebra, accompanied by less realistic claims about capabilities (q.v., [113]). On the positive side, the attention of many scientists has now been drawn to computer algebra and to the use of computer algebra tools in research and education. Another advantage has been the growing interest of developers of computer algebra systems in friendly user interfaces, good documentation, and ample user support.

The aforementioned general purpose systems manipulate formulae if the entire formula can be stored inside the main memory of the computer. This is the only limit to the size of formulae. The symbolic manipulation program FORM [119] has been designed to deal with formulae of virtually infinite size. On the other hand, the size of the set of instructions in FORM is somewhat limited.

Last (but not least) in the row is Scratchpad [38, 39, 74, 115]. It is a powerful general purpose system developed in the eighties at the IBM Thomas J. Watson Research Laboratory. In contrast to other general purpose systems, which only allow calculations in a specific algebraic domain, e.g., the field of rational numbers or the ring of polynomials over the integers, Scratchpad II allows its users to define and handle distinct types of algebraic structures. It was released in 1992 under the name of AXIOM on IBM RS/6000 machines. In 1993 AXIOM will be released on other Unix platforms as well.

1.3 Some Properties of Computer Algebra Systems

Computer algebra systems differ from one another, but they share many properties. We shall illustrate common properties with examples from Maple.

Computer algebra systems are *interactive* programs that, in contrast to numerical computer programs, allow mathematical computations with *symbolic* expressions. Typically, the user enters a mathematical expression or an instruction, which the computer algebra system subsequently tries to execute. Given the result of the computation the user may enter a new instruction. This may lead to a fruitful computer algebra session. As an easy example of the use of Maple, we shall compute the stationary point of the real function

$$x \mapsto \arctan\left(\frac{2x^2 - 1}{2x^2 + 1}\right),$$

as well as the value of the function at this point. As we shall see later on in this section, Maple can compute the minimum on its own. Here, we only use the example to show some of the characteristics of computer algebra systems. What follows is screen dump of a complete work session with Maple V Release 2, on a Unix-type computer running the worksheet interface.

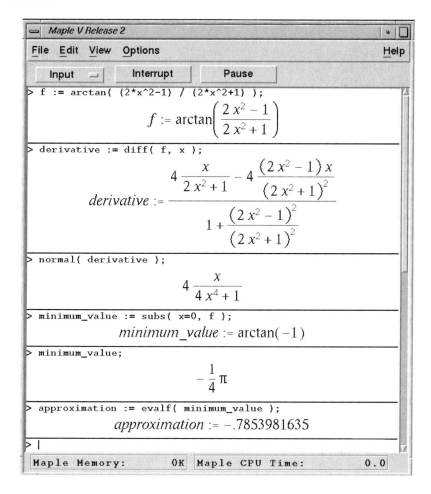

Let us take a closer look at this example. When Maple is started under the X Window System with **xmaple**, an empty worksheet appears, except that the system prints the greater-than symbol ">" on the first line in order to prompt the user to enter an instruction. The symbol ">" is called the *Maple prompt*. In the first command we enter the formula f, ending the input line with a semicolon, and pressing the Return key. The last two key strokes signal Maple to start to work. In this case, the formula is shown in two-dimensional mathematical notation of textbook quality.

What strikes one most is that the system allows the use of symbols like x. In most numerical programming languages this would immediately cause an error; but not in systems for *symbolic* computations!

Each time Maple has executed an instruction, it prints a horizontal line to separate pairs of input/output lines (this is optional), it prints the prompt and waits for another command. We decide to consider f as a function, **differ**entiate it, and assign the result to the variable called *derivative*. Maple's answer is a rather complicated expression. So, we **normal**ize the rational function. The answer is a simple expression, from which we can immediately see that the original function has a minimum at $x = 0$. The minimum value $-\frac{1}{4}\pi$ is obtained by **subst**itution of $x = 0$ in f. We obtain an approximate floating-point result by use of the command **evalf**. The name **evalf** — short for "**eval**uate using **f**loating-point arithmetic" — is already the fourth example that shows Maple's general philosophy in chosing names: Use a short, easy-to-remember name for a procedure which describes its functionality. In addition to this, we have given meaningful names to variables, which describe their use.

We see that Maple leaves it to us to find our way through the computation. *We* must decide, on the basis of the second result, to try and find a less complicated formula for the derivative. One may wonder why the system itself does not perform this more or less obvious simplification. But remember, it is not always clear when and how to simplify. In many cases more than one simplification is possible and it is the mathematical context that actually determines which simplification is appropriate. For example, the rational expression

$$\frac{(x^2 - 1)(x^2 - x + 1)(x^2 + x + 1)}{(x - 1)^6}$$

can be transformed into the compact expression

$$\frac{x^6 - 1}{(x - 1)^6},$$

but also into a form suitable for integration, viz.,

$$1 + \frac{6}{(x - 1)^5} + \frac{15}{(x - 1)^4} + \frac{20}{(x - 1)^3} + \frac{15}{(x - 1)^2} + \frac{6}{x - 1}.$$

Another problem with automatic simplification is that in many computations one cannot predict the size and shape of the results and therefore must be able to intervene at any time. A procedure which works fine in one case might be a bad choice in another case. For example, one might think that it is always a good idea to factorize an expression. For example, the factorization of

$$x^8 + 8x^7 + 28x^6 + 56x^5 + 70x^4 + 56x^3 + 28x^2 + 8x + 1$$

is
$$(x+1)^8.$$

However (surprise!) apart from being expensive, the factorization of the relatively simple
$$x^{26} + x^{13} + 1$$

yields
$$(x^{24} - x^{23} + x^{21} - x^{20} + x^{18} - x^{17} + x^{15} - x^{14} + x^{12} - x^{10} + x^9 - x^7 + x^6 - x^4 + x^3 - x + 1)(x^2 + x + 1).$$

For these reasons, Maple only applies automatic simplification rules when there is no doubt about which expression is simpler: $x + 0$ should be simplified to x, $3x$ is simpler than $x + x + x$, x^3 is better than $x * x * x$, and $\sin(\pi)$ should be simplified to 0. Any other simplification is left to the user's control; Maple only provides the tools for such jobs.

Automatic simplification sometimes introduces loss of mathematical correctness. For example, the automatic simplification of $0 * f(1)$ to 0 is not always correct. An exception is the case $f(1)$ is undefined or infinity. The automatic simplification is only wanted if $f(1)$ is finite but difficult to compute. In cases like this, designers of computer algebra systems have to choose between rigorous mathematical correctness and usability/efficiency of their systems (q.v. [42]). In Maple and many other systems the scales sometimes tip to simplifications which are not 100% safe in every case.

Another remarkable fact in the first example is that Maple computes the exact value $-\frac{1}{4}\pi$ for the function in the origin and does not return an approximate value like 0.785398. This is a second aspect of computer algebra systems: the emphasis on *exact arithmetic*. In addition, computer algebra systems can carry out floating-point arithmetic in a *user-defined precision*. For example, in Maple the square $\tan^2(\pi/12)$ can be computed exactly, but the numerical approximation in 25-digits floating-point notation can also be obtained.

```
> real_number := tan(Pi/12)^2;
```
$$real\_number := \left(2 - \sqrt{3}\right)^2$$

```
> real_number := expand( real_number );
```
$$real\_number := 7 - 4\sqrt{3}$$

```
> approximation := evalf( real_number, 25 );
```
$$approximation := .07179676972449082589 0216$$

Computer algebra systems like Maple contain a substantial amount of built-in mathematical knowledge. This makes them good mathematical assistants. In calculus they differentiate functions, compute limits, and compute series expansions. Integration (both definite and indefinite), is one of the highlights in computer calculus. Maple uses non-classical algorithms such as the Risch algorithm for integrating elementary functions [53], instead of the heuristic integration methods which are described in most mathematics textbooks.

With the available calculus tools, one can easily explore mathematical functions. In the following worksheet we explore the previously defined function f. The *sharp symbol* # followed by text is one of Maple's ways of allowing comments during a session; in combination with the names of variables and Maple procedures, this should explain the script sufficiently. If an input line is ended by a colon instead of a semicolon, then Maple does not print its results. Spaces in input commands are optional, but at several places we have inserted them to make the input more readable.

```
> # enter the formula
> f := arctan( (2*x^2-1) / (2*x^2+1) );
```

$$f := \arctan\left(\frac{2\ x^2\ -\ 1}{2\ x^2\ +\ 1} \right)$$

```
> # integrate f
> integrate( f, x );
```

$$x \arctan\left(\frac{2\ x^2\ -\ 1}{2\ x^2\ +\ 1} \right) - \frac{1}{4} \ln(\ 2\ x^2\ -\ 2\ x\ +\ 1\ )$$

$$- \frac{1}{2} \arctan(\ 2\ x\ -\ 1\ ) + \frac{1}{4} \ln(\ 2\ x^2\ +\ 2\ x\ +\ 1\ )$$

$$- \frac{1}{2} \arctan(\ 2\ x\ +\ 1\ )$$

```
> # check the answer
> normal( diff(",x) );
```

$$\arctan\left(\frac{2\ x^2\ -\ 1}{2\ x^2\ +\ 1} \right)$$

```
> # here, the " is used to refer to the previous result
> # load the library function `extrema`
> readlib( extrema ):
```

```
> # let Maple compute the extrema
> extrema( f, {}, x, stationary_points );
```

$$\left\{ -\frac{1}{4}\,\pi \right\}$$

```
> stationary_points;
```

$$\{ \{ x = 0 \} \}$$

```
> # this value was assigned by the call of `extrema´
> # compute the zero´s of f
> solve( f=0, x );
```

$$\frac{1}{2}\sqrt{2}\,,\ -\frac{1}{2}\sqrt{2}$$

```
> # compute the Taylor series approximation of f
> series( f, x=0, 15 );
```

$$-\frac{1}{4}\,\pi + 2\,x^2 - \frac{8}{3}\,x^6 + \frac{32}{5}\,x^{10} - \frac{128}{7}\,x^{14} + O(\,x^{15}\,)$$

```
> # load package for numerical approximation of functions
> with( numapprox ):
> pade( f, x, [6,4] );
```

$$\frac{1}{12}\,\frac{-15\,\pi + 120\,x^2 - 36\,\pi\,x^4 + 128\,x^6}{5 + 12\,x^4}$$

```
> # compute the Chebyshev-Pade approximation of f
> chebpade( f, x, [2,2] );
```

$$(\,-.007904471007\ T(\,0,\ 1.000000000\ x\,)$$
$$+\ .4715125862\ T(\,2,\ 1.000000000\ x\,)\,)\big/(\,$$
$$T(\,0,\ 1.000000000\ x\,)$$
$$+\ .4089934686\ T(\,2,\ 1.000000000\ x\,)\,)$$

```
> # compute limit of f when x goes to infinity
> limit( f, x=infinity );
```

$$\frac{1}{4}\,\pi$$

```
> # compute the asymptotic form of f
> asympt ( f, x );
```

$$\frac{1}{4}\,\pi\;-\;\frac{1}{2}\,\frac{1}{x^2}\;+\;O\!\left(\frac{1}{x^6}\right)$$

```
> # finally, draw the graph of f
> plot ( f, x=-4..4, -1..1, title=`graph of f` );
```

graph of f

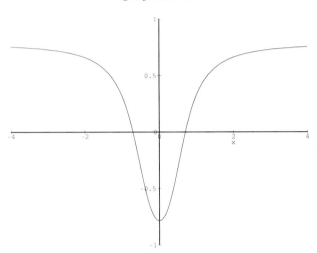

Other impressive areas of computer algebra are polynomial calculus, the solution of systems of linear and nonlinear equations, the solution of recurrence equations and differential equations, calculations on matrices with numerical and symbolic coefficients, and tensor calculus. Various tools for manipulation of formulae are present: selection and substitution of parts of expressions, restricted simplification, simplification rules, pattern matching, and so on. We may call computer algebra systems *mathematical expert systems* with which mathematical problems can be solved in a more productive and accurate way than with pencil and paper.

In addition to functioning as symbolic and algebraic calculators, most computer algebra systems can be used as *programming languages* for implementing new mathematical algorithms. By way of illustration we write a Maple program which computes the Bessel polynomials $y_n(x)$. Recall [65] that they can be recursively defined by

$$y_0(x) = 1,$$
$$y_1(x) = x + 1,$$
$$y_n(x) = (2n - 1)\,x\,y_{n-1}(x) + y_{n-2}(x), \quad \text{for } n > 1.$$

```
> Y := proc( n:nonnegint, x:name )
>    if n=0 then 1
>    elif n = 1 then x+1
>    else Y(n,x) := expand( (2*n-1)*x*Y(n-1,x) + Y(n-2,x) )
>    fi
> end:
> Y(5,z);
```

$$945 \ z^5 + 945 \ z^4 + 420 \ z^3 + 105 \ z^2 + 15 \ z + 1$$

The Maple programming language is reminiscent of Algol68 without declarations, but also includes several functional programming paradigms.

1.4 Advantages of Computer Algebra

The long-term goal of computer algebra is to automate as much as possible the mathematical problem solving process. Although present computer algebra systems are far from being automatic problem solvers, they are already useful, if not indispensable, tools in research and education. Of course, it takes time to familiarize oneself with a computer algebra system, but this time is well-spent. In this section, some of the more important reasons for learning and using a computer algebra system will be illustrated with Maple examples, a few of which are rather advanced mathematically. All computations will be carried out with Maple V Release 2, on a Silicon Graphics Indigo Server running Irix 4.0.5F, with a 50 MHz IP20 processor of MIPS R4000 type, and having 64 MB main memory plus 200 MB swap space. This does not imply that the same results could not have been obtained on a much smaller machine, but the timings would be different.

The main advantage of a computer algebra system is its ability to carry out large algebraic computations. Although many calculations are straightforward standard manipulations which can be calculated with pencil and paper, the larger the formulae, the harder the work and the less the chance of success. For this kind of computation a computer algebra system is an excellent tool. The next three examples demonstrate this.

The first example is one of the problems posed by R. Pavelle [100] as a challenge for computer algebra systems. The object is to prove that

$$\frac{\sin \left(\dfrac{nz\sqrt{x^2 + y^2 + z^2}}{\sqrt{y^2 + z^2}} \right)}{\sqrt{x^2 + y^2 + z^2}}$$

is a solution of the fourth order partial differential equation

$$\left(\frac{\partial^2}{\partial x^2} \left(\frac{\partial^2}{\partial x^2} + \frac{\partial^2}{\partial y^2} + \frac{\partial^2}{\partial z^2} \right) + n^2 \left(\frac{\partial^2}{\partial x^2} + \frac{\partial^2}{\partial y^2} \right) \right) f = 0.$$

The simplification procedures of Maple are powerful enough to solve this problem in a few seconds.

```
> settime := time():    # start timing
> f := sin( n*z*sqrt(x^2+y^2+z^2) / sqrt(y^2+z^2) ) /
>    sqrt(x^2+y^2+z^2);
```

$$f := \frac{\sin\left(\dfrac{n\, z\, \sqrt{x^2 + y^2 + z^2}}{\sqrt{y^2 + z^2}} \right)}{\sqrt{x^2 + y^2 + z^2}}$$

```
> simplify( diff( diff(f,x$2) + diff(f,y$2) + diff(f,z$2),
>    x$2 ) + n^2 * ( diff(f,x$2) + diff(f,y$2) ) );
```

$$0$$

```
> cpu_time = (time()-settime) * seconds; # computing time
```

$$cpu\_time = 3.667\ seconds$$

In the second example, the objective is find the generating function for dimensions of representations of the Lie group of type G_2 (q.v. [29, 30]). So, the attempt is made to find a rational function $F(x, y)$ such that

$$F(x, y) = \sum_{k, l \geq 0} G2(k, l) x^k y^l,$$

where $G2(k, l)$ is the following polynomial expression.

```
> G2 := (k,l) -> 1/5! * (k+1) * (l+1) * (k+l+2) *
>    (k+2*l+3) * (k+3*l+4) * (2*k+3*l+5);
```

$$G2 := (k,\ l) \to \frac{1}{120}\ (k + 1)\ (l + 1)\ (k + l + 2)$$

$$(k + 2\ l + 3)\ (k + 3\ l + 4)\ (2\ k + 3\ l + 5)$$

Here, we have used Maple's arrow notation for functional operators. In this way $G2$ is a function with values defined in terms of its arguments instead of just a formula. Maple has a procedure **ztrans** for computing z-transforms. Recall that the z-transform of an infinite sequence f_n with respect to z is defined as $\sum_{n \geq 0} f_n z^{-n}$. We use this to solve our problem.

```
> readlib( ztrans ):    # load library function
> settime := time():    # start timing
> ztransform := ztrans( ztrans( G2(k,l), k, x), l, y ):
> gen_fun := sort( normal(
>    subs( { x=1/x, y=1/y }, ztransform ) ) );
```

$$gen\_fun := (x^4 \ y^4 + 8 \ x^4 \ y^3 + x^3 \ y^4 + 8 \ x^4 \ y^2 - 26 \ x^3 \ y^3$$

$$+ \ x^4 \ y - 41 \ x^3 \ y^2 + 15 \ x^2 \ y^3 - 6 \ x^3 \ y + 78 \ x^2 \ y^2$$

$$- \ 6 \ x \ y^3 + 15 \ x^2 \ y - 41 \ x \ y^2 + y^3 - 26 \ x \ y + 8 \ y^2$$

$$+ \ x + 8 \ y + 1)\Big/\!\Big((x - 1)^6 \ (y - 1)^6 \Big)$$

```
> cpu_time = (time()-settime) * seconds; # computing time
```

$$cpu\_time = 3.384 \ seconds$$

An example taken from scientific life where Maple could have played the role of mathematical assistant can be found in [124]. In this paper the Laplace-Beltrami operator Δ in hyperspherical coordinates is wanted. To this end, the Jacobian of the coordinate mapping, the metric tensor, and its inverse are calculated. Following are quotations from the paper:

"It is not difficult to compute $\frac{\partial \mathbf{Y}}{\partial q_i}$, and it is not difficult, but tedious, to compute the traces in Eq.(32B). After quite some algebra we find, ..."

"It is also tedious to invert $\mathbf{g}$. After several pages of computation of minors we find, ..."

These remarks are indeed true when one carries out these calculations with pencil and paper; but not if one lets Maple carry out the computations! Below is the Maple calculation, as much as possible in the notation of [124]. Don't worry if you do not fully understand individual commands: details will be provided later in this book.

The first step in the computation is to define the coordinate mapping Y and to build the metric tensor G. This turns out to be the most time-consuming step in the computation.

```
> settime := time():    # start timing
> with( linalg ): # load linear algebra package
Warning: new definition for    norm
Warning: new definition for    trace
```

```
> R[z] := x -> matrix( 3, 3, [ cos(x), -sin(x), 0,
>                               sin(x),  cos(x), 0,
>                                    0,       0, 1 ] ):
> ´R[z](phi)´ = R[z](phi);
```

$$R_{[z]}(\phi) = \begin{bmatrix} \cos(\phi) & -\sin(\phi) & 0 \\ \sin(\phi) & \cos(\phi) & 0 \\ 0 & 0 & 1 \end{bmatrix}$$

```
> R[y] := x -> matrix( 3, 3, [ cos(x), 0, -sin(x),
>                                   0, 1,      0,
>                              sin(x), 0,  cos(x) ] ):
> ´R[y](phi)´ = R[y](phi);
```

$$R_{[y]}(\phi) = \begin{bmatrix} \cos(\phi) & 0 & -\sin(\phi) \\ 0 & 1 & 0 \\ \sin(\phi) & 0 & \cos(\phi) \end{bmatrix}$$

```
> T := x -> matrix( 3, 3, [ cos(x) + sin(x), 0, 0,
>                           0, cos(x) - sin(x), 0,
>                           0,              0, 0 ] ):
> ´T(phi)´ = T(phi);
```

$$T(\phi) = \begin{bmatrix} \cos(\phi) + \sin(\phi) , & 0 , & 0 \\ 0 , & \cos(\phi) - \sin(\phi) , & 0 \\ 0 , & 0 , & 0 \end{bmatrix}$$

```
> # define macros for greek characters
> macro( a=alpha, b=beta, c=gamma, f=phi, t=theta ):
> # coordinate mapping Y is a product of matrices
> Y := evalm( r/sqrt(2) * R[z](a) &* R[y](b) &* R[z](c/2)
>    &* T(t/2) &* R[z](f/2) ):
> # compute the metric tensor G
> Y1 := map( diff, Y, r ):  Y2 := map( diff, Y, a ):
> Y3 := map( diff, Y, b ):  Y4 := map( diff, Y, c ):
> Y5 := map( diff, Y, t ):  Y6 := map( diff, Y, f ):
> # build the metric tensor
> G := array( symmetric, 1..6, 1..6 ):
```

```
> for i to 6 do for j from i to 6 do

>   G[i,j] := simplify( trace( transpose(Y.i) &* Y.j ) ) )

> od od:

> intermediate_cpu_time = (time() - settime) * seconds;
```

$$cpu\_time = 50.517 \; seconds$$

Now, we apply some simplification procedures to obtain the formulae in [124]. To shorten the output of the session, we continue to suppress most results. We also show a slightly polished session, admittedly not the first interactive session when the problem was solved.

```
> G := subs( cos(t/2)^2 = 1/2 + 1/2*cos(t),

>   cos(c/2)^2 = 1/2 + 1/2*cos(c), sin(t/2) = sin(t) /

>   ( 2*cos(t/2) ), sin(c/2) = sin(c) / ( 2*cos(c/2) ),

>   eval(G)):

> G := map( normal, G ): # normalize each matrix entry

> G[2,2] := normal( subs( -1/2 * r^2 * cos(c) * sin(t) =

>   -1/2 * r^2 * (cos(b)^2 + sin(b)^2) * cos(c) * sin(t),

>   G[2,2] ) ):

> G := map( factor, G );   # this the formula in the paper!
```

$$G :=$$

$$[\, 1 \; , \; 0 \; , \; 0 \; , \; 0 \; , \; 0 \; , \; 0 \,]$$

$$\left[\, 0 \; , \right.$$

$$\frac{1}{2} \, r^2 \left(\cos(\beta)^2 + 1 - \sin(\theta) \cos(\gamma) \sin(\beta)^2 \right) ,$$

$$\frac{1}{2} \, r^2 \, \sin(\gamma) \, \sin(\beta) \, \sin(\theta) \; , \; \frac{1}{2} \, r^2 \, \cos(\beta) \; , \; 0$$

$$\left. , \; \frac{1}{2} \, r^2 \, \cos(\beta) \, \cos(\theta) \,\right]$$

$$\left[\, 0 \; , \; \frac{1}{2} \, r^2 \, \sin(\gamma) \, \sin(\beta) \, \sin(\theta) \; , \right.$$

$$\left. \frac{1}{2} \, r^2 \, (1 + \sin(\theta) \cos(\gamma)) \; , \; 0 \; , \; 0 \; , \; 0 \,\right]$$

$$\left[0 \ , \ \frac{1}{2} \ r^2 \ \cos(\ \beta\ ) \ , \ 0 \ , \ \frac{1}{4} \ r^2 \ , \ 0 \ , \ \frac{1}{4} \ r^2 \ \cos(\ \theta\ ) \right]$$

$$\left[0 \ , \ 0 \ , \ 0 \ , \ 0 \ , \ \frac{1}{4} \ r^2 \ , \ 0 \right]$$

$$\left[0 \ , \ \frac{1}{2} \ r^2 \ \cos(\ \beta\ ) \ \cos(\ \theta\ ) \ , \ 0 \ , \ \frac{1}{4} \ r^2 \ \cos(\ \theta\ ) \ , \ 0 \right.$$

$$\left. , \ \frac{1}{4} \ r^2 \right]$$

Due to the screen width and the length of expressions Maple was not able to produce a nice layout, but it can translate the formulae automatically into a format suitable for text processing programs like LaTeX [84].

```
> latex( eval( G ), `metric_tensor` ):
```

The LaTeX code is not shown, but the result after typesetting is

$$\begin{bmatrix} 1 & 0 & 0 & 0 & 0 & 0 \\ 0 & \frac{r^2(\cos(\beta)^2+1-\sin(\theta)\cos(\gamma)\sin(\beta)^2)}{2} & \frac{r^2\sin(\gamma)\sin(\beta)\sin(\theta)}{2} & \frac{r^2\cos(\beta)}{2} & 0 & \frac{r^2\cos(\beta)\cos(\theta)}{2} \\ 0 & \frac{r^2\sin(\gamma)\sin(\beta)\sin(\theta)}{2} & \frac{r^2(1+\sin(\theta)\cos(\gamma))}{2} & 0 & 0 & 0 \\ 0 & \frac{r^2\cos(\beta)}{2} & 0 & \frac{r^2}{4} & 0 & \frac{r^2\cos(\theta)}{4} \\ 0 & 0 & 0 & 0 & \frac{r^2}{4} & 0 \\ 0 & \frac{r^2\cos(\beta)\cos(\theta)}{2} & 0 & \frac{r^2\cos(\theta)}{4} & 0 & \frac{r^2}{4} \end{bmatrix}$$

Let us compute the Jacobian.

```
> determinant := simplify( det( G ) ):
> determinant := normal( subs( cos(b)^2 = 1 - sin(b)^2,
>    cos(t)^4 = cos(t)^2 * (1 - sin(t)^2), determinant) ):
> Jacobian :=   subs( cos(t) = sin(2*t) / (2*sin(t)),
>    sqrt( determinant ) );
```

$$Jacobian \ := \ \frac{1}{32} \ r^5 \ \sin(\ 2\ \theta\ ) \ \sin(\ \beta\ )$$

This is formula (33) in the paper. Now we compute the inverse of the metric tensor.

```
> GINV := map( simplify, inverse( G ) ):
> GINV := subs( cos(t)^2 = 1 - sin(t)^2,
>    cos(b)^2 = 1 - sin(b)^2, eval( GINV ) ):
```

```
> cpu_time = (time()-settime) * seconds; # computing time
```

$$cpu\_time = 55.983 \ seconds$$

We do not show the inverse metric tensor, but all entries except GINV[4,4] are in the shape of formula (34) in the paper. Casting GINV[4,4] into good shape is not difficult; we skip this last part of the computation. Anyway, the calculation can easily be done in less than one minute computing time and paper-ready formulae are obtained too!

Another example from science where computer algebra enables the researcher to finish off a proof of a mathematical result which requires a lot of straightforward but tedious computations can be found in [32]. There, a purely algebraic problem, related to proving the existence of a certain finite subgroup of a Lie group, could be reduced to the problem of solving a set of linear equations in 240 variables with coefficients from the field of 1831 elements. This system of linear equations was easily shown to have a unique solution by computer. By hand this is almost impossible, but by computer this is quite feasible.

In the last two worked-out examples we have used Maple to determine a generating function and a metric tensor and its inverse, respectively. Now, one may not think much of mathematical results obtained by a computer program, but remember that there are many independent ways to check the answers. One may even use Maple itself to check the answers or to enlarge one's confidence in the results: e.g., one can compute the first terms of the Taylor series and compare them with the original coefficients, and one can multiply the metric tensor and its inverse as an extra check on the answers.

Symbolic and algebraic computation often precedes numerical computation. Mathematical formulae are first manipulated to cast them into good shape for final numerical computation. For this reason, it is important that a computer algebra system provides a good interface between these two types of computation. Maple can generate FORTRAN and C expressions from Maple expressions. Double precision arithmetic and code optimization are optional. For example, the metric tensor G in the previous example can be converted into FORTRAN as shown below.

```
> precision := double:
> fortran( G, 'optimized' );
        t1 = r**2
        t4 = dsin(beta)
        t5 = dsin(theta)
        t9 = t5*dcos(0.5772156649015329D0)
        t12 = dcos(beta)
        t13 = t12**2
        t14 = t4**2
        t18 = dcos(theta)
        t20 = t1*t12
```

```
G(1,3)  = 0
G(1,5)  = 0
G(1,2)  = 0
G(1,4)  = 0
G(4,5)  = 0
G(2,3)  = t1*dsin(0.5772156649015329D0)*t4*t5/2
G(6,6)  = t1/4
G(4,4)  = t1/4
G(5,6)  = 0
G(3,3)  = t1*(1+t9)/2
G(5,5)  = t1/4
G(1,6)  = 0
G(2,5)  = 0
G(2,2)  = t1*(t13+1-t9*t14)/2
G(3,5)  = 0
G(4,6)  = t1*t18/4
G(3,6)  = 0
G(2,4)  = t20/2
G(1,1)  = 1
G(3,4)  = 0
G(2,6)  = t20*t18/2
```

The answers obtained with a computer algebra system are either exact or in a user-defined precision. They can be more accurate than hand calculations [80]; and can lead to many correction to integral tables. Below, we give the example of an integral incorrectly tabulated in one of the most popular tables [60] as

$$\int \frac{1}{x\sqrt{(bx+cx^2)^3}}\,dx = \frac{2}{3}\left(-\frac{1}{bx} + \frac{4c}{3b^2} - \frac{8c^2x}{3b^3}\right)\frac{1}{\sqrt{bx+cx^2}},$$

whereas Maple gives the correct answer which can be verified too!

```
> normal(
>     integrate( 1 / (x * sqrt(( b*x + c*x^2 )^3)), x ) );
```

$$\frac{2}{3}\frac{-b^2 + 8\ c^2\ x^2 + 4\ c\ x\ b}{b^3\ x\ \sqrt{b\ x + c\ x^2}}$$

```
> normal( diff(",x) );    # check the result
```

$$\frac{1}{x\ (b\ x + c\ x^2)^{3/2}}$$

In many cases of integration, conditions on parameters are important. Below is an example of exact arithmetic in the computation of the definite integral

$$\int_0^\infty \frac{t^{1/3}\ln(at)}{(b+2t^2)^2}\,dx, \quad a,b > 0.$$

```
> # assume that a and b are positive numbers
> assume( a>0 );   assume( b>0 );
```

```
> normal( integrate( t^(1/3) * ln(a*t) / (b + 2*t^2)^2,
>    t = 0..infinity ) );
```

$$-\frac{1}{36}\,\pi\,2^{1/3}\left(-2\,\ln(a\~)\,\sqrt{3}\,-\,\pi\,+\,3\,\sqrt{3}\,+\,\sqrt{3}\,\ln(2)\right.$$

$$\left.-\,\sqrt{3}\,\ln(b\~)\,\right)\Big/b\~^{4/3}$$

The tildes after a and b in the above result indicate that these variables have certain assumed properties. Maple can inform its user about these properties.

```
> about( a );
Originally a, renamed a~:
  is assumed to be: RealRange( Open(0), infinity )
```

Integration is also a good illustration of another advantage of computer algebra: it provides easy access to advanced mathematical techniques and algorithms. When input in Maple, the following two integrals

$$\int x^2 \exp(x^3)\,dx \quad\text{and}\quad \int x \exp(x^3)\,dx$$

give different kinds of response:

$$\frac{1}{3}\exp(x^3) \quad\text{and}\quad \int x \exp(x^3)\,dx.$$

This means more than just the system's incompetence to deal with the latter integral. Maple can decide, via the Risch algorithm [53], that for this integral no closed form in terms of elementary functions exists. This contrasts with the heuristic methods usually applied when one tries to find an answer in closed form. In the heuristic approach one is never sure whether indeed no closed form exists or that it is just one's mathematical incompetence. The Risch algorithm however is a complicated algorithm, which is based on rather deep mathematical results and algorithms and which involves many steps that cannot be done so easily by pencil and paper. Computer algebra enables its user to apply such advanced mathematical results and methods without knowing all details.

Using a computer algebra system, one can concentrate on the analysis of a mathematical problem, leaving the computational details to the computer. Computer algebra systems also invite one to do "mathematical experiments". They make it easy to test mathematical conjectures and to propose new ones on the basis of calculations. As an example of such a mathematical experiment, we shall conjecture a formula for the determinant of the $n \times n$ matrix A_n defined by

$$A_n(i,j) := x^{\gcd(i,j)}.$$

The first thing to do is to compute a few determinants, and look and see.

```
> numex := 7:    # number of experiments
> dets := array( 1..numex ):
> for n to numex do
>    A[n] := array( 1..n, 1..n, symmetric ):
>    for i to n do
>      for j to i do
>        A[n][i,j] := x^igcd(i,j)
>    od od:
>    dets[n] := factor( linalg[det]( A[n] ) ):
>    print( dets[n] )
> od:
```

$$x$$

$$x^2 (x - 1)$$

$$x^3 (x + 1) (x - 1)^2$$

$$x^5 (x + 1)^2 (x - 1)^3$$

$$x^6 (x^2 + 1) (x + 1)^3 (x - 1)^4$$

$$x^7 (x^2 + 1) (x^3 + x - 1) (x + 1)^4 (x - 1)^5$$

$$x^8 (x^2 + 1) (x^2 - x + 1) (x^2 + x + 1) (x^3 + x - 1)$$
$$(x + 1)^5 (x - 1)^6$$

At first sight, it has not been a success. But, look at the quotients of successive determinants.

```
> for i from 2 to numex do
>    quo( dets[i], dets[i-1], x )
> od;
```

$$x^2 - x$$

$$x^2 (x - 1)$$

$$x^3 (x + 1) (x - 1)^2$$

$$x^5 (x + 1)^2 (x - 1)^3$$

$$x^6 \ (\ x^2 \ + \ 1 \ ) \ (\ x \ + \ 1 \ )^3 \ (\ x \ - \ 1 \ )^4$$

$$x^7 \ (\ x^2 \ + \ 1 \ ) \ (\ x^3 \ + \ x \ - \ 1 \ ) \ (\ x \ + \ 1 \ )^4 \ (\ x \ - \ 1 \ )^5$$

In the nth polynomial only powers of x appear that have divisors of n as exponents. Thinking of Möbius like formulae and playing a little more with Maple, the following conjecture comes readily to mind:

Conjecture. $\det A_n = \displaystyle\prod_{j=1}^{n} \phi_j(x)$, where the polynomials $\phi_j(x)$ are

defined by $x^n = \displaystyle\sum_{d|n} \phi_d(x)$.

Some Properties.

(i) If p is a prime number, then

$$\phi_p(x) = x^p - x,$$

and for any natural number r,

$$\phi_{p^r}(x) = \phi_p(x^{p^{r-1}}).$$

(ii) If p is a prime number, not dividing n, then

$$\phi_{pn}(x) = \phi_n(x^p) - \phi_n(x).$$

(iii) Let $n = p_1^{r_1} \ldots p_s^{r_s}$ be a natural number with its prime factorization, then

$$\phi_n(x) = \phi_{p_1 \ldots p_s}(x^{p_1^{r_1-1} \ldots p_s^{r_s-1}}).$$

(iv) We have

$$\phi_n(x) = \sum_{d|n} \mu\left(\frac{n}{d}\right) x^d = \sum_{d|n} \mu(d) x^{\left(\frac{n}{d}\right)},$$

where μ is the Möbius function such that $\mu(1) = 1$, $\mu(p_1 \ldots p_s) = (-1)^s$ if $p_1, \ldots, p_s$ are distinct primes, and $\mu(m) = 0$ if m is divisible by the square of some prime number.

For the interested reader: $\frac{1}{d}\phi_d(q)$ is equal to the number of monic irreducible polynomials of degree d in one variable and with coefficients in a finite field with q elements [90].

However much mathematical knowledge has been included in a computer algebra system, it is still important that an experienced user can enhance the system by writing procedures for personal interest. The author implemented in Maple several algorithms for inversion of polynomial mappings according to the methods developed in [41]. With these programs it is possible to determine whether a polynomial mapping has an inverse which is itself a polynomial mapping, and if so, to compute the inverse. We show an example of an invertible mapping in three unknowns.

```
> read `invpol.m`; # load user-defined package
> P := [ x^4 + 2*(y+z)*x^3 + (y+z)^2*x^2 + (y+1)*x
>    + y^2 + y*z, x^3 + (y+z)*x^2 + y, x + y + z ];
```

$$P := \left[x^4 + 2 \ (y + z) \ x^3 + (y + z)^2 \ x^2 + (y + 1) \ x \right.$$

$$\left. + y^2 + y \ z, \ x^3 + (y + z) \ x^2 + y, \ x + y + z \right]$$

```
> settime := time(): # start timing
> invpol( P, [x,y,z] ); # compute inverse mapping
```

$$[x - y \ z, \ y - x^2 \ z + 2 \ z^2 \ y \ x - z^3 \ y^2,$$

$$-x - y + z + y \ z + x^2 \ z - 2 \ z^2 \ y \ x + z^3 \ y^2]$$

```
> cpu_time = (time()-settime) * seconds; # computing time
```

$$cpu\_time = 1.650 \ seconds$$

Computing the inverse of a polynomial mapping with pencil and paper is almost impossible; one needs a computer algebra system for the symbol crunching. However, one cannot expect designers of computer algebra systems to anticipate all of the needs of their users. One can expect good programming facilities to implement new algorithms oneself.

1.5 Limitations of Computer Algebra

What has been said about computer algebra systems so far may have given the impression that these systems offer unlimited opportunities, and that they are a universal remedy for solving mathematical problems. But this impression is too rosy. A few warnings beforehand are not out of place.

Computer algebra systems often make great demands on computers because of their tendency to use up much memory space and computing time. The price one pays for exact arithmetic is often the exponential increase in size of expressions and the appearance of huge numbers. This may even happen in cases where the final answer is simply "yes" or "no". For example, it is well-known that Euclid's algorithm yields the greatest common divisor (gcd) of two polynomials. However, this "naive" algorithm does not perform very well. Look at the polynomials

```
> f[1] := 7*x^7 + 2*x^6 - 3*x^5 - 3*x^3 + x + 5;
```

$$f_{[1]} := 7 \ x^7 + 2 \ x^6 - 3 \ x^5 - 3 \ x^3 + x + 5$$

```
> f[2] := 9*x^5 - 3*x^4 - 4*x^2 + 7*x + 7;
```

$$f_{[2]} := 9\ x^5\ -\ 3\ x^4\ -\ 4\ x^2\ +\ 7\ x\ +\ 7$$

We want to compute the $\gcd(f_1, f_2)$ over the rational number by Euclid's algorithm. In the first division step we construct polynomials q_2 and f_3, such that $f_1 = q_2 f_2 + f_3$, where $\mathrm{degree}(f_3) < \mathrm{degree}(f_2)$ or $f_3 = 0$. This is done by long division.

```
> f[3] := sort( rem( f[1], f[2], x, q[2] ) );
```

$$f_{[3]} := \frac{70}{27}\ x^4\ -\ \frac{176}{27}\ x^3\ -\ \frac{770}{81}\ x^2\ -\ \frac{94}{81}\ x\ +\ \frac{503}{81}$$

```
> q[2];
```

$$\frac{7}{9}\ x^2\ +\ \frac{13}{27}\ x\ -\ \frac{14}{81}$$

Next, polynomial q_3 and f_4 are computed such that $f_2 = q_3 f_3 + f_4$, where $\mathrm{degree}(f_4) < \mathrm{degree}(f_3)$ or $f_3 = 0$, etc. until $f_n = 0$; then $\gcd(f_1, f_2) = f_{n-1}$. The following Maple program computes the polynomial remainder sequence.

```
> Euclid_gcd := proc( f:polynom, g:polynom, x:name )
>    local r:
>    if g = 0 then  sort( f )
>    else
>       r := sort( rem( f, g, x ) );
>       if r <> 0 then print( r ) fi;
>          Euclid_gcd( g, r, x )
>    fi
> end:
> Euclid_gcd( f[1], f[2], x ):
```

$$\frac{70}{27}\ x^4\ -\ \frac{176}{27}\ x^3\ -\ \frac{770}{81}\ x^2\ -\ \frac{94}{81}\ x\ +\ \frac{503}{81}$$

$$\frac{100881}{1225}\ x^3\ +\ 72\ x^2\ -\ \frac{14139}{2450}\ x\ -\ \frac{98037}{2450}$$

$$-\ \frac{16726864175}{10176976161}\ x^2\ -\ \frac{5255280625}{10176976161}\ x\ +\ \frac{19754564375}{10176976161}$$

$$\frac{35171085032244648729}{456796710414528050}\ x\ +\ \frac{6605604895087335357}{456796710414528050}$$

$$\frac{2406814310427212456610119901925}{121549387831506345564025862481}$$

The conclusion is that the polynomials f_1 and f_2 are relatively prime, because their greatest common divisor is a unit. But look at the tremendous growth in the size of the coefficients from 1-digit integers to rational numbers with thirty digits (even though the rational coefficients are always simplified). In [53, 81] one can read about more sophisticated algorithms for gcd computations, which avoid blowup of coefficients as much as possible.

The phenomenon of tremendous growth of expressions in intermediate calculations turns up frequently in computer algebra calculations and is known as *intermediate expression swell*. Although it is usually difficult to estimate the computer time and memory space required for a computation, one should always do one's very best to optimize calculations, both by using good mathematical models and by efficient programming. It is worth the effort. For example, Maple computes the inverse of the 5×5 matrix with (i, j)-entry equal to $(iu + x + y + z)^j$ in 70 seconds requiring 1350 Kbytes of memory space on a Silicon Graphics Indigo Server. The obvious substitution $x + y + z \rightarrow v$ reduces the computer time to 3 seconds and the memory requirements to 575 Kbytes.

A second problem in using a computer algebra system is psychological: how many lines of computer output can one grasp? And when one is faced with large expressions, how can one get enough insight to simplify them? For example, it would be difficult to recover the polynomial composition

$$f(x, y) = g\big(u(x, y),\ v(x, y)\big),$$

where

$$g(u, v) = u^3 v + uv^2 + uv + 5,$$
$$u(x, y) = x^3 y + xy^2 + x^2 + y + 1,$$
$$v(x, y) = y^3 + x^2 y + x,$$

from its expanded form.

While it is true that one can do numerical computations with a computer algebra system in any precision one likes, there is also a negative side of this feature. Because one uses software floating-point arithmetic instead of hardware arithmetic, numerical computation with a computer algebra system is 100 to 1000 times slower than numerical computation in a programming language like FORTRAN. Hence, for numerical problems, one must always ask oneself "Is exact arithmetic with rational numbers or high-precision floating-point arithmetic really needed, or is a numerical programming language preferable?"

In an enthusiastic mood we characterized computer algebra systems as mathematical expert systems. How impressive the amount of built-in mathematical knowledge may be, it is only a small fraction of mathematics known today. There are many mathematical areas where computer algebra is not of much help yet, and where more research is required: partial differential equations, indefinite and definite integration involving non-elementary functions like Bessel functions, contour integration, surface integration, calculus of special functions, and non-commutative algebra are just a few examples.

Another serious problem and perhaps the trickiest, is the wish to specify at an abstract level the number domain in which one wants to calculate. For example, there are an infinite number of fields, and one may want to write algorithms in a computer algebra system using the arithmetic operations of a field, without the need to say what particular field you work with. Moreover, one may want to define one's own mathematical structures. Scratchpad II/AXIOM [38, 39, 74, 115] is the first computer algebra system making steps in this direction. In Maple V Release 2, the package Gauss allows its user to create domains in a similar way that AXIOM allows.

As far as the syntax and the semantics are concerned, the use of a computer algebra system as a programming language is more complicated than programming in a numerical language like FORTRAN. In a computer algebra system one is faced with many built-in functions which may lead to unexpected results. One must have an idea of how the system works, how data are represented, how to keep data of manageable size, and so on. Efficiency of algorithms, both with respect to computing time and memory space, requires a thorough analysis of mathematical problems and a careful implementation of algorithms. For example, if we had forgotten to expand intermediate results in the procedure for calculating Bessel polynomials as defined in §1.3, it would have resulted in unnecessarily large expressions. The rather unsuccessful implementation of $\mathbf{Y}$ would compute $Y_5(z)$ as

```
9 z ( 7 z ( 5 z ( 3 z ( z + 1 ) + 1 ) + z + 1 )

        + 3 z ( z + 1 ) + 1 ) + 5 z ( 3 z ( z + 1 ) + 1 )

        + z + 1
```

Familiarity with the basic features of a computer algebra system, such as elementary data structures and built-in facilities, makes it easier to program efficiently and to foresee some of the many pitfalls in symbolical computation. Good understanding of the computer algebra systems which one has at one's disposal is also prerequisite to making the right choice for the system to use when studying a particular problem. For example, the formula manipulation system FORM [119] is better suited than Maple for doing computations in most non-commutative algebras because in this system non-commutative objects are of basic type and pattern matching is an amply supported basic operation.

Finally, we mention the technical difficulties in using computer algebra systems. Sometimes, input and output formats and the reuse of expressions are confusing and too far removed from standard mathematical notation. In comparison to global manipulations, local manipulations in formulae are often difficult to carry out. Interfaces with other programming languages are frequently absent or inadequate. And last but not least, bugs are a major issue. See [113] for an entertaining discussion on this issue. It is hoped that some of these remarks will soon be outdated.

1.6 Maple

The name Maple is not an acronym of **ma**thematical **ple**asure — great fun as it is to use a computer algebra system — but was chosen to draw attention to its Canadian origin. Since November 1980 a lot of work has gone into the development of the Maple system by the Symbolic Computation Group of the University of Waterloo.

Maple is a computer algebra system open to the public and fit to run on a variety of computers, from a supercomputer like the Cray Y/MP down to desktop computers like Macintosh and IBM PC or compatibles. The user accessibility shows up best on a mainframe with a time-sharing operating system, where several users of Maple can work simultaneously without being a nuisance to each other or other software users, and without excessive load put on the computer. This is possible because of the modular design of Maple. It consists of three parts: the user interface called the *Iris*, the basic algebraic engine or *kernel*, and the external *library*.

The Iris and the kernel form the smaller part of the system, which has been written in the programming language C; they are loaded when a Maple session is started. The Iris handles input of mathematical expressions (parsing and notification of errors), display of expressions ("prettyprinting"), plotting of functions, and support of other user communication with the system. There are special interfaces called *worksheets* for the X Window System (under Motif), VMS, Amiga, Macintosh, NeXT, and MS-Windows.

The Maple kernel interprets the user input and carries out the basic algebraic operations such as rational arithmetic and elementary polynomial arithmetic. It also contains certain algebraic routines which are so often used that they must be present in the lower-level systems language, for efficiency reasons. To the latter category belong routines for manipulation of polynomials like **degree**, **coeff**, and **expand**. The kernel also deals with storage management. A very important feature of Maple is that the system keeps only one copy of each expression or subexpression within an entire session. In this way testing for equality of expressions is an extremely inexpensive operation, viz., one machine instruction. Subexpressions are reused instead of being recomputed over and over again.

Most of the mathematical knowledge of Maple has been coded in the Maple programming language and resides as functions in the external library. When a user needs a library function, Maple is in most cases smart enough to load the routine itself. Only infrequently used Maple procedures must be loaded explicitly by the user. Maple must also be informed about the use of separate packages like the linear algebra, number theory, and statistics packages, to name a few. This makes Maple a compact, easy-to-use system. But what is more important, in this setting Maple uses memory space only for essential things and not for facilities in which a user is not interested. This is why many people can use Maple on one computer simultaneously, and why Maple runs on computers with little memory.

Below is a small table that summarizes the design of the Maple system as just described:

The Maple System	
Part	**Function**
Iris	parser
	display of expressions ("prettyprinting")
	graphics
	special user interfaces:
	worksheet version for X11 (Motif),
	Macintosh, NeXT, MS-Windows, etc.
Kernel	interpreter
	memory management
	basic & time-critical procedures for
	computations in $\mathbb{Z}$, $\mathbf{Q}$, $\mathbb{R}$, $\mathbb{C}$, $\mathbb{Z}_n$, $\mathbf{Q}[x]$, etc.
Library	library functions
	application packages
	on-line help

The Maple language is a well-structured, comprehensible, high-level programming language. It supports a large collection of data structures: functions, sequences, sets, lists, arrays, tables, etc. There are also plenty of easy-to-use operations on these data structures like type-testing, selection and composition of data structures, and so on. These are the ingredients of the programming language in which almost all mathematical algorithms of Maple are implemented, and which is the same language users will employ in interactive calculator mode. Furthermore, anyone who is interested in the algorithms that Maple uses and who is interested in the way these algorithms are implemented can look at the Maple code in the library; the procedures are available in readable form or can be reproduced as such inside a Maple session. If desired, a user can enlarge the library with self-written programs and packages. Maple also provides its with user facilities to keep track of the execution of programs, whether self-made or not.

The last advantage of Maple we shall mention is its user-friendly design. Many computer algebra systems require a long apprenticeship or knowledge of a low-level systems language if one really wants to understand what is going on in computations. In many systems one has to leaf through the manual to find the right settings of programming flags and keywords. Nothing of the kind in Maple. First, there is the help facility, which is basically the on-line manual for Maple procedures. Secondly, the secret to why Maple is so easy to use is the hybrid algorithmic structure of the computer algebra system, where the system itself can decide which algorithm is favorable. As an example we look at some invocations of the Maple procedure **simplify**, which does what its name suggests.

```
> trig_formula := cos(x)^6 + sin(x)^6
>    + 3*sin(x)^2*cos(x)^2:
> exp_ln_formula := exp( a +1/2*ln(b) ):
> radical_formula := (x-2)^(3/2) / (x^2-4*x+4)^(1/4):
> trig_formula = simplify( trig_formula );
```

$$\cos(x)^6 + \sin(x)^6 + 3\,\sin(x)^2\,\cos(x)^2 = 1$$

```
> exp_ln_formula = simplify( exp_ln_formula );
```

$$e^{a\,+\,1/2\,\ln(b)} = e^a\,\sqrt{b}$$

```
> radical_formula = simplify( radical_formula );
```

$$\frac{(x-2)^{3/2}}{(x^2-4\,x+4)^{1/4}} = x - 2$$

You see that just one procedure, viz., **simplify**, carries out distinct types of simplifications: trigonometric simplification, simplifications of logarithms and exponential functions, and simplification of powers with rational exponentials. On the other hand, the concept of pattern matching and transformation rules (rewrite rules) is currently underdeveloped in Maple. It is difficult, if not impossible in Maple to program mathematical transformations that must be applied globally.

At many places Maple makes decisions which way to go; we mention four examples. Computation of the determinant of a matrix is done by the method of minor expansion for a small matrix, otherwise Gaussian elimination is used. Maple has essentially three numerical methods at its disposal to compute definite integrals over a finite interval: the default integration method is Clenshaw-Curtis quadrature, but when convergence is slow (due to nearby singularities) the system tries to remove the singularities or switches to an adaptive double-exponential quadrature method. An adaptive Newton-Cotes method is available when low precision (e.g., `Digits <= 15`) suffices. By the way, generalized series expansions and variable transformations are two of the techniques used in the Maple procedure **evalf/int** to deal with singularities in an analytic integrand. The interested reader is referred to [48, 52]. At present, there are six algorithms coded into the Maple procedure **fsolve**: Newton, Secant, Dichotomic, inverse parabolic interpolation, a method based on approximating the Jacobian (for systems), and a method of partial substitutions (for systems again). As a user of Maple you normally do not need to know about or act on these details; the system finds its own way. This approach turns Maple into an easy-to-learn and easy-to-use system for mathematical computations on computers.

The First Steps: Calculus on Numbers

In this chapter, we shall cover some of the basics needed to start using Maple, to access the on-line help, and to compute with numbers. A discussion at length of how to interact with Maple will follow in chapter 4. During the overview of the number fields that are supported by Maple, we shall also introduce you gently to the way Maple stores data internally.

We assume that Maple V Release 2 is used in combination with the worksheet interface under the X Window System. Henceforth, all computations will be done on a Silicon Graphics Indigo Server running Irix 4.0.5F, with a 50 Mhz IP20 processor of MIPS R4000 type, and having 64 MB main memory plus 200 MB swap space. Most of this book applies equally well to other computers and/or operating systems, but there may be implementation differences in areas like plotting and filenames. We assume that the reader knows how to log onto the computer and is using a workstation or X terminal.

2.1 Getting Started

To start Maple, type **xmaple** from a Unix shell. Look for local assistance and documentation if this does not work. When Maple has been started successfully, the worksheet appears and the system indicates with a *prompt*, such as the greater-than symbol, ">", that it is waiting for a command. Now, you can use Maple as an ordinary pocket calculator.

```
> 2 + 100 / 5^2 * 3 ;
```

$$14$$

```
> 5! / 21 ;
```

$$\frac{40}{7}$$

All arithmetic operations which you are familiar with are present: addition $(+)$, multiplication $(*)$, division $(/)$, exponentiation ($\char`\^$ or $**$), and factorial (!). The usual precedence rules apply, and in doubtful cases, or just for the sake of clarity, you may use parentheses. But there are a few differences in the input mode when using Maple as a pocket calculator:

- Each command must be terminated by a semicolon or a colon. Don't forget these punctuation marks, otherwise the system will sit waiting for more input. Termination by a semicolon informs Maple that input is complete, causes the instruction to be carried out by the system and displays the result. A colon can be used instead of a semicolon if you do not want to see the output. This is convenient when you are interested in computing an intermediate result, but do not need to look at it. The process of carrying out an instruction is called *evaluation*.

- Maple only deals with an input line when the *newline* character, which is either the carriage return or the line feed character, is sent by pressing the Return or Enter key, respectively. After the evaluation of the command Maple prints a prompt at the beginning of a new line, again indicating that it is waiting for input.

The Maple input mode and particularly the roles of the semicolon and the colon are exemplified below.

```
> 2*5;  2^5:  100/4;  100

                              10

                              25

>                          /6

> ;

                              50
                              --
                              3

> 1\
> 2345\
> 6789;
```
                              123456789

As you see, more than one instruction may be entered in one line. Maple deals with them one by one, as if they were given separately. To enhance readability you may stretch a command across several lines and you may insert spaces. But be careful, this is not allowed everywhere. For example, you cannot type the number 1000000 as 1 000 000; but you may group the digits into groups of three by typing 1\000\000. The *backslash* is used in Maple as the *continuation character*, which is ignored. When you stretch a command across two or more lines, Maple splits the parts of the command by newline characters, unless you end a line with the backslash; in this case both backslash and newline character are ignored.

If Maple does not understand your input because of syntactical errors, it will tell you so.

```
> this is a line Maple does not understand;

syntax error:
this is a line Maple does not understand;
         ^
```

The *caret* (^) points to the token that was being read when the error occurred. Maple does not say anything more. You must find out yourself what went wrong; Maple just waits for new input.

You can correct the previous input by placing the cursor on this input line and then making all necessary changes. The tty version of Maple has both a vi- and emacs-like command line editor available which allows you to edit up to one hundred previously entered input lines. If your typing skills are really poor, you can also use the command completion facility. Command completion is also a useful capability for novice and casual users of Maple who have gaps in their knowledge about the system. It is invoked by pressing the T key while holding down the Control key. Command completion works as follows: it completes the command as far as possible, shows a list of remaining matches, and then redraws the (partially completed) input line. You can then type more characters and finish the command. A simple example:

```
> eva

eval   evala   evalb   evalc   evalf   evalgf   evalhf   evalm
   evaln   evalr   evalstat
> eval
```

You quit Maple by successively clicking on the File and Exit menu items; the system will ask you to confirm this action. Alternatively, you press the X key while holding down the Alt key. You can immediately leave Maple by entering the command **quit** or **done** followed by the newline character.

In the worksheet interface there are (at the bottom of the Maple window) two message regions about the amount of storage allocated and computing time. In the tty version, Maple will print so-called *bytes-used* messages about the use of computer memory and computing time. Such messages also appear during lengthy computations. Just ignore them for the moment or consider them as indicators that Maple is still working for you.

You can interrupt a lengthy Maple calculation which is in progress by clicking on the $\boxed{\text{Interrupt}}$ button so that the system receives the *interrupt* character (usually Control-C). You may also send the interrupt character directly from the keyboard by pressing the C key while holding down the Control key. After the interrupt is recognized you may enter another command.

You may stop and restart a lengthy stream of Maple output by alternatively clicking on the $\boxed{\text{Pause}}$ button.

Inside Maple you can always start afresh by entering

```
> restart;
```

This statement will clear Maple's internal memory and reread the initialization file(s) so that it acts as if you had started Maple from scratch.

2.2 Getting Help

When you click on the $\boxed{\text{Help}}$ button of a Maple worksheet, or alternatively press the Alt and H keys simultaneously, you get a menu of available help facilities. The most important is the hierarchal help topic browser for accessing the on-line help information. You select it by clicking on $\boxed{\text{Help Browser}}$ or by entering a B. A typical search in the Help Browser is shown on the next page: it is a screen dump of the Help Browser while searching for information about graphics in a polar coordinate system. The help window with the actual information on how to plot a parametric curve in polar coordinates is also shown on the next page: it appears after clicking on the $\boxed{\text{Help}}$ button in the Help Browser, when the (sub)topics library, plot, and polar are highlighted. The same help window appears when you enter:

```
> ?plot,polar
```

The advantage of the Help Browser is that it allows you to explore or to find your way through Maple without browsing through the Maple Library Reference Manual [24]. The ?<*topic*> command-line syntax is a faster way of getting information when you know what command you are looking for and only want to refresh your knowledge or look at an example.

Via the Help Browser you can get more information about the help system by asking for information about the library function **help** You can also enter just the question mark for this purpose.

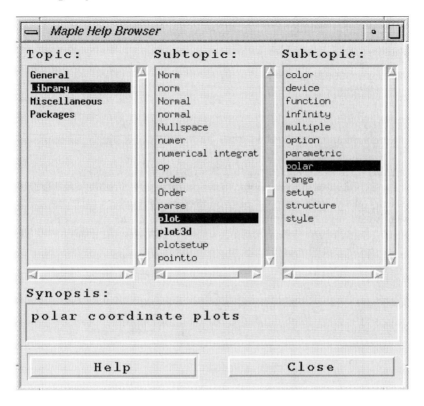

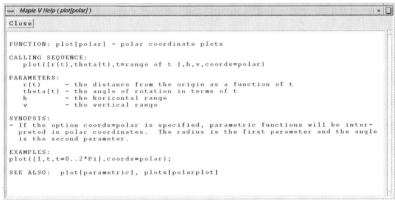

As a more concrete example of available on-line help, let us ask for help about integer factorization.

```
> ?ifactor
```

The corresponding help message is a clear illustration of the general format of Maple's descriptions of syntax, data types, and functions. Below, we have split the contents of the help window accordingly.

```
FUNCTION: ifactor - integer factorization

CALLING SEQUENCE:
    ifactor(n)
    ifactor(n, method)

PARAMETERS:
    n        - integer or a rational
    method - (optional) name of base method for factoring
```

The procedure **ifactor** is explained first: what it is meant for and how you can use it. Obviously, you can factorize an integer with it, but the help text informs you that **ifactor** can also be used to factorize a rational number. If you desire a particular factorization method, then you can specify this with an extra argument in the procedure call. Hereafter, the procedure and its options are described in more detail.

```
SYNOPSIS:
- ifactor returns the complete integer factorization of n.

- The answer is in the form:
  u * ``(f1) ^ e1 * ... * ``(fn) ^ en   such that
  n = u * f1 ^ e1 * ... * fn ^ en   where u equals
  sign(n), f1,..., fn are the distinct prime factors of n,
  and e1, ..., en are their multiplicities (negative in
  the case of the denominator of a rational).

- The expand function may be applied to cause the factors
  to be multiplied together again.

- If a second parameter is specified, the named method
  will  be used when the front-end code fails to achieve
  the factorization. By default, the Morrison-Brillhart
  algorithm is used as the base method. Currently
  accepted names are:

          'squfof'        - D. Shanks' undocumented square-free
                            factorization;
          'pollard'       - J.M. Pollard's rho method;
          'lenstra'       - Lenstra's algorithm; and
          'easy'          - which does no further work.

- If the 'easy' option is chosen, the result of the
  ifactor call will be a product of the factors that
  were easy to compute, and a name _c.m indicating an
  m-digit composite number that was not factored.

- The pollard base method accepts an additional optional
  integer: ifactor(n,pollard,k), which increases the
  efficiency of the method when one of the factors is of
  the form k*m+1.
```

What follows are a few examples. In many cases you can immediately learn from these examples how to do your work in Maple.

```
EXAMPLES:
> ifactor( 61 );
                                          (61)
```

```
> ifactor( 60 );
                                        2
                               (2)  (3)  (5)

> ifactor( -144 );
                                 4      2
                            -  (2)   (3)

> expand(");
                                 -144

> ifactor( 60, easy );
                                        2
                               (2)  (3)  (5)
> ifactor( 4/11 );
                                     2
                                  (2)
                                  ----
                                  (11)

> n := 8012940887713968000041:
> ifactor( n, easy );
                            (13)  (457)  _c19

> ifactor( n );
                  (13)  (457)  (473638939)  (2847639359)
```

Finally, Maple refers to related matter.

```
SEE ALSO:   ifactors, isprime, factor, type[facint]
```

It may be the case that you know more or less about a procedure in Maple, but do not recall exactly its name or abbreviation. If you happen to ask for help using a word that is not present in Maple's list of keywords, then a nearby search is done.

```
> ?sub

Try one of the following topics:

    { substring, subsop, subvector, substitute, subgraph,

       submatrix, subscript, subscripted, subtract,

       suball, subgrel, subsets }
```

So you see that you can get plenty of help directly from the system. When you don't use the Help Browser, you can get a list of help categories when you enter **?index**. The categories *library*, *libmisc*, and *packages* are listed among others. When you enter

```
> ?library
```

you get a list of all standard library functions present in Maple. After the command **?libmisc** you will see more rarely used procedures present in the "miscellaneous library". Entering the command **?packages** will provide you with a list of all packages present in Maple. If you want to know what procedures are available in the linear algebra package, for example, just enter **?linalg**. Or if you want to know more about the trace function in the linear algebra package, enter **?linalg,trace** or **?linalg[trace]**. If you omit the first part and simply enter **?trace**, then you will get information about the debugging tool **trace** in Maple which resides in the standard library. In cases of no ambiguity, e.g., **det** for computing the determinant of a matrix, you may use the abbreviation **?det** instead of **?linalg,det**. Once a package is loaded, you can use abbreviations when you ask for help about a procedure in that package.

Good advice: familiarize yourself with the help system because it will be your best assistant in learning and using Maple.

Now we are ready for our tour through Maple, which will be in the form of short Maple sessions interleaved with explanatory remarks. Unless explicitly stated, we assume that in each example all history of previous examples has been forgotten by Maple, as if a new session has been started. Have a close look at the examples, try them yourself with Maple, and change the examples as you like. Only through direct confrontation with the computer algebra system can you acquire the right skills and experience the applicability and limitations of computer algebra personally. For the same reason we have added a set of exercises at the end of each session. Work through these exercises to become more and more proficient at Maple.

2.3 Integers and Rational Numbers

Like a true computer algebra system, Maple is averse to approximations in arithmetic computations. In contrast to pocket calculators, Maple never changes spontaneously arithmetic expression into decimal numbers. The quotient of two integers with nonzero denominator is only simplified. More precisely, the greatest common divisor is removed automatically from the numerator and the denominator of a rational number. For exact arithmetic on rational numbers, Maple must be able to deal with very large integers.

```
> 5 / 8149152832478977343456112695961115894

> - 101 / 101983469161384038564394426 3;

    -8230644360293849771083753636300987983979/8310788 \

         765825251740419901735045140451894517651 62 \

         144347024416122

> number := 4^(4^4);
```

```
 number := 13407807929942597099574024998205846 12 \

        747936582059239337772356144372176403 00735 \

        469768018742981669034276900318581864 86050 \

        853753882811946569946433649006084096
```

```
> length( number );   # number of digits
```

```
                        155
```

Note that Maple spontaneously uses a backslash to indicate that output continues on the next line.

Of course, there is a maximum integer that can be represented by Maple, but it has a much higher value than in most other programming languages; the number of digits is limited to $2^{19} - 9 = 524279$. The secret of Maple's capability of computing with large numbers up to 10^{524279} lies in the internal representation of integers. Most programming languages make use of the hardware facilities for calculus on so-called *single-precision integers*. This limits the range of values for integers to those numbers which can be represented in one computer word. Maple has implemented *multiple-precision integer arithmetic* by using several consecutive computer words for the internal representation of an integer [25, 52]. We call such a linear list a *dynamic data vector* and define the *length* of the data vector as the number of computer words used. The internal data structure in Maple representing an integer has the following format.

intpos	integer i_0	integer i_1	. . . .	integer i_n

The first word in this vector encodes all the information about the data structure: it indicates that the vector represents a positive integer and that the vector length is equal to $n + 2$. The next $n + 1$ words contain single-precision nonnegative integers i_0, i_1, i_2, ..., i_n. Let B be the base of the number system used inside the computer, then the above vector represents the integer

$$i_0 + i_1 B + i_2 B^2 + i_3 B^3 + \cdots + i_n B^n .$$

Maple uses as base B the largest power of 10 such that B^2 can be represented in the single-precision integer arithmetic of the computer ($B = 10^4$ on a 32-bit machine). Because the length of the vector may be chosen dynamically, instead of being of a pre-defined fixed length, very large integers can be represented in Maple. The only restriction is that the number of computer words necessary for representation of an integer must be specifiable in the first word of the dynamic data vector. Maple uses seventeen bits for specification of the vector length, and this explains the "magic number"

$2^{19} - 9 = 4\big((2^{17} - 1) - 1\big) - 1$. Maple is clever enough to decide beforehand whether an integer can be represented or not.

```
> 123456789 ^ 987654321;
Error, object too large
```

In Maple there are several procedures for doing calculus on integers. A few examples:

```
> number := 10^29 - 10^14 - 1;
        number := 99999999999999899999999999999
```

```
> isprime( number );  # check whether the number is prime
                              false
```

```
> settime := time():  # start timing
> ifactor( number );  # factorize the integer
    ( 61 ) ( 223 ) ( 13166701 ) ( 97660768252549 ) ( 5717 )
```

```
> cpu_time := (time()-settime) * seconds; # computing time
               cpu_time = 9.616 seconds
```

```
> nextprime( number );   # determine the next largest prime
           99999999999999900000000000157
```

```
> # integer approximation to the square root
> isqrt( number );
               316227766016838
```

Integer factorization is a time-consuming operation, and you may want to know the computing time. As you have seen before, this can be done with the help of the Maple procedure **time**, which gives back the computing time (in seconds) since the start of the Maple session. Enter the command **time()** immediately before and after a computation. By taking the differences of these two numbers, you get the computer time of that particular computation.

In all the above procedures, integer division (with remainder) and determination of greatest common divisor play a crucial role.

```
> a := 1234:   b := 56:
> q := iquo(a,b);  # quotient of integer division
```

$$q := 22$$

```
> r := irem(a,b);   # remainder of integer division
```

$$r := 2$$

```
> a = q*b + r;   # check identity
```

$$1234 = 1234$$

```
> igcd(a,b);   # greatest common divisor of integers
```

$$2$$

By use of the procedure **igcdex** Maple can compute the **ex**tended **greatest common divisor of integers**; for any two integers a and b, two integers, say s and t, are computed such that $a\,s + b\,t = \gcd(a,b)$.

```
> igcdex( a, b, 's', 't' );
```

$$2$$

```
> 's' = s, 't' = t;
```

$$s = 1, \quad t = -22$$

```
> a*s + b*t;
```

$$2$$

The quotes around s and t in the above examples are used to suppress evaluation of variables. This will be explained in more detail in the next chapter.

Modular arithmetic plays an important role in integer factorization and primality tests [81]. The operator **mod** gives, in modular arithmetic with respect to a nonzero integer n, an answer in the sequence $0, 1, 2, \ldots, |n| - 1$. If you prefer an answer in the sequence

$$-\left\lfloor \frac{|n|-1}{2} \right\rfloor, \ldots, -1, 0, 1, \ldots, \left\lfloor \frac{|n|}{2} \right\rfloor - 1, \left\lfloor \frac{|n|}{2} \right\rfloor,$$

i.e., symmetrically around zero, then you can specify this beforehand.

```
> 1/2345 mod 6;
```

$$5$$

```
> `mod` := mods:   1/2345 mod 6;
```

$$-1$$

A drawback of Maple's modular arithmetic is that you cannot specify in one step that all computations are to be done modulo some fixed integer. In each separate command you need to call the **mod** routine.

As we have noted before, Maple simplifies a rational number spontaneously into a unique standard form. The system automatically removes the greatest common divisor from the numerator and the denominator of the rational number, and it guarantees that the denominator is a positive number. If you represent a rational number as a pair of integers (*numerator, denominator*) with positive denominator, this standard form, referred to as *canonical form*, is the most compact one. You would not like to represent $\frac{1}{3}$ as

$$\frac{-41152263041152263041152263041152263041152263}{-123456789123456789123456789123456789123456789}.$$

Now, you might think that Maple represents a rational number internally as a data vector consisting of three components, the first component specifying the nature of the data vector, the second component representing the numerator, and the third component representing the positive denominator. However, because the developers of Maple wanted to make Maple as memory-efficient as possible, they have chosen a different design, based on the rule [23]

every (sub)expression in Maple appears internally only once.

Therefore, in a data vector representing a rational number, the last two components do not consist of the multiple-precision integers representing the numerator and denominator themselves, but only contain reference pointers to these integers. In this way, any integer which occurs in several rational numbers, appears internally only once. For example, the rational numbers $-\frac{1}{2}$, $\frac{2}{3}$, and $\frac{3}{5}$, when used in the same Maple session, are internally represented as follows:

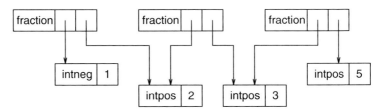

2.4 Irrational Numbers and Floating-Point Numbers

In the previous section you have seen that Maple simplifies rational numbers automatically. In general, Maple only carries out computations when it is specifically ordered to do so.

```
> 25^(1/6);
```

$$25^{1/6}$$

```
> simplify(");
```

$$5^{1/3}$$

```
> evalf("");
```

$$1.709975947$$

```
> convert( """, ´float´ );
```

$$1.709975947$$

Here, the procedures **simplify** and **evalf** put Maple to work here. With the double quote in the command **simplify(")** you refer to the previously evaluated expression, in this case $25^{1/6}$. Two double quotes return the second last expression evaluated; more than three double quotes for referring to previously evaluated expressions are not allowed. Double quotes which are used in the above sense are called *ditto operators*.

You might have expected in the above example that Maple would immediately yield an approximate result for the cube root, but this is against the principle of exact arithmetic. You may want to compute the third power of this cube root and expect the exact result. In approximate floating-point arithmetic you would get a different result.

```
> 25.0^(1/6);
```

$$1.709975947$$

```
> "^6;
```

$$25.00000003$$

Any number containing a dot is interpreted as a floating-point number, and henceforth Maple computes with it as such. In this case, Maple will also take care of automatic type conversions from integers to floating-point numbers.

```
> 90005*0.15;
```

$$13500.75$$

Other Maple notations for a floating-point number, say 0.000001, are: $0.1 * 10^{-5}$, **1E-6**, and **Float(10,-6)**. The latter notation is of the form **Float**(*mantissa, exponent*) and resembles Maple's internal representation of floating-point number: a data vector consisting of the header **Float**, and pointers to the multiple-precision integers *mantissa*, and *exponent*. This vector represents the number *mantissa* $\times 10^{exponent}$. In other words, the significant digits of a floating-point number are stored in the *mantissa* and the overall magnitude is given by the *exponent*. As a consequence of the internal representation of floating-point numbers, the limit of the floating-point precision coincides with the maximum number of digits that an integer can have in Maple. However, the internal addition and multiplication routines which compute the integer values of the exponent are written in C. This means that exponent arithmetic is restricted to C's integer arithmetic.

The precision of floating-point arithmetic can be defined by setting different values to the Maple variable Digits, whose default value is equal to ten. There are several functions that make Maple compute in floating-point arithmetic, the most important being **evalf** (**eval**uate using **f**loating-point arithmetic).

```
> evalf( sqrt(2) );
```
$$1.414213562$$

```
> Digits;
```
$$10$$

```
> Digits := 20:    evalf( sqrt(2) );
```
$$1.4142135623730950488$$

```
> evalf( Pi, 150 );
```

```
    3.14159265358979323846264338327950288419716939  9 \

        3751058209749445923078164062862089986280  3 \

        4825342117067982148086513282306647093844  6 \

        0955058223172535940813
```

The procedure **evalf** approximates its first argument; the number of digits used is equal to the value of its second argument. If there is no second argument to **evalf**, then Maple takes the value of Digits as the number of digits to be used in floating-point arithmetic.

Maple knows, of course, some mathematical constants, like the base e of the natural logarithm and the number π. They are stored in the sequence called constants. You may add your own symbolic constants.

```
> constants;
```
$$\textit{false, } \gamma, \ \infty, \ \textit{true, Catalan, E, } \pi$$

```
> constants := constants, electron_rest_mass, kg;
```
$$\textit{constants := false, } \gamma, \ \infty, \ \textit{true, Catalan, E, } \pi,$$

electron_rest_mass, kg

```
> type( electron_rest_mass, `constant` );
```

true

```
> electron_rest_mass := 9.109558 * 10^(-31) * kg;
Error, may not assign to a system constant
```

You can associate the value $9.10955810^{-30} kg$ with the symbolic constant electron_rest_mass by use of the procedure **macro**. In this way, electron_rest_mass is just an abbreviation of a specific value; but it still cannot be assigned a value by accident.

```
> macro( electron_rest_mass = 9.109558 * 10^(-31) * kg ):

> electron_rest_mass;
```

$$.91095580000000000000 \ 10^{-30} \ kg$$

```
> electron_rest_mass := 5.48593 * 10^(-4)

>    * atomic_mass_units;
Error, may not assign to a system constant
```

Mathematical Constants in Maple		
Mathematical Constant	**Maple Name**	**Value (approx)**
π, the area of a unit circle	Pi	3.141592654
e, the natural log base	E, exp(1)	2.718281828
Catalan's number C $= \sum_{n=0}^{\infty} \frac{(-1)^n}{(2n+1)^2}$	Catalan	0.9159655942
Euler-Mascheroni's constant γ $= \lim_{n \to \infty} \left((\sum_{k=1}^{n} \frac{1}{k}) - \ln n \right)$	gamma	0.5772156649
logical values *true, untrue*	true, false	
∞	infinity	

With a scientific pocket calculator you can compute with mathematical functions like the exponential function, the natural logarithm, and trigonometric functions. In Maple these functions are also present, but the system contains many more. Below we list commonly used mathematical functions and their names in Maple. A more complete list can be obtained by the command **?inifcns** (help about **ini**tially known **f**unctio**ns**).

Commonly Used Functions Known to Maple	
Mathematical Function	**Maple Name**
exponential function	exp
natural logarithm	ln, log
logarithm with base 10	log10
square root function	sqrt
absolute value	abs
trigonometric functions	sin, cos, tan, csc, sec, cot
inverse trigonometric functions	arcsin, arccos, arctan, arccsc, arcsec, arccot
hyperbolic functions	sinh, cosh, tanh, csch, sech, coth
inverse hyperbolic functions	arcsinh, arccosh, arctanh, arccsch arcsech, arccoth
hypergeometric function	hypergeom
Bessel functions	BesselI, BesselJ, BesselK, BesselY
Gamma function	GAMMA
binomial coefficient	binomial
polygamma function	Psi
Riemann zeta function	Zeta
dilogarithm	dilog
error function	erf

Recall the definitions of

the Gamma function
$$\Gamma(z) = \int_0^\infty t^{z-1} e^{-z}\, dz, \quad \Re(z) > 0,$$

the Riemann zeta function
$$\zeta(z) = \sum_{n=1}^\infty \frac{1}{n^z},$$

the dilogarithm function
$$\mathrm{dilog}(x) = \int_0^x \frac{\ln t}{(1-t)}\, dx,$$

and the error function
$$\mathrm{erf}(x) = \frac{2}{\sqrt{\pi}} \int_0^x e^{-t^2}\, dt.$$

Maple knows exact values of many of these functions. Trigonometric functions applied to multiples of $\frac{\pi}{8}$, $\frac{\pi}{10}$, and $\frac{\pi}{12}$ yield exact numerical results. The Riemann zeta function yields exact numbers when applied to even, natural numbers less than fifty; for larger arguments, you must explicitly **expand** it. $\lim_{x \to \infty} \mathrm{erf}(x)$ is known to be equal to one.

```
> sin(Pi/10), ln(E), Zeta(2), limit( erf(x), x=infinity );
```

$$\frac{1}{4}\sqrt{5} - \frac{1}{4}, \quad 1, \quad \frac{1}{6}\pi^2, \quad 1$$

```
> Zeta(50) = expand( Zeta(50) );
```

$$Zeta(\,50\,)$$

$$3960457641928637185699820\,2/28525877145754676446 \ \backslash$$

$$3363635252374414183254365234375\ \pi^{50}$$

Numerical approximations can be obtained with **evalf**.

```
> Zeta(3); evalf(");
```

$$Zeta(\,3\,)$$

$$1.2020569031595942854$$

The next examples give more food for thought about exact arithmetic versus floating-point arithmetic.

```
> sin(4)-2*sin(2)*cos(2); combine(",'trig'); evalf("");
```

$$sin(\,4\,)\ -\ 2\ sin(\,2\,)\ cos(\,2\,)$$

$$0$$

$$-.1\ 10^{-9}$$

```
> (1+sqrt(2))^2-2*(1+sqrt(2))-1; simplify("); evalf("");
```

$$\left(\sqrt{2}\ +\ 1\right)^2\ -\ 3\ -\ 2\ \sqrt{2}$$

$$0$$

$$-.1\ 10^{-8}$$

You may wonder how the Maple procedure **evalf** distinguishes all these mathematical functions. Maple shows its secrets when you set a higher value to the Maple variable `printlevel`, whose default value is equal to 1.

```
> printlevel := 5:    evalf( sin(1) + ln(2) );
--> enter sin, args = 1
<-- exit sin = sin(1)
--> enter ln, args = 2
<-- exit ln = ln(2)
--> enter evalf/sin, args = 1
```

$$x\ :=\ 1.$$

```
<-- exit evalf/sin = .8414709848
--> enter evalf/ln, args = 2
```

$$x\ :=\ 2.$$

```
<-- exit evalf/ln = .6931471806
                1.534618165
```

This example indicates that there exists in the Maple library a procedure called **evalf/func** for each mathematical function *func* for which numerical values can be computed. Whenever you apply the procedure **evalf** on a Maple expression, the system finds out what functions are present and automatically applies the appropriate **evalf/func** procedures. In this way, it is only necessary for you to recall the name of *one* procedure for numerical approximation, instead of remembering several distinct procedures. We shall see that similar techniques are used in other areas, such as, integration, differentiation, and simplification.

Maple also has a the procedure **evalhf** (**eval**uate using **h**ard**w**are **f**loating-point arithmetic) for the purpose of gaining speed in numerical computations (e.g., in plotting graphs of functions) or for users who want hardware floating-point arithmetic. This procedure converts all its arguments to hardware floating-point numbers, computes the answer in double precision (which is equivalent to a setting of `Digits` around fifteen), and converts it to a Maple floating-point result. We illustrate the use of **evalhf** with the calculation of the values of the function g defined by

```
> f := x -> arctan( (2*x^2-1)/(2*x^2+1) ):

> g := (x,y) -> f(x) * f(y):

> g(x,y);
```

$$\arctan\left(\frac{2\ x^2\ -\ 1}{2\ x^2\ +\ 1}\right)\arctan\left(\frac{2\ y^2\ -\ 1}{2\ y^2\ +\ 1}\right)$$

on a two-dimensional rectangular 50 by 50 grid at equally spaced points in the ranges $[-3, 3]$ and $[-3, 3]$, respectively.

```
> settime := time(): # start timing

> for i to 50 do

>     for j to 50 do

>         evalf( g( -3 + 6*i/50, -3 + 6*j/50 ) )

>     od

> od:

> cpu_time := (time()-settime) * seconds; # computing time
```

$$cpu\_time := 14.117\ seconds$$

```
> settime := time():

> for i to 50 do

>     for j to 50 do

>         evalhf( g( -3 + 6*i/50, -3 + 6*j/50 ) )
```

```
>     od
> od:
> cpu_time := (time()-settime) * seconds; # computing time
```

$$cpu\_time := .933 \; seconds$$

```
> evalf( g(1,1) );
```

$$.1035234193$$

```
> evalhf( g(1,1) );
```

$$.1035234192545466$$

Hardware floating-point arithmetic is used by Maple in plot routines, e.g., in **plot3d**, with which you can graph the function g.

```
> plot3d( g, -3..3, -3..3,
>   grid=[50,50], style=patchnogrid );
```

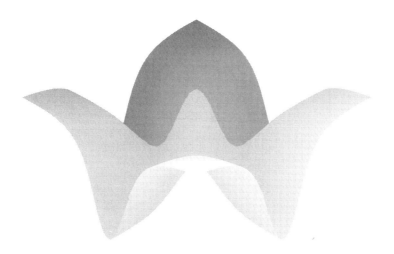

2.5 Algebraic Numbers

We have already seen examples of radical numbers such as square roots and cube roots of integers. Maple has little problems in computing with them.

```
> ( 1/2 + 1/2*sqrt(5) )^2;
```

$$\left(\frac{1}{2} + \frac{1}{2} \sqrt{5} \right)^2$$

```
> expand(");
```

$$\frac{3}{2} + \frac{1}{2}\sqrt{5}$$

```
> (-8)^(1/3);
```

$$(-8)^{1/3}$$

```
> simplify(");
```

$$-2$$

In the last example, Maple uses the principal branch of the complex, cube root function.

Radical numbers are instances of so-called algebraic numbers. In general, an *algebraic number* is a root of an irreducible univariate polynomial over the rational numbers: $\sqrt{2}$ is a root α of the polynomial $x^2 - 2$, $\sqrt{2}+\sqrt{3}+\sqrt{5}$ is a root α of the polynomial $x^8 - 40x^6 + 352x^4 - 960x^2 + 576$, the nested radical $\sqrt{1+\sqrt{2}}$ is a root α of the polynomial $x^4 - 2x - 1$. A root α of the polynomial $x^5 + x + 1$ cannot be expressed in terms of radicals. Note that in these examples the symbol α can be any of the roots of the polynomial, just as the square root of two can be approximately 1.4142 or -1.4142.

Computing with algebraic numbers is complicated and time-consuming [108], but Maple has computational methods built in. An algebraic number is represented in the system by means of the procedure **RootOf**, which plays the role of a placeholder. For example, $\sqrt{2}$ can be represented as an algebraic number by

```
> alpha := RootOf( z^2 - 2, z );
```

$$2$$

Here, Maple reveals that it will use the underscore name _z internally. The procedure **simplify** makes use of the fact that $\alpha^2 = 2$ to simplify expressions containing α.

```
> simplify( alpha^2 );
```

$$2$$

```
> simplify( 1/(1+alpha) );
```

$$RootOf(\_Z^2 - 2) - 1$$

These calculations become much clearer when an **alias** is used for the square root.

```
> alias( beta = RootOf( z^2 - 2, z ) ):
> # beta denotes a root of z^2 - 2 = 0, i.e., sqrt(2)
> 1/(1+beta) + 1/(beta-1);  simplify(");
```

$$\frac{1}{1 + \beta} + \frac{1}{\beta - 1}$$

$$2 \beta$$

You can easily **convert** the representation of an algebraic number from *radical* into *RootOf*, and vice versa.

```
> convert( (-8)^(1/3), `RootOf` );
```

$$\mathrm{RootOf}(\_Z^3 + 8)$$

```
> convert( ", `radical` );
```

$$(-8)^{1/3}$$

Actually, in the above example, α and β can be any of the square roots of two, and the procedure **allvalues** does its very best to show them all.

```
> allvalues( alpha );
```

$$\sqrt{2}, \ -\sqrt{2}$$

In Maple you can do polynomial calculus over algebraic number fields. Below, we shall use this facility to check that $\zeta = \sqrt{2} + \sqrt{3} + \sqrt{5}$ is a root of the polynomial $x^8 - 40x^6 + 352x^4 - 960x^2 + 576$ and that in this case $\sqrt{2} = \frac{1}{576}\zeta^7 - \frac{7}{144}\zeta^5 - \frac{7}{72}\zeta^3 + \frac{5}{3}\zeta$. First, we use resultants to compute the defining polynomial for ζ (q.v., [87]).

```
> polynomial := resultant(
>    resultant( x^2-5, (x-y)^2-3, x ),   (y-z)^2-2, y );
```

$$polynomial := z^8 - 40 \ z^6 + 352 \ z^4 - 960 \ z^2 + 576$$

```
> expand( subs( z=sqrt(2)+sqrt(3)+sqrt(5), polynomial ) );
```

$$0$$

```
> # sqrt(2)+sqrt(3)+sqrt(5) is indeed a root
> # introduce algebraic number zeta
> alias( zeta = RootOf( polynomial, z ) ):
> factor( x^2-2, zeta ); # factorize over Q(zeta)
```

$$\frac{1}{331776}\left(576 \ x - 960 \ \zeta + 56 \ \zeta^3 + 28 \ \zeta^5 - \zeta^7\right)$$

$$\left(576 \ x + 960 \ \zeta - 56 \ \zeta^3 - 28 \ \zeta^5 + \zeta^7\right)$$

```
> roots( x^2-2, zeta );  # find the two roots over Q(zeta)
```

$$\left[\left[\frac{1}{576}\,\zeta^7 + \frac{5}{3}\,\zeta - \frac{7}{72}\,\zeta^3 - \frac{7}{144}\,\zeta^5,\ 1\right],\right.$$

$$\left.\left[-\frac{1}{576}\,\zeta^7 - \frac{5}{3}\,\zeta + \frac{7}{72}\,\zeta^3 + \frac{7}{144}\,\zeta^5,\ 1\right]\right]$$

The procedure **roots** computes the roots of the polynomial with multiplicities. In this case, $\frac{1}{567}\zeta^7 + \frac{5}{3}\zeta - \frac{7}{72}\zeta^3 - \frac{7}{144}\zeta^5$ is a root of 2 in $\mathbf{Q}(\zeta)$ with multiplicity 1, where ζ satisfies $\zeta^8 - 40\zeta^6 + 352\zeta^4 - 960\zeta^2 + 576 = 0$.

2.6 Complex Numbers

In contrast to algebraic numbers, complex numbers are of basic type. The complex number i ($\sqrt{-1}$) is represented in Maple by I. Numeric complex number arithmetic is automatic.

```
> complex_number := ( 2 + 3*I ) * ( 4 + 5*I );
```

$$complex\_number := -7 + 22\ I$$

```
> Re(");  Im("");  conjugate(""");
```

$$-7$$

$$22$$

$$-7 - 22\ I$$

```
> argument( complex_number );
```

$$-\arctan\left(\frac{22}{7}\right) + \pi$$

```
> 1 / complex_number;
```

$$-\frac{7}{533} - \frac{22}{533}\ I$$

In Maple, many mathematical functions are regarded as complex functions.

```
> cos(I), ln(I), arccoth(0);
```

$$\cosh(1),\ \frac{1}{2}\ I\ \pi,\ \frac{1}{2}\ I\ \pi$$

```
> sqrt( (1+I)^2 - 1 );
```

$$\sqrt{\frac{1}{2}\sqrt{5}-\frac{1}{2}}+I\sqrt{\frac{1}{2}\sqrt{5}+\frac{1}{2}}$$

```
> GAMMA ( 1 + 2*I );
```
$$\Gamma (1 + 2 \ I)$$

```
> evalf(");
```
$$.1519040027 + .01980488016 \ I$$

```
> plot3d( abs( GAMMA(x+y*I) ), x=-Pi..Pi, y=-Pi..Pi,
>    view=0..5, grid=[30,30], orientation=[-120,45],
>    axes=framed, style=patchcontour );
```

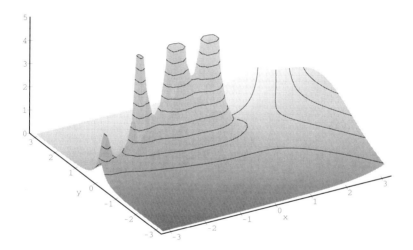

In the above **plot3d** command, we have specified all options necessary to generate this picture. Many of these options can be manually changed after the surface has been drawn. For more details you are referred to §14, in which graphics is discussed in great detail.

The next example illustrates that Maple uses the principal branch of complex, multiple-valued functions.

```
> sqrt(-8);
```
$$2 \ I \sqrt{2}$$

To activate Maple's knowledge about complex numbers in *symbolic* expressions you must use the procedure **evalc** (**eval**uate using **c**omplex number arithmetic). **evalc** assumes that all variables in an expression represent real-valued quantities and puts a complex number in its canonical form $a + b\,\mathrm{I}$, where a and b are real numbers.

```
> 1 / (2 + a - b*I);
```

$$\frac{1}{2 + a - \mathrm{I}\ b}$$

```
> evalc(");
```

$$\frac{2 + a}{(2 + a)^2 + b^2} + \frac{\mathrm{I}\ b}{(2 + a)^2 + b^2}$$

```
> abs("");
```

$$\frac{1}{\left|\ 2 + a - \mathrm{I}\ b\ \right|}$$

```
> evalc(");
```

$$\frac{1}{\sqrt{4 + 4\ a + a^2 + b^2}}$$

```
> sqrt( a + b*I );
```

$$\sqrt{a + \mathrm{I}\ b}$$

```
> evalc(");
```

$$\sqrt{\frac{1}{2}\sqrt{a^2 + b^2} + \frac{1}{2}\ a}$$

$$+\ \mathrm{I}\ \mathrm{csgn}(\,b - \mathrm{I}\ a\,)\ \sqrt{\frac{1}{2}\sqrt{a^2 + b^2} - \frac{1}{2}\ a}$$

The complex sign function **csgn** is defined by

$$\mathrm{csgn}(z) = \begin{cases} 1 & \text{if } \Im(z) > 0 \text{ or } (\Im(z) = 0 \text{ and } \Re(z) > 0); \\ 1 & \text{if } z = 0; \\ -1 & \text{elsewhere.} \end{cases}$$

```
> assume( a>0 ):   assume( b>0 ):
> evalc( sqrt( a + b*I ) );
```

$$\sqrt{\frac{1}{2}\sqrt{a\tilde{\ }^2 + b\tilde{\ }^2} + \frac{1}{2}\ a\tilde{\ }} + \mathrm{I}\ \sqrt{\frac{1}{2}\sqrt{a\tilde{\ }^2 + b\tilde{\ }^2} - \frac{1}{2}\ a\tilde{\ }}$$

When you apply transformation rules like $\ln z_1 z_2 \longrightarrow \ln z_1 + \ln z_2$, you yourself are responsible for checking whether these rules may be applied or not for specific values of z_1 and z_2. In this respect, the automatic simplifications $(z^n)^{1/n} \longrightarrow z$, (for $n \in \mathbb{N}$), and $\sqrt{z_1 z_2} \longrightarrow \sqrt{z_1}\sqrt{z_2}$, (for all z_1 and z_2), are a disaster in Maple V Release 2.

2.7 Exercises

1. Consider the following Maple session.

    ```
    > 3^2:
    > 4^2;
    ```
                                        16
    ```
    > " + "";
    ```

    Does the last instruction make sense? If so, what is the result? If not, why?

2. Explain the different results of the following Maple commands.

    (a) x:y;

    (b) x/y;

    (c) x\y;

3. In this exercise you can practise your skills in using the help system of Maple.

    (a) Suppose that you want to select from an equation, e.g., $\ln(xy) = \ln x + \ln y$, only the left or right side. How can you easily do this in Maple?

    (b) Suppose that you want to compute the continued fraction approximation of the exponential function; can Maple do this for you? If yes, carry out the computation.

    (c) Suppose that you want to factor the polynomial $x^8 + x^6 + 10x^4 + 10x^3 + 8x^2 + 2x + 8$ modulo 13. Can Maple do this? If yes, carry out this factorization.

    (d) Suppose that you want to determine all subsets of the set $\{1, 2, 3, 4, 5\}$. How can you do this in Maple?

4. (a) Find the prime factors of 9876543210123456789.

    (b) What is the prime factorization of 5^{5^5}?

5. In Maple, what is the difference between $1/3 + 1/3 + 1/3$ and $1.0/3.0 + 1.0/3.0 + 1.0/3.0$?

6. Find the floating-point approximation of $e^{\frac{1}{3}\pi\sqrt{163}}$ using a precision of ten, twenty, and thirty digits, respectively.

7. Calculate $\pi^{(\pi^\pi)}$ to nine decimal places.

8. Compute this exercise in a floating-point precision of 8 decimal places. What is the result of $310.0 * 320.0 * 330.0 - \text{sqrt}(310.0 * 320.0) * \text{sqrt}(320.0 * 330.0) * \text{sqrt}(310.0 * 330.0)$?

9. Do you remember which of the numbers $\frac{19}{6}$, $\frac{22}{7}$, and $\frac{25}{8}$ is a fairly good rational approximation of π? Use Maple to find the best of these three numbers. Find the best rational approximation $\frac{a}{b}$ of π, where a and b are natural numbers less than 1000 (Hint: look at the continued fraction expansion of π).

10. Check that $\sqrt{2\sqrt{19549} + 286}$ is equal to $\sqrt{113} + \sqrt{173}$.

11. In Maple, transform $\dfrac{1}{\sqrt{3} + 1}$ into an expression of the form $a + b\sqrt{3}$, with rational numbers a and b.

12. Let θ be a root of the polynomial $\theta^3 - \theta - 1$ and consider the extension of the field of rational numbers with θ. So, we consider expressions of the form $a + b\theta + c\theta^2$, where $a, b, c \in \mathbf{Q}$, and in calculations with these expressions, we apply the identity $\theta^3 = \theta + 1$. Transform with Maple $\dfrac{1}{\theta^2 + 1}$ into an expression of the form $a + b\theta + c\theta^2$, where $a, b, c \in \mathbf{Q}$.

13. Let $\alpha = \sqrt{2}$, $\beta = \sqrt{3}$, and $\gamma = \sqrt{5}$. Use the procedure **Primfield** to compute a primitive element ζ for the field extension $\mathbf{Q}(\alpha, \beta, \gamma)$, and compare the result with the last example of §2.5.

14. Show that Maple knows that the exponential power of a complex number can be written in terms of cosine and sine of the real and imaginary parts of that number. Also calculate $e^{\frac{\pi}{6}i}$ in that form.

15. Show with Maple that
$$\tanh(z/2) = \frac{\sinh x + i \sinh y}{\cosh x + \cos y},$$
for any complex number $z = x + yi$ with $x, y \in \mathbb{R}$.

16. Compare the results of the following Maple commands.

```
evalc( sqrt( (Pi+I) / (Pi-I) ) );
sqrt( evalc( (Pi+I) / (Pi-I) ) );
```

Variables and Names

A Maple session usually consists of a series of statements in which values are computed, assigned names, and used in further computations. In this chapter we shall discuss what are valid Maple names, how to assign a name to a value, and how to unassign a variable.

Unlike programming languages such as FORTRAN, Algol, and C, there is no need in Maple to declare the types of variables. Maple figures out the type of an expression on the basis of how it is internally represented and how it is used. In this chapter we shall have a look at the basic data types. Moreover, we shall describe the way symbolic expressions are normally evaluated, viz., full evaluation.

3.1 Assignment and Evaluation

The secret behind the success of computer algebra systems in scientific computation is that you can manipulate formulae and solve mathematical problems where unknowns and parameters are involved. As an example of the use of such variables we ask Maple about the general formulae for the solutions of a quadratic equation. Solving equations is usually done in Maple with **solve**.

```
> solve( a*x^2 + b*x + c, x );
```

$$\frac{1}{2} \frac{-b + \sqrt{b^2 - 4\,a\,c}}{a}, \; \frac{1}{2} \frac{-b - \sqrt{b^2 - 4\,a\,c}}{a}$$

The variables a, b, and c are parameters and x is an unknown; they are used as symbols, neither more nor less. This use of *free* or *unbound variables*, which do not point to any value except their own name, is characteristic of computer algebra systems.

On the other hand, a variable can be bound to, or assigned, a value. The use of *assigned variables* is twofold: you often want to label a calculated result or some complicated expression for further reference, and when you use Maple as a programming language, you want to specify data in an algorithm by name instead of using the data themselves. When data only have some fixed value, we speak of *symbolic constants*. We have seen in §2.4 what symbolic constants Maple initially has available and how new constants can be introduced. In Maple, when you want to use assigned variables, the two-character symbol := is the assignment operator.

```
> polynomial := 9*x^3 - 37*x^2 + 47*x - 19;
```

$$polynomial := 9\ x^3 - 37\ x^2 + 47\ x - 19$$

```
> # compute roots of the polynomial with multiplicities
> roots( polynomial );
```

$$\left[\left[\frac{19}{9},\ 1\right],\ [\ 1,\ 2\ ]\right]$$

```
> # substitute x for the root 19/9 into the polynomial
> subs( x=19/9, polynomial );
```

$$0$$

```
> polynomial, x;
```

$$9\ x^3 - 37\ x^2 + 47\ x - 19,\ x$$

In the above example, the effect of the first statement is that the variable polynomial is bound to 9*x^3 - 37*x^2 + 47*x - 19. Each time Maple encounters this variable, it takes its value; this is called *evaluation*. So, the instruction

$$roots(\ polynomial\ )$$

is read by Maple as

$$roots(\ 9*x^3\ -\ 37*x^2\ +\ 47*x\ -\ 19\ )$$

In the meantime, the variable x has no value, except its own name. Through the instruction

$$subs(\ x=19/9,\ polynomial\ )$$

x in the expression labeled by polynomial, i.e., in 9*x^3 - 37*x^2 + 47*x - 19 is replaced by 19/9: a *substitution*. But x itself remains unchanged and still points to itself. The same holds for the polynomial; polynomial has not been assigned a value through the substitution. You can also check the root 19/9 by assignment of x.

```
> x := 19/9;
```

$$x := \frac{19}{9}$$

```
> polynomial;
```
$$0$$

The way Maple carries out the last instruction can be understood as follows:

- Maple sees the variable `polynomial` and evaluates it first to
  `9*x^3 - 37*x^2 + 47*x - 19`,
- then it evaluates each `x` in this expression to `19/9`,
- and finally simplifies the result to `0`, i.e., does the arithmetic.

The disadvantage of checking a root by assignment instead of substitution is that `x` now points to some number. If you want `x` to point to something else, you can achieve this by a new assignment.

```
> x := unknown:
```
```
> polynomial;
```
$$9 \ unknown^3 - 37 \ unknown^2 + 47 \ unknown - 19$$

When you assign a value, say `7`, to the variable `unknown`

```
> unknown := 7;
```
$$unknown := 7$$

then `x` evaluates to `unknown`, and this for its part evaluates to 7.

```
> x;
```
$$7$$

You see that Maple evaluates in the current environment and as far as possible. We refer to this general rule as *full evaluation*.

```
> polynomial;
```
$$1584$$

We shall come back to full evaluation of expressions in §3.3.

```
> x := ´x´;
```
$$x := x$$

The last instruction gives `x` back its own name as its value. So, you can use *apostrophes* (also referred to as *forward quotes*, *right quotes*, and *acute accents*) to unassign variables. Whenever apostrophes surround an expression, Maple does not apply evaluation to the enclosed expression. In this particular case, evaluation of `x` is avoided.

Meanwhile, you have seen two exceptions to the general rule of full evaluation:

- expressions which are enclosed by apostrophes are not evaluated, and
- the name to the left of the assignment operator `:=` is not evaluated.

3.2 Unassignment

In the previous section you have seen that you can unassign a variable, say x, by

```
> x := ´x´;
```

$$x := x$$

Unassignment of a variable can also be achieved by the procedure **evaln** (**eval**uate to a **n**ame).

```
> x := 7;    x := evaln( x );
```

$$x := 7$$

$$x := x$$

This procedure is especially needed for unassigning an indexed name like $A_{[i]}$ or a concatenated name like $A.i$, where i has been assigned some value.

```
> i := 1;    A[i] := 2;    A.i := 3;
```

$$i := 1$$

$$A_{[\,1\,]} := 2$$

$$A1 := 3$$

```
> A[i] := evaln( A[i] );   A[i];   # unassignment of A[i]
```

$$A_{[\,1\,]} := A_{[\,1\,]}$$

$$A_{[\,1\,]}$$

Note the difference with the unassignment-method using apostrophes.

```
> A.i := ´A.i´;   # no unassignment of A.i
```

$$A1 := A.i$$

```
> A.i;   # but infinite recursion occurs
```

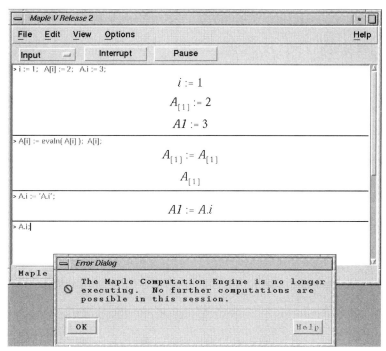

As is shown in the above screen dump, when Maple enters an infinite recursion, it will give up at some point, stop the kernel, and inform you with an error dialog box. The only thing you can do is to further edit the worksheet and save it. However, no further computations can be done in this session; you have to leave Maple first. Sometimes, Maple warns you for recursive definitions of names.

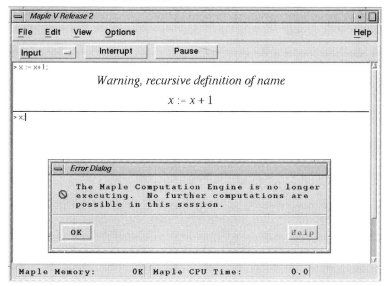

At the beginning of this two-line Maple session, x has its own name as a value and in the first instruction gets a new value x+1. In the second instruction, Maple is asked to evaluate the expression and due to full evaluation re-evaluates x over and over again until stack overflow occurs.

Because it is hardly possible to recall which variables have been assigned values and which not, the computer algebra system provides for this purpose with a few utility functions.

Procedure	Effect
anames	shows assigned names, i.e., the names of bound variables
unames	shows all unassigned names, i.e., the names of all free variables
assigned	checks whether a variable is bound to a value different from its name or not

The next sample session illustrates the use of these Maple procedures.

```
> unames();

  fraction, uneval, !, or, Copyright 1980-92 by G \

        aston Gonnet & Keith Geddes, Univ. of Wat \

                         . . .

      relation, integer, atatsign, indexed,

      algebraic, <=, polynom, <>

> nops( {"} );   # number of unassigned names
                         54
```

We have omitted most of the output of **unames**, but from the few names shown and from the number of names it is already clear that the procedure is of little use because it gives too many details. Not only the user-defined names are listed, but also the unassigned names generated and used by Maple itself. Below is the **selec**tion of all initially known, unassigned three-character names.

```
> select( s -> length(s)=3,  { unames() } );

                  { set, and, not }
```

For a description of the use of the anonymous function s -> length(s)=3 in the selection process, you are referred to §8.7.

Let us look more closely at the procedure **anames** (in a fresh Maple session).

```
> p := q;   r := q*s;
```

$$p := q$$

$$r := q\ s$$

```
> anames();
```

$$p,\ r$$

The procedure **anames** returns a sequence of names that are currently assigned values other than their own name. Here, they are user-defined variables. But when you ask for names which are assigned values of specific type, you will also get Maple-defined names.

```
> anames( `*` );
```

$$r$$

```
> anames( ´name´ );
```

$$mod,\ integrate,\ p,\ libname$$

```
> anames( ´integer´ );
```

$$Order,\ Digits,\ printlevel$$

The meaning of the quotes and data types will be explained in the last two sections of this chapter.

With the procedure **assigned** you can get the status of individual variables.

```
> assigned( r );
```

$$true$$

```
> assigned( q );
```

$$false$$

Meanwhile, you have seen two more exceptions of the general rule of full evaluation:

- the argument of the procedure **evaln** is not evaluated, and
- the argument of the procedure **assigned** is not evaluated.

We end this section with an application of the two Maple procedures **assign** and **unassign**. Their names suggest their functionality, but there are some differences from what we have previously learned about assignments and unassignments.

$$\textbf{assign}(name,\ expression)$$

has the same effect as

$$name := expression$$

except that the first argument of the procedure **assign** is fully evaluated, whereas this general rule is not applied to the left operand of the assignment operator :=. What makes the procedure **assign** worthwhile is that it can be applied to sets of equations returned by the **solve** function when it is desired to assign the solution values to the variables.

```
> eqns := { x + y = a,   b*x - 1/3*y = c }:
> vars := { x, y }:
> sols := solve( eqns, vars );
```

$$sols := \left\{ y = 3\ \frac{b\ a\ -\ c}{3\ b\ +\ 1},\quad x = \frac{3\ c\ +\ a}{3\ b\ +\ 1} \right\}$$

```
> assign( sols );
> x, y;
```

$$\frac{3\ c\ +\ a}{3\ b\ +\ 1},\quad 3\ \frac{b\ a\ -\ c}{3\ b\ +\ 1}$$

unassign can be used to unassign several variables in one statement.

```
> readlib( unassign ):   # load library function
> unassign( ´x´, ´y´ ):   x, y;
```

$$x,\ y$$

You may be tempted to use it in combination with **anames** in order to clear all your assigned values, but look what a drastic effect this can have on the behavior of Maple.

```
> # compute some integral
> integral := integrate( 1/(x^2+1), x );
```

$$integral := \arctan(x)$$

```
> unassign( anames() ):   # unassign variables
> integrate( 1/(x^2+1), x );   # recompute the integral
Error, (in int) type int/type does not exist in maple
```

The reason for Maple's malfunctioning is that we did not only unvaluate user-defined variables like integral, but also system-defined variables like int/type. You had better use the **restart** statement to clear internal memory and start Maple afresh without leaving the system.

3.3 Full Evaluation

In general, when Maple encounters a name in an instruction, it searches
for the object to which the name points: we say that Maple *evaluates* the
name. When a name points to another name, the system will search again
for the object to which that name points, and so on, until it arrives at an
object which is not a name or which points to itself. The last object is now
used as if it were substituted in the instruction. So, the normal process is
for every expression to be *fully evaluated.* This explains the next sample
session.

```
> a := b;   b := c;   c:= 3;
```
$$a := b$$
$$b := c$$
$$c := 3$$
```
> a;   # evaluation of a
```
$$3$$

In order to get a better understanding of full evaluation, we look at the
effect of assignments in terms of internal data structures. In Maple, a
variable is internally represented by a data vector with three components,
viz., a first component indicating that the vector represents a variable, a
second component pointing to the current value of the variable, and a third
component to name the variable. When we assign a value to a variable, we
simply set a pointer from the named data vector to the assigned value. In
the above example, this results in the following internal representation.

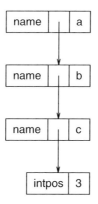

The second component of the data vector representing the variable a points
to the value of a: so, the value of a is equal to b. Similarly, the value of b
is equal to c. We can check this internal representation by use of the **eval**
procedure.

```
> eval(a,1);   # value of a
                              b
> eval(b,1);   # value of b
                              c
> eval(c,1);   # value of c
                              3
> eval(a,2);   # two-level evaluation of a
                              c
> eval(a,3);   # three-level evaluation of a
                              3
```

When we fully evaluate a, we walk down all pointers, starting at the data vector representing a and ending at the object of type "positive integer" and value 3. We say "a evaluates to 3." When the variable c is now assigned a new value, say 5, then the variable a evaluates to 5. However, the value of a remains b; it can only be changed by an assignment.

```
> c := 5:
> a;   # a now evaluates to 5
                              5
> eval(a,1);   # but the value of a remains the same
                              b
> a := 4:
> a, eval(a,1);
                         4, 4
> # the value of a and its full evaluation are both 4
```

In the process of full evaluation of expressions, variables are substituted by the values which they received in their most recent assignments. The next example illustrates this.

```
> x := y:  y := 7:
> # the value of x is y, but x evaluates to 7
> eval(x,1), x;
                         y, 7
> x := x;
                         x := 7
```

```
> # now, the value of x is 7 and x also evaluates to 7
> y := 9:
> x;   # the value and evaluation of x remain unchanged
```

$$7$$

The instruction **x := x** suggests that x points to x. This is not the case as you have seen before! If you want to achieve this, you should have entered the command **x := ´x´**. Here, the apostrophes prevent the full evaluation of x.

The easiest way to make sure that a name is passed through as an argument to a Maple procedure is to use *apostrophes* to suppress evaluation. For example, the fourth parameter of the procedure **rem**, which is used for storage of the quotient, must be a name.

```
> # suppose that quotient has been assigned some value
> quotient := 0:
> rem( x^3 + x + 1, x^2 + x + 1, x, ´quotient´ );
```

$$2 + x$$

```
> quotient; # value has been set in previous command
```

$$x - 1$$

If you really want to go savely, then you should reset the value of a variable first to its own name with the command *variable* := **evaln**(*variable*).

But what if you forget the apostrophes in the above example?

```
> quotient := 0:
> rem( x^3 + x + 1, x^2 + x + 1, x, quotient );
Error, (in rem) Illegal use of a formal parameter
```

What went wrong? Through the first instruction, the variable quotient gets the value 0. When the second instruction is carried out, Maple first evaluates its arguments, which leads to rem(x^3+x+1, x^2+x+1, x, 0). Maple gives an error because it expects a name to which the computed quotient can be assigned as its fourth argument. If the variable quotient points to x, then an infinitely recursive structure would appear!

```
> quotient := x:
> rem( x^3 + x + 1, x^2 + x + 1, x, quotient );
```

$$2 + x$$

```
> eval(quotient,1), eval(quotient,2);
```

$$x, \ x - 1$$

So, internally an assignment $x := x - 1$ is carried out, and this will cause an error when you later refer to x.

In other instances, you also want to or actually need to suppress full evaluation of expressions or of parts of expressions. Let us, for example, compute the sum of the first 5 prime numbers with the procedure **sum**.

```
> i := 0: # assume i has been assigned some value

> sum( ithprime(i), i=1..5 );

Error, (in ithprime) argument must be a positive integer
```

When Maple evaluates the argument `ithprime(i)` in the above function call it notices that it has gotten an invalid argument.

```
> sum( 'ithprime(i)', i=1..5 );

Error, (in sum) summation variable previously assigned,
               second argument evaluates to, 0 = 1 .. 5
```

The error message explains the problem. So, you must ensure that the summation index evaluates to a name.

```
> sum( 'ithprime(i)', 'i'=1..5 );
```

$$28$$

Good advice: in commands like **sum**, always use quote marks around the summand and the summation index unless you are *sure* that they can be omitted.

The result of evaluation of an expression enclosed by apostrophes can be best described as peeling off a pair of quotes.

```
> x := 1: # in this example x always has the value 1

> x+1;
```

$$2$$

```
> 'x'+1;
```

$$x + 1$$

```
> 'x+1';
```

$$x + 1$$

```
> '''x'+1'';
```

$$''x' + 1'$$

```
> ";
```

$$'x' + 1$$

```
> ";
```

$$x + 1$$

```
> ";
```

$$2$$

3.4 Names of Variables

In Maple, the simplest kind of names of variables and constants are *strings*, i.e., sequences of letters, digits, and underscores, the first of which must be a letter or underscore. Strings are restricted to a maximum length of 499 characters. A few examples:

```
> x, a_long_name_containing_underscores, H2O;
```

$$1, \; a\_long\_name\_containing\_underscores, \; H2O$$

```
> unknown, UNKNOWN, UnKnOwN;
```

$$unknown, \; UNKNOWN, \; UnKnOwN$$

Note that Maple uses both upper- and lower-case letters. Keep this in mind when using Maple names for mathematical constants: π is denoted in Maple by Pi, but the system does not associate the name pi with this constant. Be careful with the Maple name for the base of the natural logarithm: not e, but E. The complex square root of -1 is denoted by I, not by i.

Names starting with an underscore are used by Maple itself (recall the result of **RootOf** in §2.5). There are also reserved words that Maple does not accept right away as valid names.

Reserved Names				
and	by	do	done	elif
else	end	fi	for	from
if	in	intersect	local	minus
mod	not	od	option	options
or	proc	quit	read	save
stop	then	to	union	while

Furthermore, there are names which already have a meaning in Maple, e.g., names of mathematical functions like **sin**, **cos**, **exp**, **sqrt**, ..., names of Maple procedures like **copy**, **indices**, **lhs**, **rhs**, **type**, **coeff**, **degree**, **order**, ..., and names of data types in Maple like **set**, **list**, **matrix**, ...

Good advice: avoid reserved names of variables unless you want to deliberately overrule Maple. Also avoid names starting with an underscore. Otherwise, you may get puzzled by results.

```
> _Z:=sqrt(2):
> RootOf(x^2-x,x);
Error, (in RootOf) expression independent of, 2**(1/2)
> type( {a,b,c}, set );
```
$$true$$
```
> set := {1,2,3}:
> type( {a,b,c}, set );
```
$$false$$
```
> indices := {1,2}:
> with( linalg ):   # (try to) load the linalg package
Error, (in with) invalid arguments to sort
```

If you want to use spaces in a name for reasons of readability, or if you want to use special characters such as dots, colons, or slashes, then you must surround the name with *left quotes* (also referred to as *back quotes, grave accents*, and *reversed apostrophes*). These left quotes themselves are not part of the name and disappear when the string is displayed; they only mark the boundaries of the name. Two consecutive left quotes appearing after the opening or before the ending of a string are parsed as an enclosed back quote character. Below are few more examples of valid Maple names.

```
> `exercise 1`, `/usr/local/lib/maple/lib/cat.m`;
```
$$exercise\ 1,\ /usr/local/lib/maple/lib/cat.m$$
```
> `Answer:`; # the colon is part of the name
```
$$Answer:$$
```
> ``; # the null string or empty name
> ```/usr/local/lib/maple/lib/cat.m```;
```
$$`/usr/local/lib/maple/lib/cat.m`$$

Don't associate Maple names enclosed by left quotes with strings in conventional programming languages like FORTRAN. The following example shows you this.

```
> miscellanea := `apparent_text`;
```
$$miscellanea := apparent\_text$$
```
> apparent_text := cos(Pi);
```
$$apparent\_text := -1$$

```
> miscellanea, `miscellanea`;
```

$$-1, \ -1$$

As you see, these left quotes have no influence here. Occasionally, rather strange things happen with these quotes.

```
> `Here starts a name which is

Warning: String contains newline character.
Close strings with ` quote.

>   concatenated` := 0;
```

$$\textit{Here starts a name which is \ concatenated}:= 0$$

If you happen to type an opening left quote but forget about the closing one, Maple does not seem to accept input anymore. To get you out of this deadlock, follow Maple's advice: enter a closing left quote followed by a semicolon and everything should work fine again.

Now and then, but mostly when using Maple as a programming language, concatenation of names is handy. A few examples of the use of the procedure **cat** and the concatenation operator (.) follow.

```
> libname,  cat(libname,`/cat.m`);
```

$$\textit{/usr/local/lib/maple/lib,}$$

$$\textit{/usr/local/lib/maple/lib/cat.m}$$

```
> # alternative way of concatenation
> `` . libname . `/cat.m`;
```

$$\textit{/usr/local/lib/maple/lib/cat.m}$$

```
> X.Y, X.1;
```

$$\textit{XY, \ X1}$$

```
> X . ( Y, 1 );
```

$$\textit{XY, \ X1}$$

```
> X . (1..8);
```

$$\textit{X1, X2, X3, X4, X5, X6, X7, X8}$$

```
> `` . ( X, Y ) . ( 1 .. 4 );
```

$$\textit{X1, X2, X3, X4, Y1, Y2, Y3, Y4}$$

```
> i:=4:  X.i, i.X;
```

$$\textit{X4, \ iX}$$

The last example shows that, when using the concatenation operator, the first name does not get evaluated. The obvious design choice has been that, for example, x.1 should always evaluate to x1, regardless whether x has been assigned a value or not. This explains why we have used in some of the above examples the empty name as first argument in concatenation.

Don't confuse the use of quote marks in Maple; we summarize their effects.

Quote Marks	
Quote	**Purpose**
` ` ` `	markers for a name with special characters
´ ´	delay of evaluation
"	reference to previously evaluated expression
" "	reference to the second last expression evaluated
" " "	reference to the third last expression evaluated

3.5 Basic Data Types

Values of data are divided into classes — the *data types*. The data type fixes, among other things, what values can be taken or what operations are allowed on the data. The usual elementary data types like *integer, floating-point number*, and *string* are present in Maple, but there are many more. Maple can show you the basic type of data with the command **whattype**.

```
> whattype( 5.0 );
                          float

> whattype( `an example of a long name` );
                          string

> whattype( { 1, 2, 3 } );
                          set
> whattype( 1, 2, 3 );
                          exprseq
```

The result of **whattype** is a description of the header of the data vector. Therefore, all such data types are also called *surface data types*. At the end of this chapter we list the most common surface data types available in Maple. You get a more complete list with **?surface**.

Maple provides two other tools for type testing, viz., **type** and **hastype**.

```
> type( x + y, `+` );
```
true

```
> hastype( x + y, `+` );
```
true

```
> hastype( x + 1/2 * y, ´fraction´ );
```
true

```
> hastype( x + 2 * y, ´fraction´ );
```
false

These two type testing functions test not only for surface data types, but also test more general types of expressions.

```
> type( x^2 + x + 1, ´polynom´ );
```
true

```
> type( x^2 + x + Pi, ´polynom(integer,x)´ );
```
false

```
> type( x^2 + x + 1, ´quadratic( x )´ );
```
true

The apostrophes around the second argument of the procedures **hastype** and **type** are used to prevent evaluation of these arguments, just in case they have values different from their names. You are again advised to get into the habit of adding quotes in such cases. Note that an expression can be of several data types at the same time.

In a conventional programming languages like FORTRAN you have to specify the type of a variable and it cannot be changed within a program. Nothing of the kind in Maple: a variable has no fixed type. Otherwise, your interactive work would be overloaded with type declarations, which are almost always superfluous because of the mathematical context, and type conversions would be cumbersome. A few illustrative examples:

```
> number := 1:  whattype( number );
```
integer

```
> number := 0.75:   whattype( number );
```
float

```
> number := convert( number, ´fraction´ );
```

$$number := \frac{3}{4}$$

```
> convert( number, ´binary´ );

Error, (in convert/binary) invalid argument for convert
```

The last statement illustrates that not all type changes are allowed in Maple: type changes must make sense to the system. For example, the rational number $\frac{3}{4}$ can be written as the **con**tinued **frac**tion

$$0 + \cfrac{1}{1 + \cfrac{1}{3}}$$

```
> convert( number, ´confrac´ );

                    [ 0, 1, 3 ]
```

Again, the apostrophes around the second argument of the procedure **convert** are used to prevent evaluation. More readable, two-dimensional output is obtained by the procedure **numtheory[cfrac]**.

```
> # load the function cfrac from the numtheory package

> with( numtheory, cfrac ):

> cfrac( number, 2 );
```

$$\cfrac{1}{1 + \cfrac{1}{3}}$$

Maple also has the *padic* package to compute with *p-adic numbers*. Let us, for example, write the fraction $\frac{3}{4}$ as a 3-adic number.

```
> with( padic ):   # load the p-adic number package

> # write the number as a 3-adic number in standard size

> evalp( number, 3 );
```

$$3 + 2 \cdot 3^2 + 2 \cdot 3^4 + 2 \cdot 3^6 + 2 \cdot 3^8 + O(3^{10})$$

3.6 Exercises

1. What is the difference in the use of the variables a and b in

```
> a := ´a´;    b:= ´b´;    a := b;    b := 10;
```

and

```
> a := ´a´;    b := ´b´;    b := 10;    a := b;
```

Can you add one extra assignment at the end of the sentence below, so that the total effect of carrying out the instructions on this line is the same as the result of entering the first of the above sentences?

```
> a := ´a´;  b := ´b´;   b:= 10;
```

2. Explain in detail what happens when you enter the following commands in sequence.

```
> p := ´p´ ; q := ´q´ ;
> 7 * 5 ;
> p = 10 ;
> q : 3 ;
> """ ; """ ; """ ;
> p ; q ;
```

3. Explain the different result of the following Maple commands.
   x*y;, **x·y;**, and **x\y;**.

4. Describe in detail the difference between the two Maple sessions below (e.g., by drawing pictures of the internal data structures).

```
> a := b;
> b := 3;
> a;
> b := 4;
> a;
```

and

```
> b := 3;
> a := b;
> a;
> b := 4;
> a;
```

5. Predict the results of entering the following commands and check your answers with Maple.

```
> X1 := 5;    j := 1;
> X . j;
> ´X . j´;
> ´X´ . j;
> `X . j`;
```

6. Suppose that the variables v1, v2, and v3 are bound. Why can't you unassign these variables by the following repetition statement (or do-loop)?

```
> for i to 3 do   v.i := ´v.i´ od:
```

7. Explain what goes wrong when you enter the following commands.

```
> gcd( x^2 - 1, x - 1, x );
> x;
```

8. Carry out the following instructions, predict the Maple results and compare these with the actual answers of the system.

```
i := 3:    x := 4:
sum( x^i, i = 1..5 );
sum( x^i, ´i´ = 1..5 );
sum( ´x^i´, ´i´ = 1..5 );
sum( ´x´^i, ´i´ = 1..5 );
sum( x^´i´, ´i´ = 1..5 );
sum( ´x´^`i`, ´i´ = 1..5 );
sum( `x^i`, ´i´ = 1..5 );
´sum( x^i, i = 1..5 )´;
```

9. Successively transform the expression $a+b+c$ into $a*b*c$, and $[a, b, c]$.

10. Use Maple to find the continued fraction expansion of $\sqrt{2}$ and the golden ratio $\dfrac{1+\sqrt{5}}{2}$, respectively.

Surface Data Types		
Data	**Type**	**Example**
Numbers and Strings:		
integer	`integer`	`1`
fraction	`fraction`	`1/2`
floating-point number	`float`	`0.33333`
complex number	`complex`	`1+2*I`
alphanumeric text	`string`	`xvalue`
Arithmetic Expressions:		
sum	`` `+` ``	`x + y`
product	`` `*` ``	`x * y`
power	`` `^` `` or `` `**` ``	`x ^ y`
Relational Expressions:		
equation	`` `=` ``, `equation`	`x+1 = 1+x`
inequality	`` `<>` ``	`Pi <> pi`
less-than-relation	`` `<` ``	`2 < 3`
less-than-or-equal relation	`` `<=` ``	`E <= Pi`
Logical Expressions:		
and-expression	`` `and` ``	`P and Q`
or-expression	`` `or` ``	`P or Q`
negation	`` `not` ``	`not P`
Composite Expressions:		
expression sequence	`exprseq`	`a,b,c`
set	`set`	`{a,b,c}`
list	`list`	`[a,b,c]`
table	`table`	`table([a,b,c])`
indexed name	`indexed`	`X[1]`
function call	`function`	`f(x)`, where `f` is not defined
Miscellanea:		
unevaluated concatenation	`` `.` ``	`a.(1..n)`, where `n` has no value
range	`` `..` ``, `range`	`1 .. 3`
generalized power series	`series`	x^{-1} `- gamma + O(x)`
procedure definition	`procedure`	`proc(x) x^3 end`
unevaluated expression	`uneval`	`''x + y''`

Getting Around with Maple

This chapter describes in detail how to get around with Maple: how Maple handles input and output, how to change Maple to your own taste (prompt, width of printout, labeling, etc.), how to edit inputs, how to read and write files, how to get more information about usage of computer resources, how to trace computations, and how to get user-information about chosen techniques or algorithms. Formatted I/O and code generation are examples of interaction between Maple and programming/typesetting languages. Moreover, the setup of the Maple library (standard library, miscellaneous library, packages, and share library) is explained.

Some of the topics in this chapter depend on the user interface: we shall assume that the worksheet interface is used. Occasionally we shall describe how things work in the text-based user interface.

4.1 Input and Output

Maple can react in several ways when you enter an instruction:

- The system understands the command and returns
  - ▷ either the result in one or more lines followed by a new prompt,
  - ▷ or a new prompt at once, indicating that Maple is waiting for another instruction.

  In the former case the previous input line was closed by a semicolon; the latter reaction occurs when the input line was closed by a colon. When a colon is used Maple performs the calculation quietly. Later in this section we shall encounter some exceptions to this general rule.

- Your instruction is not finished yet, e.g., because you simply forgot to enter a semicolon or a colon to separate commands. In this case too, Maple is short in its response and only returns a new prompt. You may still finish your instruction.

```
> Digits := 25:    evalf(
>    log(cos(Pi/12)) );
              -.03466823209753695510470915
```

- You entered an instruction which Maple does not understand and you are punished with a *syntax-error* message; Maple points with the *caret* (^) to the place where the syntax error appeared. The only thing that you can do is to re-enter what you hope is a correct instruction.

```
> x*
> *3;
syntax error:
*3;
^
> x**
> 3;
```
$$x^3$$

When you use the worksheet interface, you can place the cursor at any place to correct input (in most cases, to add brackets, to insert mathematical operators like *, etc.) and re-execute it. When the *replace mode* option has been turned on, the newly generated output replaces the previous one. The text-based user interface of Maple has a command line editor built in which allows you to edit one hundred previous input lines.

- Although the command is syntactically correct, Maple refuses to carry out the instruction.

```
> read a_non_existing_file;
Error, unable to read a_non_existing_file
> 123456789 ^ 987654321;
Error, object too large
```

After an error message, Maple is usually ready for new input; and it certainly is after you have entered an empty statement in the form of a single semicolon. This does not apply if you have started a name with a left quote and forgotten about the closing left quote. In this case you must first finish the name with a left quote before Maple listens to you again.

```
> `This is a long name;
Warning, string contains newline
character. Close strings with ` quote.
> 2+3; @%!
Warning, string contains newline
character. Close strings with ` quote.
> that contains funny characters`;

    This is a long name; 2+3; @%! that contains funny\

        characters
```

- By using the *sharp symbol*, **#**, you entered a comment. Maple does not echo the text after the sharp symbol.

```
> # this is a comment
> a := 2;   # a := two
```
$$a := 2$$

```
> a;
```
$$2$$

```
> a := 2   # a := two ;
> # the semicolon on the previous line
> # was part of a comment!
> ;
```
$$a := 2$$

So, Maple's reaction to your input depends upon the way you finish your command. But you have more influence on the output. First, there is the variable `printlevel` whose default value is equal to one. When you assign a negative value to this variable, then no results are shown irrespective of whether a command is finished with a semicolon or colon. On the other hand, when you set a higher value to `printlevel` Maple tells you more of what it is doing. Values in the range from two to four are for information such as explanatory remarks about the chosen algorithm or information about parameters, local variables, and the precise statement being executed if a run-time error occurs. The higher the value of `printlevel`, the more information you get. High values of `printlevel`, say in the hundreds or thousands, are not unusual when you want to debug a Maple program. If you only want to see what technique or algorithm is chosen, then you should use the **userinfo**-facility, which can be invoked by the assignement **infolevel**[*function*] := *level* for the requested *function*. User information is available at several levels.

userinfo-facility	
Level	**Purpose**
1	all necessary information
2, 3	general information, including technique or algorithm being used
4, 5	detailed information about how the problem is being solved

Two examples make things clear.

```
> printlevel := 2:   # set printlevel a higher value

> lhs( x + y );
```

Error, (in lhs) invalid arguments
executing statement: ERROR(`invalid arguments`)
lhs called with arguments: x+y

```
> printlevel := 1:   # reset printlevel

> infolevel[ integrate ] := 1:

> integrate( 1/(x^3+x+1),   x = 0 .. infinity );
```

int/indef: first-stage indefinite integration
int/ratpoly: rational function integration
int/rischnorm: enter Risch-Norman integrator
int/risch: enter Risch integration
int/risch: exit Risch integration

$$-\left(\sum_{\_R=\%1} \_R \ \ln\left(-\frac{62}{9} \ \_R^2 + \frac{31}{9} \ \_R + \frac{4}{9} \right) \right)$$

%1 := RootOf(31 $\_Z^3$ - 3 $\_Z$ - 1)

If you still want to see a result on the terminal screen while print-level has been assigned a negative value, then you must say so. Use either one of the procedures **print** or **lprint**. The difference is in the display of results: **print** yields a so-called two-dimensional layout, which resembles common mathematical notation as much as possible. **lprint** ("linear print") displays results in one-dimensional, left-adjusted format. An example:

```
> printlevel := -1:   # Maple becomes silent

> sols := solve( a*x^2 + b*x + c, x );

> print( sols );   # 2-dimensional output
```

$$-\frac{1}{4} b + \frac{1}{4} \sqrt{b^2 - 8 \ c}, \quad \frac{1}{4} b - \frac{1}{4} \sqrt{b^2 - 8 \ c}$$

```
> lprint( sols );   # left-adjusted, 1-dimensional output
```

-1/4*b+1/4*(b^2-8*c)^(1/2)   -1/4*b-1/4*(b^2-8*c)^(1/2)

```
> printlevel := 10: # Maple gives more details

> integrate( 1/ ( x^5 + 1 ),   x = 0 .. infinity );
```

{--> enter int, args = 1/(x^5+1), x = 0 .. infinity

X := X

ra := 0

$$rb := \infty$$

$$indef := false$$

$$g := \frac{1}{x^5 + 1}$$

$$r := \frac{1}{5} \Gamma\left(\frac{1}{5}\right) \Gamma\left(\frac{4}{5}\right)$$

```
<-- exit int (now at top level)=1/5*GAMMA(1/5)*GAMMA(4/5)}
```

$$\frac{1}{5} \Gamma\left(\frac{1}{5}\right) \Gamma\left(\frac{4}{5}\right)$$

By the way, you cannot refer to the result of the procedures **print** and **lprint** by the ditto operators or in any other way, because both procedures evaluate to the special name NULL. This special name is used in Maple to indicate an empty sequence of expressions or an empty statement. When you use the ditto operator to refer to a previous result NULL is skipped. So, note the differences in the following commands.

```
> example := 11/12, evalf(exp(-10)), NULL, (1-x)/(1+x):
> `some text`;
                        some text

> lprint( example ); # display of some expressions
11/12    Float(4539992976,-14)    (1-x)/(1+x)
> ";
                        some text

> example: # evaluation to a sequence of expressions
> ";
```

$$\frac{11}{12}, \quad .00004539992976248485153559152, \quad \frac{1 - x}{1 + x}$$

```
> interface( prettyprint = false );
> ";
11/12, Float(4539992976,-14), (1-x)/(1+x)
```

The last two instructions show that you can set the value of the interface variable prettyprint to false so that henceforth Maple output is left-adjusted and in one-dimensional format. In §4.6 we shall see what other interface options you have in Maple to change the system to your own taste.

4.2 The Maple Library

The Maple library consists of four parts:

- the *standard library,*
- the *miscellaneous library,*
- *packages,* and
- the *share library.*

The size of the Maple library, the share library exclusive, is about nine megabytes, but the system loads only those functions into main memory that it actually needs.

Whenever you enter an instruction which uses a procedure from the *standard library* that has not been used before in the Maple session, the system is smart enough to load the requested procedure from the external memory into main memory itself and to carry out the computation.

The *miscellaneous library* contains more infrequently used procedures. These functions must be explicitly loaded from the external memory into main memory by the command **readlib**.

```
> f := exp(a*z) / ( 1 + exp(z) );   # some formula
```

$$f := \frac{e^{a\,z}}{1 + e^z}$$

```
> residue( f, z=Pi*I );
```

$$\mathrm{residue}\left(\frac{e^{a\,z}}{1 + e^z},\ z = I\,\pi\right)$$

The procedure **residue** for computing the residue of a complex function at a pole resides in the *miscellaneous library* and has not yet been loaded into main memory. Maple leaves it this way and waits for the moment that you define the function, i.e., load it from the library.

```
> readlib( residue );
proc(f,a) ... end
> residue( f, z=Pi*I );
```

$$-e^{I\,a\,\pi}$$

```
> residue( 1 / ( z^2 + a^2 ), z=a*I );
```

$$-\frac{1}{2}\frac{I}{a}$$

There are also packages for more specialized purposes in Maple, e.g., the orthopoly package for orthogonal polynomials (among others,

Hermite, Legendre, Laguerre, and Chebyshev polynomials). To use a function from this package you have to mention the name of the package as well. For example, to compute a Chebyshev polynomial you enter

```
> orthopoly[T](4,x);
```
$$8\ x^4\ -\ 8\ x^2\ +\ 1$$

There are four ways to avoid having to use such long names:

- Use the procedure **alias** to define a synonym.

```
> alias( T = orthopoly[T] ):
> T(5,x);
```
$$16\ x^5\ -\ 20\ x^3\ +\ 5\ x$$

  To remove the alias definition of T enter

```
> alias( T = T ):
```

- Use the procedure **macro** to define an abbreviation.

```
> macro( T = orthopoly[T] ):
> T(6,x);
```
$$32\ x^6\ -\ 48\ x^4\ +\ 18\ x^2\ -\ 1$$

  The difference between **macro** and **alias** is that the macro facility is a simple abbreviation mechanism working on the input side,

```
> ´T(6,x)´;
```
$$orthopoly_{[\ T\ ]}(\ 6,\ x\ )$$

  whereas the alias facility affects both input and output (see also the examples in §2.5). To remove the macro definition of T enter

```
> macro( T = T ):
```

- Explicitly load the Chebyshev function **T** from the *orthopoly* package.

```
> with( orthopoly, T );
```
$$[T]$$

```
> T(7,y);
```
$$64\ y^7\ -\ 112\ y^5\ +\ 56\ y^3\ -\ 7\ y$$

- Tell Maple that you want to use the complete package.

```
> with( orthopoly );
```
$$[\ G,\ H,\ L,\ P,\ T,\ U\ ]$$

The result of invoking **with(orthopoly)** is that a group of names (such as **T** or **U**) is defined to point to the same procedure as their corresponding package style names (**orthopoly[T]** or **orthopoly[U]**). The complete code of all procedures is *not* loaded from the library.

```
> T(8,z);
```

$$128 \ z^8 \ - \ 256 \ z^6 \ + \ 160 \ z^4 \ - \ 32 \ z^2 \ + \ 1$$

Only at this point is the code for the procedure **orthopoly[T]** loaded and executed for the given arguments.

Finally, there is the *share library* containing user-developed Maple procedures and packages. Enter **?share, address** to see where to get updates of the share library from, and enter **?share, contrib** to see how you can contribute yourself to the share library. When Maple is properly installed, you can access the code in the share library by entering

```
> with( share ):
```

Hereafter you can read each procedure and load each package from the share library as if it were a regular Maple procedure or package. For example, you can load Dongming Wang's implementation of Ritt-Wu's characteristic sets method [120] and use it to solve a system of polynomial equations.

```
> with( charsets );
```

$$[\ cfactor, \ charser, \ charset, \ csolve, \ ecs, \ eics, \ ics,$$

$$iniset, \ ivd, \ mcharset, \ mcs, \ mecs, \ qics, \ remset,$$

$$triser \ ]$$

```
> polys := [x^2 - 2*x*z + 5, x*y^2 + y*z^3,
>    3*y^2 - 8*z^3 ];
```

$$polys := [\ x^2 \ - \ 2 \ x \ z \ + \ 5, \ x \ y^2 + y \ z^3, \ 3 \ y^2 - 8 \ z^3 \ ]$$

```
> vars := [ x, y, z ]:
> sols := csolve( polys, vars );
```

$$\left\{ x = \%1 \ , y = -\frac{1}{8} \frac{\%1^{\ 6} + 15 \ \%1^{\ 4} + 75 \ \%1^{\ 2} + 125}{\%1^{\ 4}}, z = -\frac{1}{2} \frac{-\%1^{2} - 5}{\%1} \right\},$$

$$\left\{ z = 0, y = 0, x = I\sqrt{5} \right\}, \left\{ z = 0, y = 0, x = -I\sqrt{5} \right\}$$

$$\%1 := RootOf(3 \ \_Z^6 - 64 \ \_Z^5 + 45 \ \_Z^4 + 225 \ \_Z^2 + 375)$$

4.3 Reading and Writing Files

First of all we distinguish between

- files containing Maple code in a format that can only be understood by the computer algebra system,
- files containing Maple code in a user-readable and user-understandable format, i.e., code which has been written in the Maple programming language itself,
- files containing results of Maple calculations, which for their part cannot be used as input for further computations, and
- files containing formatted input/output, which are created by or can be read by other applications.

The latter category of files will be dealt with in the next section. Here, we shall concentrate on only the first three types of files.

Let us first look at the third category of files. Normally, the result of a Maple command which has been terminated by a semicolon is embedded in the worksheet or shown on the terminal screen. However, you can also transfer the output to a file so that you can read through the results at your leisure or print the results on paper. For example, to transfer all results in a Maple session to the file `outputfile` it suffices to enter

```
> writeto( outputfile ):
```

Henceforth, all Maple output is redirected to the file instead of to the worksheet or terminal screen. However, there is a difference between the worksheet and text-based user interface: when you use the text-based interface, then also the prompt ">", the given instructions, and the run-time messages are written into the file. The reason for this is that, when the text-based interface is used, Maple cannot write simultaneously to a file and the terminal screen. The instructions that you enter are carried out in a row. Suppose that you enter the commands

```
number := 90;
polynomial := x^2 + 81;
subs( x = number, polynomial );
writeto( terminal );
```

Everything from the last command is shown on the terminal screen again.

```
> ";
                          8181
> quit
```

The file `outputfile` looks as follows.

```
> number := 90;
                                           number := 90
> polynomial := x^2 + 81;
                                                      2
                               polynomial := x  + 81
> subs( x = number, polynomial );
                                          8181
> writeto( terminal );
```

Keep in mind that **writeto** overwrites an existing file. If you want to avoid this and just want to append output, then you should use the procedure **appendto**. As was remarked before, you cannot do very much else with the output file but reading and printing. You cannot use it as input for a new Maple session without further processing.

With the procedure **save** you can indeed save results of Maple calculations in such a way that they can be used again in a Maple session. You read data from such a file back into memory with the Maple procedure **read**. The data transfer into an output file can be done in two ways:

- in an internal format which can only be understood by Maple (when the filename ends with ".m") or otherwise
- in a human-readable format or plain text format.

Let us look at an example.

```
> polynomial := x^2 + 2*x +1;  `number four` := 4;
                        polynomial := x² + 2 x + 1

                           number four := 4

> save datafile;   save `datafile.m`;
> quit
```

Don't forget to use the back quotes around the name `datafile.m`, otherwise Maple concatenates it to `datafilem` and consequently transfers results in user-readable format instead of internal Maple format. Note that you will also need the back quotes when you want to make use of a subdirectory and need the Unix-separator /, otherwise this symbol is used as a division operator. If you work under Unix, you cannot use abbreviations like ~ for your home directory.

The files `datafile` and `datafile.m` both contain all the knowledge of Maple just before the data transfer. This can be the starting point for a new Maple session; you can read (and if desired change) the file `datafile` with an editor or look at it with the Unix command **more**.

```
canc.can.nl> more datafile

`number four` := 4;
polynomial := x^2+2*x+1;
```

You see that readability leaves a lot to be desired because of the one-dimensional layout chosen by Maple. But let us read the file in a new Maple session.

```
> read datafile;
                    number four := 4

                polynomial := x² + 2 x + 1

> `number four` * polynomial;

                    4 x² + 8 x + 4

> quit
```

You see that the instructions in the file `datafile` are dealt with as if they were entered directly from the keyboard. Therefore, you can prepare in your favorite editor a file suitable for **read** by writing down Maple instructions one after another.

When you start Maple, the system always looks first for an initialization file that can be read in the above way. For example, under the Unix operating system, Maple searches first for a system-wide initialization file called `init` in the `src` subdirectory of the Maple library, and secondly searches for an initialization file `.mapleinit` in your home directory. Using this file you can automatically load library packages which you always want to use, reset interface variables (see the last section), and so on.

When all data have been read from a file by the Maple procedure **read**, Maple resumes the handling of instructions entered from the previous input stream; this may be from the Maple worksheet, the terminal screen, or from another file.

You see that all incoming data from the **read** instruction are redisplayed on the terminal screen. In some cases this is a handy reminder, but at others it is just too much information. When data have been written in internal Maple format, i.e., in a file with the name extension ".m", redisplay of data does not occur. You could have suppressed display of data by prepending to the user-readable file two lines in which you save the current value of `printlevel` and give it the new value -1, and by appending a line in which `printlevel` gets back its old value. But this is extra work. As you will see in the session below, echoing of input from a file does not happen when the file is in internal Maple format. However, the most important advantage of using internal Maple format is that reading and writing is done more efficiently than in user-readable format. The file `datafile.m` used below is not user-readable, but in internal Maple format.

```
> read `datafile.m`;
```

```
> polynomial := factor( polynomial );
```

$$polynomial := (x + 1)^2$$

```
> square := subs( x=`number four`, polynomial );
```

$$square := 25$$

You don't have to save all variables; you may choose. As a continuation of the above session we write the variable `number four` and the expression $(x+1)^2$ to the user-readable file `output`.

```
> save `number four`, polynomial, output;
```

The file `output` will have the following contents.

```
`number four` := 4;
polynomial := (x+1)^2;
```

   Speed and silence while reading files which are in internal Maple format becomes more important when you load procedures from the Maple library. You don't want to see messages about use or definitions of library functions each time they are loaded.

   But why another Maple procedure, viz., **readlib**, for reading library functions? Why not use the **read** command? The answer lies in the hierarchical file structure that Maple presumes. Reading from and writing to a file always takes place with respect to the position where you were in the file structure when you launched Maple, unless you specify a full pathname. You can ask for the full pathname of the Maple library by asking the value of the variable `libname` within a Maple session. The answer will look like

```
> libname;
```

$$/usr/local/lib/maple/lib$$

From there you can read for instance the file `mtaylor.m` by

```
> read `/usr/local/lib/maple/lib/mtaylor.m`:
```
or
```
> read `` . libname . `/mtaylor.m`:
```

Of course it is cumbersome and error-prone to type such long names whenever you need something from the Maple library. An abbreviation is more convenient.

```
> readlib( mtaylor ):
```

Maple seems to interpret the command as

```
> read `` . libname . `/` . mtaylor . `.m`:
```

Actually, Maple does more: it checks whether a procedure with the name
mtaylor is indeed defined as a result of this read instruction or not, and it
returns the value read as the value of the **readlib** command. Hence, you
can immediately specify the arguments and compute a multivariate taylor
series.

```
> readlib( mtaylor )(  sin(x+y), [x,y]  );
```

$$x + y - \frac{1}{6} x^3 - \frac{1}{2} y\, x^2 - \frac{1}{2} y^2\, x - \frac{1}{6} y^3 + \frac{1}{120} x^5$$

$$+ \frac{1}{24} y\, x^4 + \frac{1}{12} y^2\, x^3 + \frac{1}{12} y^3\, x^2 + \frac{1}{24} y^4\, x$$

$$+ \frac{1}{120} y^5$$

```
> sort( simplify( ", {z=x+y}, [x,y,z] ) );
```

$$\frac{1}{120} z^5 - \frac{1}{6} z^3 + z$$

```
> subs( z=x+y, " );
```

$$\frac{1}{120} (x + y)^5 - \frac{1}{6} (x + y)^3 + x + y$$

Fortunately, most of the Maple procedures are loaded automatically from
the Maple library when invoked. An example of such a *readlib-defined function* is **gcd**, which is initially defined by gcd := 'readlib('gcd')'. As
we have seen above, readlib-defined functions will be automatically loaded
when invoked. So, we actually need not know the distinction between them
and functions in the kernel (you get a list of these functions by entering
?internal).

   In Maple you can use more than one library. For example, when the
share library has been loaded, the variable sharename contains the location
of the share library, and the variable libname is a sequence of names of
two libraries which are searched in order.

```
> with( share ):
> sharename;
              /usr/local/lib/maple/share
> libname;
   /usr/local/lib/maple/lib, /usr/local/lib/maple/share
```

The support of multiple libraries also allows users to override the Maple library and to have private libraries. By the assignement

```
> libname := `/ufs/heck/private_maplelib`, libname:
```

you instruct Maple to look first in the private library and, if this does lead to a result, in the standard library whenever you call the **readlib** procedure.

You can explicitly **unload** a library function so that Maple forgets all its knowledge about the function.

```
> print( igcd );
proc() options builtin; 84 end
> readlib(unload)( igcd );
```

$$igcd$$

```
> igcd(4,6);   # all information about `igcd` lost
```

$$igcd(4, 6)$$

```
> # redefine `igcd`
> igcd := proc() options builtin; 84 end:
> igcd(4,6);
```

$$2$$

4.4 Formatted I/O

Maple supports formatted input and output. This allows you to read data created by other applications and to write data for use in other applications. The I/O procedures **printf** and **sscanf**, resemble their C equivalents. The output procedure

$$\mathbf{printf}(format, arg_1, arg_2, \ldots)$$

prints the arguments $arg_1, arg_2, \ldots$, under control of the conversion specification *format*. For example, to print the numerical approximation of $\frac{5}{3}$ as a 15 digit number with 8 digits after the decimal point and 0 for the pad character you enter

```
> printf( `%015.8f`, 5/3 );
000001.66666667
```

In general, the format specification is of the form

$$\%[\text{flags}][\text{width}][.\text{precision}][\text{code}]$$

The conversion specifications elements and their meanings are as follows.

Conversion Codes in printf	
Code	Printed as
d, i	signed decimal number
u	unsigned decimal number
o	unsigned octal number
x, X	unsigned hexadecimal number, using abcdef or ABCDEF for 10, 11, ...
c	single character
s	string
p	machine address in human-readable format
f	signed decimal floating-point number
e, E	signed decimal floating-point number in scientific notation
g, G	signed decimal floating-point number in d, e, or f format, or in E format if G was specified, depending on the value to be printed
a	Maple's lprint format
%	single percent sumbol (no conversion)

Flags in printf	
Flag	Meaning
−	left adjustment within the field
0	use 0 as the pad character instead of a space (if padding is to the left of the converted value)
+	the result of a signed conversion will always start with a sign
space	a signed numeric value is output with either a leading − or a leading blank
#	if a number-sign flag is present, then an alternative output format is used

The main differences with C's printf is that %a (for algebraic) will include any algebraic expression (with no line breaks) as printed by **lprint**, and that ∗ for field lengths are not handled. Below are some examples, in which the **lprint()** instruction has been added to get each prompt on a new line.

```
> printf( `x=%d      y=%4.2f`, 12, 34.3 );  lprint():
x=12       y=34.30

> printf( `%a`, 1/(x^2+1) );  lprint():
1/(x^2+1)
```

```
> printf( `%c, %s`, abc, abc );  lprint():
a, abc

> printf( `%g, %g`, 1/2, 1/2^16 );  lprint():
0.5, 1.52588e-05

> printf( `%d`, 10^10 );  lprint():
Maple integer too large to convert to int0

> printf( `%a`, 10^10 );  lprint():
10000000000
```

Escape characters are also convenient when using the text-based user interface of Maple V Release 2. For example, they allow you to add newline characters so that you don't need to use the **lprint()** command as in the above examples. The complete list of character escape codes is as follows.

Character Escape Codes	
Escape Code	**Meaning**
b	backspace
f	formfeed
n	newline
r	carriage return
t	horizontal tabulate
v	vertical tabulate
\	backslash
'	single quote
"	double quote
?	question mark

A few examples:

```
> printf( `\n%s\n`,

> `string enclosed by newlines\nand a newline inside` );

string enclosed by newlines
and a newline inside

> printf( `%s\f`, `a\vb\vc` );
a
 b
  c
    > printf(`\n%s\n`, `backspacing\b\b\b\b\b\b\b\bxxxxx`);

bacxxxxxing
```

```
> printf(`\n%s\n%s\n`, `x\ty\nz`,`w`);
x          y
z
w
```

The procedure **sscanf**(*string, format*) is the inverse of **printf** and decodes the *string* according to the *format*. The only difference to C's sscanf is that the Maple version returns a list of the scanned objects. Two examples:

```
> sscanf( `x = 123.45, y = 6.7E-8, 9.10`,
>    `x = %f, y = %g, %d.%d` );
```

$$[\ 123.4500000000000,\ .6700000000000000\ 10^{-7},\ 9,\ 10\ ]$$

```
> sscanf( `f = x/(1+x^2)`, `f = %a` );
```

$$\left[\frac{x}{1 + x^2} \right]$$

In general, the format specification is of the form

$$\%[*][\text{width}][\text{code}]$$

The optional * indicates that the object is to be scanned, but not returned as part of the result (i.e., it is discarded).

```
> sscanf(`0-123`,`%*d%d`);
```

$$[\ -123\ ]$$

```
> sscanf(`0-123`,`%d%d`);
```

$$[\ 0,\ -123\ ]$$

The width indicates the maximum number of characters to scan for this object. This can be used to scan one larger object as two or more smaller objects.

```
> sscanf( `date = 16121992`, `date = %2d%2d%4d` );
```

$$[\ 16,\ 12,\ 1992\ ]$$

The conversion specification elements and their meanings are given on the next page.

The **parse** command parses a string as a Maple statement. The option statement determines whether the full evaluation should take place or not.

```
> x := 1:
> parse( `x + 1`);
```

$$x + 1$$

```
> ";
```

$$2$$

```
> parse( `x + 1`, statement );
```

$$2$$

<table>
<tr><th colspan="2">Conversion Codes in sscanf</th></tr>
<tr><th>Code</th><th>Converted into</th></tr>
<tr><td>d, D, i</td><td>signed decimal number</td></tr>
<tr><td>u, U</td><td>unsigned decimal number</td></tr>
<tr><td>o, O</td><td>unsigned octal number</td></tr>
<tr><td>x, X</td><td>unsigned hexadecimal number,
using abcdef or ABCDEF for 10, 11, …</td></tr>
<tr><td>c</td><td>character</td></tr>
<tr><td>s</td><td>string</td></tr>
<tr><td>p</td><td>a pointer value of a computer memory address</td></tr>
<tr><td>e, f, g</td><td>signed decimal floating-point number</td></tr>
<tr><td>a</td><td>unevaluated Maple expression</td></tr>
<tr><td>n</td><td>number of characters read so far</td></tr>
<tr><td>%</td><td>single percent symbol</td></tr>
<tr><td>[…]</td><td>longest non-empty string of input characters
from the set between brackets</td></tr>
<tr><td>[^…]</td><td>longest non-empty string of input characters
not from the set between brackets</td></tr>
</table>

The procedures **readline** and **readdata** are utilities in Maple to read raw data from a file or terminal screen. **readline** reads in one line from the specified file or terminal. **readdata** reads in data arranged in columns from a file or terminal screen.

Consider a data file, say `data`, three lines long with the following information

```
1          .84        .54
2          .91       -.42
3          .14       -.99
```

Below are a few examples of how this file or part of it can be read.

```
> readlib( readdata ):  # load the library function
> readdata( data, 3 );  # read three columns of floats
      [ [ 1., .8400000000000000, .5400000000000000 ],

          [ 2., .9100000000000000, -.4200000000000000 ],
```

```
                [ 3., .140000000000000, -.990000000000000 ] ]
```

```
> readdata( data, 2 );   # read two columns of floats
```

```
     [ [ 1., .840000000000000 ], [ 2., .910000000000000 ],
```

```
                [ 3., .140000000000000 ] ]
```

```
> readdata( data );   # read first column of floats
```

$$[1., 2., 3.]$$

```
> # read first column of integers
> readdata( data, integer );
```

$$[1, 2, 3]$$

```
> readline( data ); # read first line
```

$$1 \qquad .84 \qquad .54$$

```
> readline( data ); # read second line
```

$$2 \qquad .91 \qquad -.42$$

4.5 Code Generation

You can find the roots of a third degree polynomial with **solve**, Maple's general equation solver.

```
> eqn := x^3 - 5*a*x^2 = 1;
```

$$eqn := x^3 - 5\ a\ x^2 = 1$$

```
> sols := solve( eqn, x );
```

$$sols := \%1^{1/3} + \frac{25}{9}\frac{a^2}{\%1^{1/3}} + \frac{5}{3}\ a, \ -\frac{1}{2}\ \%1^{1/3} - \frac{25}{18}\frac{a^2}{\%1^{1/3}}$$

$$+\frac{5}{3}\ a + \frac{1}{2}\ I\ \sqrt{3}\left(\%1^{1/3} - \frac{25}{9}\frac{a^2}{\%1^{1/3}}\right), \ -\frac{1}{2}\ \%1^{1/3}$$

$$-\frac{25}{18}\frac{a^2}{\%1^{1/3}} + \frac{5}{3}\ a - \frac{1}{2}\ I\ \sqrt{3}\left(\%1^{1/3} - \frac{25}{9}\frac{a^2}{\%1^{1/3}}\right)$$

$$\%1 := \frac{1}{2} + \frac{125}{27}\ a^3 + \frac{1}{18}\sqrt{27 + 500\ a^3}\ \sqrt{3}$$

If you want to use such analytical Maple results in a FORTRAN program you can have Maple translate the formulae. You cannot do this for all the solutions in the sequence simultaneously because the expression sequence data type does not exist in FORTRAN; you must translate each solution separately, or put the solutions in a vector or list.

```
> sol1 := sols[1];
```

$$sol1 := \left(\frac{1}{2} + \frac{125}{27} a^3 + \frac{1}{18} \sqrt{27 + 500\ a^3} \sqrt{3} \right)^{1/3}$$

$$+ \frac{25}{9} \frac{a^2}{\left(\frac{1}{2} + \frac{125}{27} a^3 + \frac{1}{18} \sqrt{27 + 500\ a^3} \sqrt{3} \right)^{1/3}}$$

$$+ \frac{5}{3} a$$

When you add the keyword optimized in a call of the Maple procedure **fortran** (reasonably) optimized FORTRAN code is generated. When you want double precision FORTRAN code set the variable precision the value double.

```
> precision := double: # set double precision
> fortran( sol1, 'optimized' );

      t1 = a**2
      t2 = t1*a
      t4 = dsqrt(27+500*t2)
      t5 = dsqrt(3.D0)
      t8 = (1.D0/2.D0+125.D0/27.D0*t2+t4*t5/18)**(1.D0/3.D0)
      t11 = t8+25.D0/9.D0*t1/t8+5.D0/3.D0*a
```

How well or how badly the code has been optimized can be checked with the procedure **cost**.

```
> readlib(cost)( sol1 );
```

>   *8 additions + 26 multiplications + 12 functions*

```
> cost( optimize(sol1) );
```

>   *5 additions + 12 multiplications + divisions*

>   *+ 6 functions + 6 assignments*

Note that Maple only searches for common powers and products in terms of the internal representation. For example, the obvious code optimization for sums

$$(a + b + c)(b + c) \quad \longrightarrow \quad t \overset{\text{def}}{=} b + c; \quad (a + t)\, t$$

is not found by Maple.

```
> optimize( (a+b+c)*(b+c) );
```

$$t3 = (a + b + c)(b + c)$$

The Maple procedure **C** generates C language code. An additional argument of the form `filename = `file.c`` can be used to direct the output to the file *file.c*. By the way, the previously discussed **fortran** routine also provides this storage facility.

```
> readlib(C): # load the C routine
> C( sol1, filename = `file.c` ); # generate code
```

You can store more than one formula in a file.

```
> C( sol1, ´optimized´, filename = `file.c` );
```

The optimized C code for the first solution is appended to the end of the file. If the interface variable `screenwidth` equals 60 then the file will look like

```
     t0 = pow(1.0/2.0+125.0/27.0*a*a*a+sqrt(27.0+500.0\
*a*a*a)*sqrt(3.0)/18,1.0
/3.0)+25.0/9.0*a*a/pow(1.0/2.0+125.0/27.0*a*a*a+sqrt(27.0+
500.0*a*a*a)*sqrt(3.0
)/18,1.0/3.0)+5.0/3.0*a;
     t1 = a*a;
     t2 = t1*a;
     t4 = sqrt(27.0+500.0*t2);
     t5 = sqrt(3.0);
     t8 = pow(1.0/2.0+125.0/27.0*t2+t4*t5/18,1.0/3.0);
     t11 = t8+25.0/9.0*t1/t8+5.0/3.0*a;
```

Maple provides the procedure **latex** to LaTeX code. When you want to generate LaTeX code for several formulae one after another and store them in one file use the function **appendto**. In the example below, we generate the LaTeX code for two of the above solutions. Here, we also show how the **latex** procedure can be adjusted to one's needs — we add the possibility of specifying LaTeX's math mode. We assume that the text-based user interface of Maple is used.

```
> # ensure that all remember tables are present
> readlib( latex ):
> `latex/special_names`[´beginmath´] :=
>    `\\begin{displaymath}`:
```

```
> `latex/special_names`[`endmath`] :=

>    `\\end{displaymath}`:

> # suppress messages, prompts, etc.

> interface( quiet=true ):

> appendto( `file.tex` ):

latex(beginmath); latex(sols[1]); latex(endmath);

latex(beginmath); latex(2*sols[1]-sols[2]-sols[3]);

latex(endmath);

writeto(terminal); interface( quiet=false );

> quit
```

If the interface variable screenwidth equals the default value 80, then the file file.tex will look like

```
\begin{displaymath}
\sqrt [3]{1/2+{\frac {125\,a^{3}}{27}}+{\frac {\sqrt {27+500\,a^{3}}
\sqrt {3}}{18}}}+25\,a^{2}1/9{\frac {1}{\sqrt [3]{1/2+{\frac {125\,a^{
3}}{27}}+{\frac {\sqrt {27+500\,a^{3}}}\sqrt {3}}{18}}}}}+{\frac {5\,a}
{3}}
\end{displaymath}
\begin{displaymath}
3\,\sqrt [3]{1/2+{\frac {125\,a^{3}}{27}}+{\frac {\sqrt {27+500\,a^{3}
}}\sqrt {3}}{18}}}+25\,a^{2}1/3{\frac {1}{\sqrt [3]{1/2+{\frac {125\,a^
{3}}{27}}+{\frac {\sqrt {27+500\,a^{3}}}\sqrt {3}}{18}}}}}
\end{displaymath}
```

When the formulae are typeset they look like

$$\sqrt[3]{1/2+\frac{125a^3}{27}+\frac{\sqrt{27+500a^3}\sqrt{3}}{18}}+25a^2 1/9\frac{1}{\sqrt[3]{1/2+\frac{125a^3}{27}+\frac{\sqrt{27+500a^3}\sqrt{3}}{18}}}+\frac{5a}{3}$$

$$3\sqrt[3]{1/2+\frac{125a^3}{27}+\frac{\sqrt{27+500a^3}\sqrt{3}}{18}}+25a^2 1/3\frac{1}{\sqrt[3]{1/2+\frac{125a^3}{27}+\frac{\sqrt{27+500a^3}\sqrt{3}}{18}}}$$

When it bothers you to add the statements latex(beginmath) and latex(endmath) each time, you can write a small program like

```
mylatex := proc(x)
  readlib(latex):
  `latex/special_names`[`beginmath`] :=
    `\\begin{displaymath}`:
  `latex/special_names`[`endmath`] :=
    `\\end{displaymath}`:
  latex(beginmath); latex(x); latex(endmath);
end:
```

and call the procedure **mylatex** instead of the regular **latex**. When formulae are too large to fit on one line, you have to edit the LaTeX file and insert breaks yourself.

4.6 Changing Maple to your own Taste

In the worksheet interface, there are (at the bottom of the Maple window) two message regions about the amount of storage allocated and computing time. In the text-based user interface, Maple will print during lengthy Maple computations *bytes-used* messages about the use of computer memory and computing time. These messages inform you about memory usage and computing time since the start of the session. The *bytes-used* message is of the following form:

$$bytes\ used = <x>, \quad alloc = <y>, \quad time = <z>$$

Here $<x>$ is equal to the total computer memory used throughout the Maple session, whereas $<y>$ measures the currently allocated amount of memory, both measured in bytes. $<z>$ tells you the computing time since the beginning of the Maple session, measured in seconds. An example of *bytes-used* messages sent during numerical integration:

```
> readlib(`evalf/int`)( ln(x)*ln(1-x), x=0..1 );

bytes used=1000264, alloc=786288, time=1.77
bytes used=2000568, alloc=1244956, time=4.52
bytes used=3000816, alloc=1441528, time=6.95
bytes used=4001128, alloc=1441528, time=9.87

                   .3550659332
```

You can control the frequency of the *bytes-used* messages or the updates of the message regions in the worksheet with the procedure **words**.

```
> words(0):
```

Hereafter no *bytes-used* messages appear, except whenever *garbage collection* occurs, which is the case in the above example. When you enter

```
> words( 1\000\000 ):
```

bytes-used messages appear whenever one million extra computer words have been used during the Maple session.

Whereas the total number of computer words used steadily grows during a Maple session, this does not mean that the actual memory requirements grow as fast: reuse of memory takes place, and this cleaning up of memory is called *garbage collection*. Whenever this occurs Maple shows

a *bytes-used* message. You can explicitly request garbage collection with
the procedure **gc**.

```
> gc();
```

```
bytes used=1347608, alloc=786288, time=9.016
```
With the same procedure you can control the frequency of the garbage
collection. When you enter

```
> gc(0):
```

no *bytes-used* messages will occur anymore at garbage collection.

If you mind these Maple messages then you can silence the computer
algebra system in two ways.

```
> words(0): gc(0):
```

This is the method you already learned. You can always find the status of
the system with respect to the memory usage and computing time in the
Maple variable status. Another, more drastic way is to enter

```
> interface( quiet = true ):
```

This only works in the text-based user interface and its effect is that the
Maple prompt disappears and that, if you try to write results to a file with
writeto, the input lines are not written to the file anymore. To Maple,
silence means absolute silence!

With the same procedure **interface** you can arrange the output to
appear in different ways. If desired you can change the prompt, stop
Maple's automatic use of labels for common subexpressions or force the
Maple output into left-adjusted, one-dimensional format. A few examples:

```
> interface( prompt = `--->` );  # an arrow as a prompt
---> solve(x^3+x+1,x);  # labels for common subexpressions
```

$$-\%1^{1/3} + \frac{1}{3} \frac{1}{\%1^{1/3}},$$

$$\frac{1}{2} \%1^{1/3} - \frac{1}{6} \frac{1}{\%1^{1/3}} + \frac{1}{2} I \sqrt{3} \left(-\%1^{1/3} - \frac{1}{3} \frac{1}{\%1^{1/3}} \right),$$

$$\frac{1}{2} \%1^{1/3} - \frac{1}{6} \frac{1}{\%1^{1/3}} - \frac{1}{2} I \sqrt{3} \left(-\%1^{1/3} - \frac{1}{3} \frac{1}{\%1^{1/3}} \right)$$

$$\%1 := \frac{1}{2} + \frac{1}{18} \sqrt{31} \sqrt{3}$$

```
---> interface( labeling = false ); # no labels anymore
---> solve( x^3+x+1=0, x );
```

$$-\left(\frac{1}{2} + \frac{1}{18} \sqrt{31} \sqrt{3}\right)^{1/3} + \frac{1}{3} \frac{1}{\left(\frac{1}{2} + \frac{1}{18} \sqrt{31} \sqrt{3}\right)^{1/3}},$$

$$\frac{1}{2}\left(\frac{1}{2} + \frac{1}{18} \sqrt{31} \sqrt{3}\right)^{1/3}$$

$$- \frac{1}{6} \frac{1}{\left(\frac{1}{2} + \frac{1}{18} \sqrt{31} \sqrt{3}\right)^{1/3}} + \frac{1}{2} I \sqrt{3} \left(\vphantom{\left(\frac{1}{2}\right)^{1/3}}\right.$$

$$-\left(\frac{1}{2} + \frac{1}{18} \sqrt{31} \sqrt{3}\right)^{1/3}$$

$$\left. - \frac{1}{3} \frac{1}{\left(\frac{1}{2} + \frac{1}{18} \sqrt{31} \sqrt{3}\right)^{1/3}}\right),$$

$$\frac{1}{2}\left(\frac{1}{2} + \frac{1}{18} \sqrt{31} \sqrt{3}\right)^{1/3}$$

$$- \frac{1}{6} \frac{1}{\left(\frac{1}{2} + \frac{1}{18} \sqrt{31} \sqrt{3}\right)^{1/3}} - \frac{1}{2} I \sqrt{3} \left(\vphantom{\left(\frac{1}{2}\right)^{1/3}}\right.$$

$$-\left(\frac{1}{2} + \frac{1}{18} \sqrt{31} \sqrt{3}\right)^{1/3}$$

$$\left. - \frac{1}{3} \frac{1}{\left(\frac{1}{2} + \frac{1}{18} \sqrt{31} \sqrt{3}\right)^{1/3}}\right)$$

```
---> example := (1-x)/(1+x):
---> example; # 2-dimensional layout
```

$$\frac{1 - x}{1 + x}$$

```
---> interface( prettyprint = false );
```

```
---> example; # 1-dimensional layout

(1-x)/(1+x)

---> # reset prettyprint to default value

---> interface( prettyprint = true ):

---> interface( verboseproc = 2 ):

---> readlib( unassign ); # procedure body is printed


proc()
local i,j,n;
options `Copyright 1990 by the University of Waterloo`;
    i := false;
    for n in args do
        if n = `assign` then i := true else assign(n,n) fi
    od;
    if i then assign := evaln(assign) fi;
    NULL
end
```

The last example shows that you can view the source code of library functions. Only the C code of kernel functions is not viewable.

A handy interface variable is `errorbreak`. It determines what should happen when you read from a corrupted input file.

errorbreak	
Value	**Purpose**
0	report error and continue reading
1	stop reading after syntax error
2	stop reading after any error

Enter **?interface** to get a list of all interface variables, their possible values, and their purposes.

4.7 Exercises

1. Find out where the Maple library resides on your computer and read the file `isolate.m` from the library in two ways.

   (a) by **read**.

   (b) by **readlib** after you have set the interface variable `verboseproc` to two.

2. Study the interface variable `echo`.

   First, create the file `readfile` in your home directory and let the file contain the single Maple command

   ```
   b := 2;
   ```

   Secondly, create the file `testfile` in your home directory and let the file contain the following command lines.

   ```
   interface( echo = X );
   a := 1;
   read readfile;
   quit
   ```

   Thirdly, if your platform allows this, launch Maple from your home directory by

   ```
   maple < testfile
   ```

   so that all commands come from the particular file, while changing X in the first line of `testfile` into 0, 1, 2, 3, and 4, respectively.

   Finally, read the `testfile` in a Maple session with the procedure **read**, while changing X in the first line of `testfile` into 0, 1, 2, 3, and 4, respectively.

3. Create a file with the following contents

   ```
   I := 1;   # syntactically correct, but run-time error
   x := 2;   # correct input line
   wrong name := 3  # syntax error
   y := 4;   # correct input line
   ```

   For each possible value of the interface variable `errorbreak`, find out what happens when you read the file in a Maple session.

4. Consider a data file, three lines long with the following information

   ```
   1    2
   3    4
   5    6
   ```

   Read this file, convert the data into a matrix, transpose the matrix, and then printout the data in the format

   ```
   1    2    3
   4    5    6
   ```

Polynomials and Rational Functions

Maple's favorite mathematical structures are polynomials and rational functions. This chapter is a gentle introduction to univariate and multivariate polynomials, to rational functions, and to conversions between distinct forms. Keywords are: greatest common divisor (gcd), factorization, expansion, sorting in lexicographic or degree ordering, normalization of rational functions, and partial fraction decomposition.

5.1 Univariate Polynomials

Polynomials and rational functions (i.e., quotients of polynomials) are Maple's favorite data type. The computer algebra system manipulates them in full generality and at a high speed. For simplicity we start with polynomials in one indeterminate, say x; these are symbolic expressions which are from mathematical point of view equivalent to

$$a_n x^n + a_{n-1} x^{n-1} + \cdots + a_2 x^2 + a_1 x + a_0 \ .$$

This is called the *expanded canonical form* with coefficients a_0, a_1, ..., a_{n-1}, and a_n. If $a_n \neq 0$ then we call a_n the *leading coefficient* and the natural number n the *degree* of the polynomial. Later on you will see that the coefficients of a polynomial are not subject to many restrictions, but for the moment we shall restrict ourselves to "ordinary" numbers like integers, rational numbers, or real numbers. We say that a polynomial in x is in *collected form*, when all the coefficients with the same power of x have been collected together. The only distinction from the expanded canonical form is that in a polynomial in collected form all terms are not necessarily sorted in descending order with respect to the degree. An example:

```
> p1 := -3*x + 7*x^2 - 3*x^3 + 7*x^4; # collected form
```

$$p1 := -3\ x + 7\ x^2 - 3\ x^3 + 7\ x^4$$

```
> type( p1, `polynom` );
```

$$true$$

```
> ``leading coefficient`` = lcoeff(p1);
```

$$leading\ coefficient = 7$$

```
> `degree` = degree(p1);
```

$$degree = 4$$

Addition and multiplication of polynomials are carried out quickly and correctly by Maple. The next example carries on from the previous example.

```
> # p2 is in expanded canonical form
> p2 := 5*x^5 + 3*x^3 + x^2 - 2*x + 1;
```

$$p2 := 5\ x^5 + 3\ x^3 + x^2 - 2\ x + 1$$

```
> 2*p1 - 3*p2 + 3;
```

$$11\ x^2 - 15\ x^3 + 14\ x^4 - 15\ x^5$$

```
> p1 * p2;
```

$$(-3\ x + 7\ x^2 - 3\ x^3 + 7\ x^4)$$

$$(5\ x^5 + 3\ x^3 + x^2 - 2\ x + 1)$$

```
> expand(");
```

$$-17\ x^6 + 11\ x^4 - 20\ x^3 + 13\ x^2 - 3\ x + 56\ x^7 + 4\ x^5$$

$$- 15\ x^8 + 35\ x^9$$

Contrary to multiplication of numbers, the product of polynomials is not worked out automatically by Maple; you must give a separate command, viz., **expand**. This looks like a handicap, but really it is not. It is better to leave a factored form like $(3x + 5)^{10}$ intact as long as possible in computations. This is clearer than the expanded form

$$59049x^{10} + 984150x^9 + 7381125x^8 + \cdots + 58593750x + 9765625\,.$$

Although Maple computes the product of two polynomials correctly, the terms in the answer are mixed up and not in ascending or descending order with respect to the degree. This often leads to sloppy expressions which are difficult to read. Terms in polynomials are not sorted into some standard ordering for efficiency reasons (both with respect to computing time and memory storage). If you really want to rearrange terms of a polynomial in descending order with respect to the degree, then you should apply the procedure **sort**.

```
> sort(");
```

$$35\ x^9\ -\ 15\ x^8\ +\ 56\ x^7\ -\ 17\ x^6\ +\ 4\ x^5\ +\ 11\ x^4\ -\ 20\ x^3$$
$$+\ 13\ x^2\ -\ 3\ x$$

Actually, **sort** will change the internal data structure. This is necessary because Maple only stores one copy for each expression or subexpression in memory, or more precisely in its *simplification table*. For any new expression Maple checks by "internal algebra" whether the expression can be simplified by elementary operations to an expression which has been used before and stored in the simplification table. If this is the case, then Maple skips the new expression and uses the old expression from the simplification table instead. Otherwise the expression, together with its subexpressions, is stored in the simplification table. Changing terms in a sum or factors in a product are examples of elementary simplifications which are used to test mathematical equivalence of expressions.

```
> p := 1+x+x^3+x^2; # random order
```

$$p\ :=\ 1\ +\ x\ +\ x^3\ +\ x^2$$

```
> x^3+x^2+x+1; # no rearrangement, but still random order
```

$$1\ +\ x\ +\ x^3\ +\ x^2$$

```
> q := (x-1)*(x^3+x^2+x+1); # the same for subexpressions
```

$$q\ :=\ (\ x\ -\ 1\ )\ (\ 1\ +\ x\ +\ x^3\ +\ x^2\ )$$

```
> sort(p); # rearrange w.r.t. descending degree order
```

$$x^3\ +\ x^2\ +\ x\ +\ 1$$

```
> q; # subexpression of q has also changed
```

$$(\ x\ -\ 1\ )\ (\ x^3\ +\ x^2\ +\ x\ +\ 1\ )$$

Maple offers many procedures to manipulate polynomials; we shall have a look at some of them. Until further notice, p1 and p2 are equal to the previously defined polynomials.

```
> `p1`=p1,  `p2`=p2;
```
$$p1 = -3\ x\ +\ 7\ x^2\ -\ 3\ x^3\ +\ 7\ x^4,$$
$$p2 = 5\ x^5\ +\ 3\ x^3\ +\ x^2\ -\ 2\ x\ +\ 1$$

The **coeff**icient of a power or monomial can be determined with the procedure **coeff**.

```
> coeff( p2, x^3 ),   coeff( p2, x, 2 );
```
$$3,\ 3$$

The leading and **t**railing **coeff**icients can be found with **lcoeff** and **tcoeff**, respectively.

```
> lcoeff( p2, x ),   tcoeff( p2, x );
```
$$5,\ 1$$

You get a sequence of all **coeff**icients and the corresponding powers with the procedure **coeffs**.

```
> coeffs( p2, x, `powers` );   powers;
```
$$1,\ 1,\ 3,\ -2,\ 5$$
$$1,\ x^2,\ x^3,\ x,\ x^5$$

Maple insists that polynomials be in collected form before you use **coeff** and **degree**.

```
> coeff( x^2-x*(x-1), x );
Error, unable to compute coeff
> coeff( (x^2-1)*(x^2+1), x^2 );
Error, unable to compute coeff
> degree( x^2-x*(x-1), x );
```
$$2$$

One of the most fundamental operations with polynomials is *division with remainder*. Maple has two procedures, viz., **quo** and **rem** — **quo**tient and **rem**ainder — to do this.

```
> q := quo( p2, p1, x, `r` );
```
$$q := \frac{5}{7}\ x\ +\ \frac{15}{49}$$

```
> r; # remainder has been set in previous command
```

$$- \frac{53}{49}\, x^3 + x^2 - \frac{53}{49}\, x + 1$$

```
> testeq( p2 = expand( q*p1 + r ) ); # test equality
```

true

```
> rem( p2, p1, x, ´q´ );
```

$$- \frac{53}{49}\, x^3 + x^2 - \frac{53}{49}\, x + 1$$

```
> q, # quotient has been set in previous command
```

$$\frac{5}{7}\, x + \frac{15}{49}$$

Mind the use of apostrophes around the fourth argument of these procedures to suppress unintended evaluation of the arguments.

Another important function is **gcd** to compute greatest common divisors of polynomials over the rational numbers.

```
> gcd( p1, p2 );
```

$$x^2 + 1$$

The computation of greatest common divisors is so important for so many mathematical calculations that much attention is paid to gcd-algorithms by developers of computer algebra systems (q.v., [53, 81]) and therefore the determination of the greatest common divisor goes quickly.

An even more complicated algorithm is factorization of polynomials; the interested reader is referred to [76, 77, 79]. The procedure **factor** writes polynomials with rational coefficients as a product of irreducible (over **Q**) polynomials.

```
> polynomial := expand( p1*p2 );
```

$$polynomial := -17\ x^6 + 11\ x^4 - 20\ x^3 + 13\ x^2 - 3\ x$$
$$+ 56\ x^7 + 4\ x^5 - 15\ x^8 + 35\ x^9$$

```
> factor( polynomial );
```

$$x\ (7\ x - 3)\ (5\ x^3 - 2\ x + 1)\ (x^2 + 1)^2$$

Computations with polynomials over domains differing from the integers or rational numbers are possible, e.g., over finite fields or over algebraic number and function fields. Examples of factorizations of the above polynomial over such domains are:

- Factorization over $\mathbb{Z}[i]$, the ring of Gaussian integers.

  ```
  > factor( polynomial, I );
  ```

  $$(5\ x^3\ -\ 2\ x\ +\ 1)\ (7\ x\ -\ 3)\ x\ (x\ +\ I)^2\ (x\ -\ I)^2$$

- Factorization over $\mathbb{Z}_2$, the field of two elements, 0 and 1.

  ```
  > sort( polynomial mod 2 ); # polynomial over {0,1}
  ```

  $$x^9\ +\ x^8\ +\ x^6\ +\ x^4\ +\ x^2\ +\ x$$

  ```
  > Factor(polynomial) mod 2;
  ```

  $$(x\ +\ 1)^6\ x\ (x^2\ +\ x\ +\ 1)$$

  ```
  > expand(") mod 2;
  ```

  $$x^9\ +\ x^8\ +\ x^6\ +\ x^4\ +\ x^2\ +\ x$$

Note the use of the upper-case character in **Factor**. The purpose of this is to suppress factorization over the integers; **Factor**(...) is just a placeholder for representing the factorization of the polynomial and the **mod** operator actually gets the computation going. Otherwise, the polynomial is first factored over the rational numbers, and then modulo arithmetic is applied.

```
> factor( polynomial) mod 2;
```

$$x\ (x\ +\ 1)\ (x^3\ +\ 1)\ (x^2\ +\ 1)^2$$

- Factorization over the Galois field GF(4), in particular the algebraic extension of $\mathbb{Z}_2$ with respect to the irreducible polynomial $x^2 + x + 1$.

  ```
  > alias( alpha=RootOf(x^2+x+1,x) ):
  > Factor( polynomial, alpha ) mod 2;
  ```

  $$x\ (x\ +\ 1)^6\ (x\ +\ \alpha)\ (x\ +\ \alpha\ +\ 1)$$

The mechanism of placeholders for manipulations of polynomials is used for other procedures like **Gcd**, **Divide**, **Expand**, and so on. A few examples:

```
> Gcd(p1,p2) mod 2;
```

$$x^3 + x^2 + x + 1$$

```
> Expand( p1 * p2 ) mod 2;
```

$$x^6 + x^4 + x^2 + x + x^8 + x^9$$

```
> q := Quo( p2, p1, x, ´r´ ) mod 2;
```

$$q := x + 1$$

```
> r;
```

$$x^3 + x^2 + x + 1$$

```
> Expand( p2 - q*p1 - r ) mod 2;
```

$$0$$

5.2 Multivariate Polynomials

Multivariate polynomials are polynomials in more than one unknown. An example of a polynomial in two indeterminates x and y is

```
> polynomial := 6*x*y^5 + 12*y^4 + 14*y^3*x^3
>    - 15*x^2*y^3 + 9*x^3*y^2 - 30*x*y^2 - 35*x^4*y
>    + 18*y*x^2 + 21*x^5;
```

$$polynomial := 6\ x\ y^5 + 12\ y^4 + 14\ y^3\ x^3 - 15\ x^2\ y^3$$
$$+ 9\ x^3\ y^2 - 30\ x\ y^2 - 35\ x^4\ y + 18\ y\ x^2 + 21\ x^5$$

You see that Maple has no personal feelings about term orderings or orderings of indeterminates within monomials; it just takes the ordering which it saw first. Again, you can do something about it with the procedure **sort**.

```
> sort( polynomial, [x,y], ´plex´ );
```

$$21\ x^5 - 35\ x^4\ y + 14\ x^3\ y^3 + 9\ x^3\ y^2 - 15\ x^2\ y^3$$
$$+ 18\ x^2\ y + 6\ x\ y^5 - 30\ x\ y^2 + 12\ y^4$$

Here, the terms are ordered in a **p**ure **lex**icographic ordering defined by

$$x^i y^j \prec x^{i'} y^{j'} \iff i < i' \text{ or } (i = i' \text{ and } j < j').$$

So,

$$1 \prec y \prec y^2 \prec \ldots \prec x \prec xy \prec x^2 \ldots .$$

You can also use the **t**otal **deg**ree term ordering defined by

$$x^i y^j \prec x^{i'} y^{j'} \iff i+j < i'+j' \text{ or } (i+j = i'+j' \text{ and } i < i').$$

So,

$$1 \prec y \prec x \prec y^2 \prec xy \prec x^2 \prec y^3 \prec xy^2 \prec x^2 y \prec x^3 \prec \dots .$$

In this term ordering, which is the default ordering used by **sort**, we get

```
> sort( polynomial );
```

$$14\ x^3\ y^3\ +\ 6\ x\ y^5\ +\ 21\ x^5\ -\ 35\ x^4\ y\ +\ 9\ x^3\ y^2\ -\ 15\ x^2\ y^3$$
$$+\ 12\ y^4\ +\ 18\ x^2\ y\ -\ 30\ x\ y^2$$

The above polynomial can also be considered as a polynomial in the indeterminate x, with polynomials in y as coefficients. You can bring the polynomial into this form with the procedure **collect**.

```
> collect( polynomial, x );
```

$$21\ x^5\ -\ 35\ x^4\ y\ +\ (\ 14\ y^3\ +\ 9\ y^2\ )\ x^3$$
$$+\ (\ 18\ y\ -\ 15\ y^3\ )\ x^2\ +\ (-30\ y^2\ +\ 6\ y^5\ )\ x\ +\ 12\ y^4$$

Alternatively, you can consider polynomial as a polynomial in the main variable y.

```
collect( polynomial, y );
```

$$6\ x\ y^5\ +\ 12\ y^4\ +\ (-15\ x^2\ +\ 14\ x^3\ )\ y^3$$
$$+\ (\ 9\ x^3\ -\ 30\ x\ )\ y^2\ +\ (-35\ x^4\ +\ 18\ x^2\ )\ y\ +\ 21\ x^5$$

Many of the Maple procedures for manipulation of univariate polynomials work as well for polynomials in more than one unknown. We only show a few examples, and invite you to experiment with multivariate polynomials yourself.

```
> coeff( polynomial, x^3 ),    coeff( polynomial, x, 3 );
```

$$14\ y^3\ +\ 9\ y^2,\ 14\ y^3\ +\ 9\ y^2$$

```
> coeffs( polynomial, x, ´powers´ );    powers;
```

$$12\ y^4,\ 14\ y^3\ +\ 9\ y^2,\ 18\ y\ -\ 15\ y^3,\ -30\ y^2\ +\ 6\ y^5,$$
$$-35\ y,\ 21$$
$$1,\ x^3,\ x^2,\ x,\ x^4,\ x^5$$

```
> settime := time(): # start timing
> factor( polynomial );
```

$$(3 \ x^2 - 5 \ x \ y + 2 \ y^3) \ (7 \ x^3 + 6 \ y + 3 \ x \ y^2)$$

```
> cpu_time := (time()-settime) * seconds; # computing time
```

$$cpu\_time := .85 \ seconds$$

No human can come near in speed to such a factorization; just ask your mathematical friends and colleagues to do such a factorization with pencil and paper! There is a lot of mathematical knowledge and complicated programming behind the procedures **factor** and **Factor**.

5.3 Rational Functions

A rational function in the unknown x is an expression which can be written in the the form f/g, where f and g are polynomials in x, and g is not equal to 0. For example,

```
> f := x^2 + 3*x + 2:    g := x^2 + 5*x + 6:    f/g;
```

$$\frac{x^2 + 3 \ x + 2}{x^2 + 5 \ x + 6}$$

You can select the **numer**ator and the **denom**inator of a rational expression with the procedure **numer** and **denom**, respectively.

```
> numer("), denom(");
```

$$x^2 + 3 \ x + 2, \ x^2 + 5 \ x + 6$$

Note that contrary to calculations with rational numbers, Maple does not simplify rational expressions into a form where numerator and denominator are relatively prime by itself. Simplifications are carried out automatically only when Maple immediately recognizes common factors.

```
> ff := (x-1)*f; gg := (x-1)^2*g;
```

$$ff := (x - 1) \ (x^2 + 3 \ x + 2)$$

$$gg := (x - 1)^2 \ (x^2 + 5 \ x + 6)$$

```
> ff/gg;
```

$$\frac{x^2 + 3 \ x + 2}{(x - 1) \ (x^2 + 5 \ x + 6)}$$

If you want to bring a rational expression into such form, then you should apply the procedure **normal**. This procedure leaves factors in numerator and denominator in factored form as much as possible for efficiency reasons.

```
> normal(f/g);
```

$$\frac{x + 1}{x + 3}$$

```
> normal(ff/gg);
```

$$\frac{x + 1}{(x + 3)(x - 1)}$$

There are three reasons for not doing **normal**ization of rational expressions automatically:

▷ it does not always give simpler results, e.g., $(x^{10000} - 1)/(x - 1)$ is more compact than its normalization, which is a polynomial with ten thousand terms;

▷ it is too time-consuming to do normalization for every rational expression that appears in a Maple computation;

▷ a user may want other manipulations, e.g., partial fraction decompositions.

We end this section with an example of a rational expression in more than one unknown.

```
> f := 161*y^3 + 333*x*y^2 + 184*y^2 + 162*x^2*y
>      + 144*x*y + 77*y + 99*x + 88:
> g := 49*y^2 + 28*x^2*y + 63*x*y + 147*y + 36*x^3
>      + 32*x^2 + 117*x + 104:
> ratexpr := f/g;
```

$$ratexpr := (161 \ y^3 + 333 \ x \ y^2 + 184 \ y^2 + 162 \ x^2 \ y$$
$$+ 144 \ x \ y + 77 \ y + 99 \ x + 88)/(49 \ y^2 + 28 \ x^2 \ y$$
$$+ 63 \ x \ y + 147 \ y + 36 \ x^3 + 32 \ x^2 + 117 \ x + 104)$$

```
> normal( ratexpr );
```

$$\frac{18 \ x \ y + 23 \ y^2 + 11}{4 \ x^2 + 7 \ y + 13}$$

5.4 Conversions

For efficiency reasons we sometimes want to write a polynomial in *Horner form*. We illustrate this with the previously defined polynomial p1. The number of additions and multiplications can be tabulated with the procedure **cost**.

```
> p1;
```
$$-3\ x\ +\ 7\ x^2\ -\ 3\ x^3\ +\ 7\ x^4$$

```
> readlib(cost)( p1 );
```
$$3\ additions\ +\ 10\ multiplications$$

```
> convert( p1, 'horner' );
```
$$(\ -3\ +\ (\ 7\ +\ (\ 7\ x\ -\ 3\ )\ x\ )\ x\ )\ x$$

```
> cost(");
```
$$3\ additions\ +\ 4\ multiplications$$

Conversion of rational expressions into their **continued fraction** forms can also speed up computations.

```
> (x^3 + x^2 - x + 1) / p1;
```
$$\frac{x^3\ +\ x^2\ -\ x\ +\ 1}{-3\ x\ +\ 7\ x^2\ -\ 3\ x^3\ +\ 7\ x^4}$$

```
> cost(");
```
$$6\ additions\ +\ 14\ multiplications\ +\ divisions$$

```
> convert( "", 'confrac', x );
```

$$\frac{1}{7}\ 1 \Bigg/ \left(x\ -\ \frac{10}{7}\ +\ \dfrac{24}{7}\ \dfrac{1}{x\ +\ \dfrac{11}{6}\ +\ \dfrac{1}{9}\ \dfrac{1}{x\ -\ \dfrac{71}{24}\ +\ \dfrac{429}{64}\ \dfrac{1}{x\ +\ \dfrac{17}{8}}}} \right)$$

```
> cost(");
```
$$7\ additions\ +\ 4\ multiplications\ +\ 4\ divisions$$

Partial fraction decomposition — **convert** to **partial fraction** form — can easily be done in Maple.

```
> convert( "" , 'parfrac', x );
```

$$\frac{143}{87} \quad \frac{1}{7\ x\ -\ 3} \quad - \quad \frac{1}{3}\ \frac{1}{x} \quad + \quad \frac{1}{29}\ \frac{3\ +\ 7\ x}{x^2\ +\ 1}$$

From the partial fraction decomposition you can almost immediately tell the indefinite integral of this rational expression.

```
> integrate(",x);
```

$$\frac{143}{609}\ \ln(7\ x\ -\ 3)\ -\ \frac{1}{3}\ \ln(x)\ +\ \frac{7}{58}\ \ln(x^2\ +\ 1)$$

$$+\ \frac{3}{29}\ \arctan(x)$$

A final example of partial fraction decomposition of a rational expression in more than one indeterminate follows.

```
> ratfun := (x-a)/(x^5+b*x^4-c*x^2-b*c*x);
```

$$ratfun := \frac{x\ -\ a}{x^5\ +\ b\ x^4\ -\ c\ x^2\ -\ b\ c\ x}$$

```
> convert( ratfun, 'parfrac', x );
```

$$\frac{a}{b\ c\ x}\ -\ ($$

$$-b^2\ c\ -\ b\ c\ a\ +\ b\ c\ x\ +\ c\ x\ a\ -\ c\ x^2\ +\ x^2\ b^2\ a\ )\Big/($$

$$c\ (c\ +\ b^3)\ (x^3\ -\ c))\ -\ \frac{b\ +\ a}{b\ (c\ +\ b^3)\ (x\ +\ b)}$$

```
> # write numerators as polynomials in x
> map( collect, ", x );
```

$$\frac{a}{b\ c\ x}\ -\ ($$

$$(-c\ +\ b^2\ a)\ x^2\ +\ (b\ c\ +\ c\ a)\ x\ -\ b^2\ c\ -\ b\ c\ a)$$

$$\Big/(c\ (c\ +\ b^3)\ (x^3\ -\ c))\ -\ \frac{b\ +\ a}{b\ (c\ +\ b^3)\ (x\ +\ b)}$$

```
> convert( ratfun, 'parfrac', x, true );
```

$$\frac{a}{b\ c\ x} - \frac{-b\ c\ -\ c\ a\ +\ x^2\ a\ b\ +\ a\ x^3}{b\ c\ (x^4\ +\ b\ x^3\ -\ c\ x\ -\ b\ c)}$$

In the last command, we add the extra argument `true` to indicate that no application of the procedure **normal** on `ratfun` is needed and that the denominator can be considered to be already in the desired factored form.

5.5 Exercises

1. Consider the rational expression $\dfrac{x^4 + x^3 - 4x^2 - 4x}{x^4 + x^3 - x^2 - x}$.
   Transform the expression into:

   (a) $\dfrac{(x+2)(x+1)(x-2)}{x^3 + x^2 - x - 1}$

   (b) $\dfrac{x^4 + x^3 - 4x^2 - 4x}{x(x-1)(x+1)^2}$

   (c) $\dfrac{(x+2)(x-2)}{(x-1)(x+1)}$

   (d) $\dfrac{x^2}{(x-1)(x+1)} - 4\dfrac{1}{(x-1)(x+1)}$

2. Consider the same rational expression as in the previous exercise.
   (a) Write it as a continued fraction.
   (b) Compute a partial fraction decomposition.

3. Let f be the polynomial $x^7 + x^5 + 2x^3 + 2x^2 + 3x + 2$.
   (a) Factor f over $\mathbb{Z}_5$, and over $\mathbb{Z}_7$.
   (b) How can you conclude from the former factorizations that f is irreducible over the ring over integers (Hint: look at the degrees of the factors). Check with Maple that f is indeed irreducible over $\mathbb{Z}$.

4. (a) Factor $x^2 - 2$ over $\mathbb{Z}_2$.
   (b) Factor $x^3 - 3$ over $\mathbb{Z}_3$.
   (c) Factor $x^5 - 5$ over $\mathbb{Z}_5$.
   (d) Factor $x^{23} - 23$ over $\mathbb{Z}_{23}$.
   (e) By now you may have an idea how $x^p - p$ factors for any prime number p; check your conjecture for some prime number distinct from previous choices. Do you understand the result?

5. Let $f = 2x^4 - 3x^2 + x + 4$ and $g = 2x^5 - 6x^4 - 4x^3 + x^2 - 3x - 2$. Consider them as polynomials over $\mathbb{Z}_7$ and compute the greatest common divisor of f and g. Determine also polynomials s and t over $\mathbb{Z}_7$ such that $sf + tg = \gcd(f, g)$ (gcd with respect to $\mathbb{Z}_7$, of course).

6. If you ask Maple to factor $x^{2458} + x^{1229} + 1$ over $\mathbb{Z}$, then the system will complain about insufficient memory, or after several hours will still not have found an answer. So, let us have a closer look at this problem and see if we can assist Maple. First, we note that 1229 is a prime number.

```
> isprime(1229);
```
                                                                          true

So, the polynomial is of the form $x^{2p} + x^p + 1$, where p is a prime number. Determine with Maple the factorization of this polynomial for low prime values of p and propose a conjecture about the form of the factored polynomial for the general case.

An experienced mathematician can tell you that the polynomial $x^n - 1$, where n is a natural number, can be factored over $\mathbb{Z}$ in the *cyclotomic polynomials* $\phi_k(x)$.

$$x^n - 1 = \prod_{k \mid n} \phi_k(x)$$

These cyclotomic polynomials are irreducible over $\mathbb{Z}$. With this knowledge and under the assumption that your conjecture is correct, it should not be too difficult to prove the result.

Internal Data Representation and Substitution

In this chapter, we shall describe in detail the internal representation of polynomials and rational functions. This is not only of theoretical interest; it is also important to know about data representation when you want to fully understand conversion between distinct data structures and substitution.

We shall generalize the concept of rational expressions, and explain how the procedures defined for polynomial and rational functions extend to more general mathematical structures.

We shall also examine Maple's procedures for type checking and selection of parts of formulae. In this way, Maple can support you when studying or manipulating data structures.

Finally, we shall discuss sequential and simultaneous substitution, and how this can be used in the process of simplifying expressions

6.1 Internal Representation of Polynomials

In the previous chapter, we have already seen some Maple procedures that transform polynomials from one shape into another. In order to fully understand these manipulations and others to come, we dot the i's and cross the t's and have a closer look at the internal data representation of polynomials in Maple.

We take the polynomial $x^4 + x^3 - x^2 - x$ as our example. The expanded canonical form is represented internally by the following set of data vectors, which is, in graph-theoretical terms, a *directed acyclic graph (DAG)*.

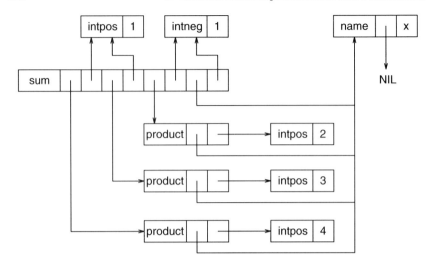

Here, you must interpret the data vector

sum	expr1	coeff1	expr2	coeff2	....

as if it consists of pairs of expressions and their numerical coefficients: the data vector represents the sum

$$\text{coeff}_1 \times \text{expression}_1 + \text{coeff}_2 \times \text{expression}_2 + \cdots.$$

Similarly, the data vector

product	expr1	expon1	expr2	expon2	....

represents the product

$$\text{expression}_1^{\text{expon}_1} \times \text{expression}_2^{\text{expon}_2} \times \cdots.$$

The NIL pointer in the picture is used to indicate that the variable x is unbound.

At the first level, the internal representation of $x^4 + x^3 - x^2 - x$ reflects the way Maple considers it, viz., as a sum of four terms, x^4, x^3, x^2, and x, with coefficients 1, 1, -1, and -1, respectively. These components are internally represented by data vectors. But, surprise, the term x^4 is internally represented by a data vector consisting of the header `product`, a pointer to the unknown x, and a pointer to the exponent 4. You might have expected a data vector of the form

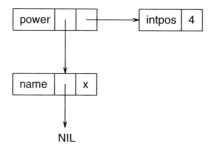

This type of DAG indeed exists in Maple, but if the exponent is a numerical constant, it is changed to the `product` structure by Maple's simplifier.

Maple only recognizes x^4, x^3, x^2, $-x^2$, x, and $-x$ as subexpressions of the polynomial $x^4 + x^3 - x^2 - x$; as far as Maple is concerned, $x^4 + x^3$ and $x^4 - x$ are no subexpressions of $x^4 + x^3 - x^2 - x$. The fact that Maple does not recognize every mathematical subexpression plays an important role in substitution. Only this can explain substitutions like

```
> subs ( 1 = 7, x^4 + x^3 - x^2 - x );
```

$$7 \; x^4 + 7 \; x^3 - x^2 - x$$

```
> subs ( 1 = 3, Pi*x + x + 1 );
```

$$3 \; \pi^3 \; x^3 + 3 \; x + 9$$

Let us have a closer look at the last example. $\pi x + x + 1$ is represented internally as

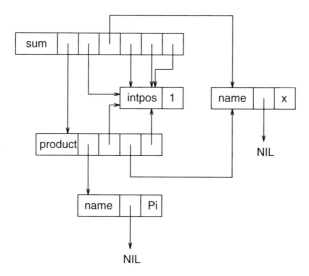

If you replace the data vector which represents 1 by a vector representing 3, then you will understand the result of the substitution of 3 for 1.

The two examples above show you that the internal representation can differ significantly from the external representation, which looks more familiar and is actually what you see on the screen. For Maple however, it is only the internal representation that counts; two expressions are identical if and only if they have the same DAG, and simplification is for the system nothing more than a transformation from one DAG into another.

Before we continue, let us think about the reasons that the designers of Maple may have had for their choice of representing sums and powers. Let us consider the representation of the monomial $x^2y^3z^4$. Maple's internal representation is

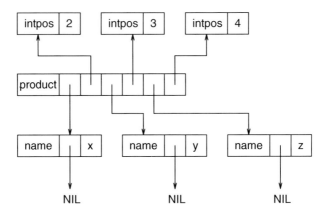

An alternative could be to consider $x^2y^3z^4$ as a product of the three power x^2, y^2, and z^2, with the following internal representation.

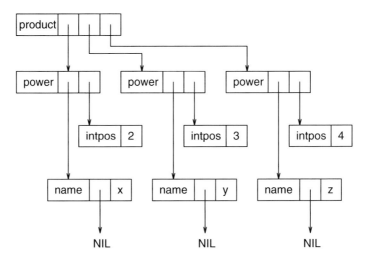

You see that more memory storage is needed in the latter representation. But what is more important, suppose that during a computation $x^2 y^3 z^4$ is multiplied by like factors, say $x^5 z^6$. Then Maple's simplifier should recognize the like factors as quickly as possible, add their exponents and build the new data structure. In the data representation chosen by Maple, this can be done easily compared to the alternative representation. Similarly, the internal representation of sums allows easy identification of like terms and addition of their coefficients. In short, Maple's internal data representation has been optimized to make polynomial arithmetic fast.

Let us forget for the moment that Maple stores (sub)expressions only once. Then the directed acyclic graph has the graph theoretical structure of a *tree*. The *representation tree* for our example is:

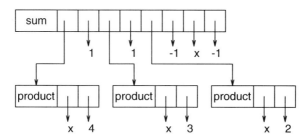

Here we have omitted the data vectors of the building blocks 1, -1, and x; they are considered as atomic elements in the formula. The representation tree of $x^4 + x^3 - x^2 - x$ also indicates that the polynomial consists of x^4, x^3, $-x^2$, and $-x$, and that x^2 is a subexpression. The main advantage of the representation tree is that it is not as messy as the directed acyclic graph. An essential difference between the directed acyclic graph and the representation tree is that in the directed acyclic graph one node is used for identical subexpressions whereas in the representation tree they are represented by separate subtrees. If one keeps this in mind, then the representation tree is an adequate and easy-to-understand description of the internal structure of a Maple expression.

Perhaps your brain is reeling from all those data vectors, directed acyclic graphs, and representation trees? Are you wondering uneasily whether you will always be able to grasp the internal structure of a Maple expression? Well, let it be a relief to you that in most cases your intuition will not fail and that in doubtful cases the system itself can assist you in the determination of the internal data structure. The surface data type of an expression can be determined by the procedure **whattype**.

```
> p1 := x^4 + x^3 - x^2 - x;   # expanded canonical form

              p1 := x^4 + x^3 - x^2 - x
```

```
> whattype( p1 );
```
$$+$$

By the symbol "+", the computer algebra system denotes that the expression is a sum. The procedure **nops** (**n**umber of **op**erands) gives you the number of summands.

```
> nops( p1 );
```
$$4$$

You get the sequence of components of a symbolic expression with the procedure **op** (extract **op**erands).

```
> op( p1 );
```
$$x^4, \quad x^3, \quad -x^2, \quad -x$$

You can unravel each subexpression separately. For example, the first term is a power of x with exponent 4.

```
> `first term` := op(1,p1);
```
$$first\ term := x^4$$

```
> whattype(");
```
$$\wedge$$

```
> op("");
```
$$x, \quad 4$$

Here, the symbol "^" is used as an indication for the data type power.

The third term, $-x^2$, is the product of -1 and the power x^2. Maple denotes the product data type as "*".

```
> `third term` := op(3,p1);
```
$$third\ term := -x^2$$

```
> whattype(");
```
$$\star$$

```
> op( `third term` );
```
$$-1, \quad x^2$$

In the same manner, you can unravel any Maple expression, not just polynomials. The only thing that you must keep in mind is that identical subexpressions are stored in Maple only once. In the above example, the character x occurs at four places, but internally it is only one Maple object. If you substitute y for x in the polynomial $x^4 + x^3 - x^2 - x$, you get the polynomial $y^4 + y^3 - y^2 - y$.

6.2 Generalized Rational Expressions

The following Maple session reveals the internal representation of a rational function.

```
> r := (y^2-1)/(y-1);
```

$$r := \frac{y^2 - 1}{y - 1}$$

```
> type( r, 'ratpoly' ); # check if rational expression
```

$$true$$

```
> whattype(r);
```

$$*$$

```
> op(r);
```

$$y^2 - 1, \frac{1}{y - 1}$$

```
> op(2,r);
```

$$\frac{1}{y - 1}$$

```
> whattype(");
```

$$\wedge$$

```
> op("");
```

$$y - 1, -1$$

```
> normal(r); # normal form
```

$$y + 1$$

Here, you see again that the internal data structure may differ from the external form shown on the worksheet or terminal screen: the rational expression is a product of the numerator and the denominator raised to the power -1. If we consider the expression as an element of the field $\mathbb{R}(y)$, then it can be normalized to the polynomial $y + 1$. Considered as real functions, $\frac{y^2 - 1}{y - 1}$ and $y + 1$ are different.

Let us now look at the following expression:

```
> r := (sin(x)^2-1)/(sin(x)-1);
```

$$r := \frac{\sin(x)^2 - 1}{\sin(x) - 1}$$

```
> type( r, ´ratpoly´ );
```
$$false$$

Maple agrees that this is not a rational function. But if you replace $\sin x$ by y, then you get back the previous rational function. This is also revealed when you inspect the internal data structure of $\dfrac{\sin^2 x - 1}{\sin x - 1}$ with the procedures **op**, **nops**, and **whattype**. Compare the following expression trees:

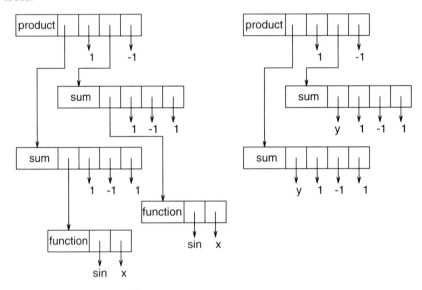

So, we may say that $\dfrac{\sin^2 x - 1}{\sin x - 1}$ is a rational expression in $\sin x$ with integer coefficients. Maple agrees.

```
> type( r, ´ratpoly´(´integer´,sin(x)) );
```
$$true$$

It explains the following result.

```
> normal( r );
```
$$sin(x) + 1$$

Maple considers $\dfrac{\sin^2 x - 1}{\sin x - 1}$ as a *generalized rational expression*. When it applies the procedure **normal**, several things happen. First, the argument of every function call to an elementary transcendental function (trigonometric function, logarithm, exponential function, square root function, etc.) is recursively normalized before it is "frozen" to a unique name. Next, **normal** is applied to the rational expression. Finally, the frozen expressions are "thawed" again. This freezing and thawing of sub-expressions is done automatically in Maple for the procedures **normal** and **factor**. Sometimes you have to help Maple in this respect with the procedure **frontend**.

```
> num := numer(r);   den := denom(r);
```

$$num := \sin(x)^2 - 1$$

$$den := \sin(x) - 1$$

```
> gcd(num,den);
Error, (in gcd)
arguments must be polynomials over the rationals
> frontend( gcd, [num,den] );
```

$$\sin(x) - 1$$

The procedure **gcd** expects polynomials over the rational numbers. **frontend** is employed to "temporarily freeze" `sin(x)` in `num` and `den` to a unique name. On the intermediate results we can apply the procedure **gcd**. Finally, the frozen names are thawed. In the next section, we shall get acquainted with another method of freezing subexpressions.

6.3 Substitution

An important tool to manipulate expressions is *substitution*. Huge expressions, which are difficult to read, can be simplified by replacement of large subexpressions by smaller ones. For example, the matrix

$$\begin{pmatrix} a & b & e & f & a & b \\ c & d & g & h & c & d \\ -e & -f & a & c & e & f \\ -g & -h & b & d & g & h \\ -a & -b & -e & -f & e & g \\ -c & -d & -g & -h & f & h \end{pmatrix},$$

can be rewritten in block form as

$$\begin{pmatrix} X & Y & X \\ -Y & X^T & Y \\ -X & -Y & Y^T \end{pmatrix},$$

where

$$X = \begin{pmatrix} a & b \\ c & d \end{pmatrix} \quad \text{and} \quad Y = \begin{pmatrix} e & f \\ g & h \end{pmatrix}.$$

On many occasions it will be more convenient to use the block matrix instead of the original matrix.

Maple introduces abbreviations in the printing of large formulae by labeling large subexpressions as %1, %2, and so on.

As a rule, you use the procedure **subs** for **subs**titution. The simplest form of a substitution command is

$$\textbf{subs}(\ var = replacement,\ expression\ ).$$

The effect is that *replacement* is substituted for all occurrences of the variable *var* in the *expression*. An example:

```
> kinetic_energy := momentum^2 / (2*mass);
```

$$kinetic\_energy := \frac{1}{2} \frac{momentum^2}{mass}$$

```
> subs( momentum = mass * velocity, kinetic_energy );
```

$$\frac{1}{2}\ mass\ velocity^2$$

```
> kinetic_energy;
```

$$\frac{1}{2} \frac{momentum^2}{mass}$$

Note that the variable kinetic_energy keeps its value after substitution. It can only be changed by an assignment.

```
> kinetic_energy := subs( momentum = mass * velocity,
>    kinetic_energy ):
> kinetic_energy;
```

$$\frac{1}{2}\ mass\ velocity^2$$

The next two examples show that the result of a substitution is simplified but not evaluated. You have to take care of this yourself.

```
> # substitution, but no evaluation
> subs( x=0, cos(x) * ( sin(x) + x^2 + 1 ) );
```

$$cos(\ 0\ )\ (\ sin(\ 0\ )\ +\ 1\ )$$

```
> eval(");   # extra evaluation
```

$$1$$

```
> sum( binomial(n,k)^2, k=1..n );
```

$$\sum_{k=1}^{n} \text{binomial}(\, n, \ k\,)^2$$

```
> subs(n=3,") = eval( subs(n=3,") );
```

$$\sum_{k=1}^{3} \text{binomial}(\, 3, \ k\,)^2 = 19$$

As an example of multiple substitution, we consider a double substitution, which is specified in Maple as

subs(*var1 = replacement1*, *var2 = replacement2*, *expression*).

The effect of this double substitution is that first *replacement1* is substituted for all occurrences of *var1* in the *expression*, and then *var2* is replaced in the intermediate result by *replacement2*. More generally, in multiple substitutions the specified replacements are applied to intermediate expressions from left to right. We call this form of multiple substitution *sequential substitution*. Two examples:

```
> kinetic_energy := momentum^2 / (2*mass);
```

$$kinetic\_energy \ := \ \frac{1}{2} \ \frac{momentum^2}{mass}$$

```
> subs( momentum = mass * velocity,
>    velocity = acceleration * time, kinetic_energy );
```

$$\frac{1}{2} \ mass \ acceleration^2 \ time^2$$

```
> expression := 1 + tan(x)^2;
```

$$expression \ := \ 1 + \tan(\, x\,)^2$$

```
> subs( tan(x) = sin(x)/cos(x), sin(x)^2 = 1 - cos(x)^2,
>    expression );
```

$$1 + \frac{1 - \cos(\, x\,)^2}{\cos(\, x\,)^2}$$

```
> normal(");
```

$$\frac{1}{\cos(\, x\,)^2}$$

Instead of sequential substitution you can also carry out so-called *simultaneous substitution*, simply by grouping the substitution equations together in a set or a list.

subs({ *var1* = *replacement1*, *var2* = *replacement2* }, *expression*)

In simultaneous substitution, the replacements in the expression take place all at once. Better stated, Maple traverses the representation tree, inspects each subexpression, and going from left to right through the set of substitution equations, checks whether there is a match between the left-hand side of a substitution equation and the particular subexpression; if so, the replacement is carried out in the original expression and not in intermediate results. The following examples show you better the difference between sequential and simultaneous substitution.

```
> subs ( x=y, y=z , x*y^2 ); # sequential substitution
```
$$z^3$$

```
> subs ( { x=y, y=z }, x*y^2 ); # simultaneous substitution
```
$$y\ z^2$$

```
> subs ( a=b, b=c, c=a, a + 2*b + 3*c );
```
$$6\ a$$

```
> subs ( { a=b, b=c, c=a }, a + 2*b + 3*c );
```
$$b\ +\ 2\ c\ +\ 3\ a$$

```
> subs ({ p=q, q=p }, f(p,q) ); # interchange p and q
```
$$f(\ q,\ p\ )$$

```
> [a+b=d,a=b^2,b=c^2];
```
$$[\ a\ +\ b = d,\ a = b^2,\ b = c^2\ ]$$

```
> subs ( ", (a+b)^2*b*a );
```
$$d^2\ c^2\ b^2$$

Not only variables can be replaced in a symbolic expression by the procedure **subs**, but also larger subexpressions. In this case, substitution is limited to subexpressions that are recognized as such by Maple. This means that only subexpressions which can be reached by (several applications of) the procedure **op** are allowed to play a role in substitution. For example,

```
> expr1 := x*y + z;   expr2 := x*y*z;
```

$$expr1 := x \, y + z$$

$$expr2 := x \, y \, z$$

```
> subs( x*y = product, expr1 );
```

$$product + z$$

```
> subs( x*y = product, expr2 );
```

$$x \, y \, z$$

```
> op( expr1 );
```

$$x \, y, \ z$$

```
> op( expr2 );
```

$$x, \ y, \ z$$

Because the product $x \, y$ in the second expression expr2 is not recognized by Maple as a subexpression, the product cannot be easily replaced. If such a substitution is desired, you will just have to make do with solutions like

```
> subs( x = product/y, expr2 );
```

$$product \, z$$

```
> subs( {x = product, y = 1}, expr2 );
```

$$product \, z$$

```
> subs( x*y*z = product*z, expr2 );
```

$$product \, z$$

The last substitution only makes sense when expr2 is part of a larger formula which contains x, and other terms involving x should stay intact.

In the same manner:

```
> expression := a + b + c;
```

$$expression := a + b + c$$

```
> subs( a + b = d, expression );
```

$$a + b + c$$

```
> subs( a = d - b, expression );
```

$$d + c$$

```
> subs( {a = d, b = 0}, expression );
```

$$d + c$$

```
subs( a + b + c = d + c, expression );
```

$$d + c$$

Maple V Release 2 contains a procedure, viz., **asubs** (algebraic **subs**titution), which is designed to work on part of a sum, and does not rely solely on syntactic substitutions as is the case with **subs**. Applied to the above example, you get:

```
> asubs( a + b = d, expression, a ); # matching variable a
```

$$d + c$$

The substitution will ordinarily take place only if the terms of matching degree in the polynomial on the left of the substitution occur with exactly the same coefficients in the target expression. You can force the substitution to occur on all parts by the optional extra parameter always, i.e., every sum s is rewritten as s - pat + replacement.

```
> pat := a^2 + 1:
> asubs( pat = d, (a^2+1)^4 + a^3 + 2*a^2 +1);
```

$$d^4 + a^3 + 2 \ a^2 + 1$$

```
> asubs( a^2 + 1 = d, (a^2+1)^4 + a^3 + 2*a^2+1,
>      ´always´ );
```

$$d^4 + a^3 + a^2 + d$$

```
> asubs( a^2 + 1 = d, b+c+ 1/(b+c), ´always´ );
```

$$b + c + \frac{1}{b + c - a^2 - 1 + d} - a^2 - 1 + d$$

Note the difference with

```
> subs( a^2 = d - 1, (a^2+1)^4 + a^3 + 2*a^2+1 );
```

$$d^4 + a^3 + 2 \ d - 1$$

For substitution in part of a product you could also make use of the procedure **powsubs** from the *student* package. First, it must be loaded from the library by the procedure **with**.

```
> with( student, powsubs ): # load the library function
```

powsubs differs from **subs** in that it is defined in terms of algebraic factors rather than in terms of the internal data structure:

```
> powsubs( x*y^2 = s, x^3*y^4 );
```

$$s^2\ x$$

You could also make implicit use of the *Gröbner basis package* by applying the procedure **simplify** with respect to side relations.

```
> simplify( x^3*y^2, {x*y=s}, [y,x,s] );
```

$$s^2\ x$$

We shall come back to simplification with respect to side relations in §13.7

When Maple checks whether a certain expression occurs as a subexpression of a given symbolic expression, the computer algebra system traverses the entire representation tree. Substitution is of a global nature in Maple: *every* occurrence of the subexpression in the original symbolic expression or intermediate results is substituted.

```
> expression := (x+y)^2 + x;
```

$$expression := (x + y)^2 + x$$

```
> op( expression );
```

$$(x + y)^2,\ x$$

```
> op( op( 1, (x+y)^2 ) );
```

$$x,\ y$$

```
> subs( x = z, expression );
```

$$(z + y)^2 + z$$

So, in case of substitution, it is important to know how a Maple expression is built-up and which subexpressions are recognized by the system.

Keep in mind that Maple stores common subexpressions only once. During substitution with **subs** all occurrences of a subexpression are substituted. There is another possibility: by **subsop** you can **subs**titute one or more **op**erands of a Maple expression. For example, the effect of the command

subsop(*num1* = *replacement1*, *num2* = *replacement2*, *expression*)

is that the subexpressions **op**(*num1, expression*) and **op**(*num2, expression*) of the given *expression* are simultaneously replaced by *replacement1* and *replacement2*, respectively. This form of substitution goes only one level deep in the internal representation of the given expression. An example:

```
> expression := x^2 + x + 1/x;
```

$$expression := x^2 + x + \frac{1}{x}$$

```
> subsop( 3 = y, expression );
```

$$x^2 + x + y$$

The third operand of `expression` is replaced by `y`. Compare

```
> subsop( 1 = z, 2 = y, expression );
```

$$z + y + \frac{1}{x}$$

```
> subs( x = y, expression);
```

$$y^2 + y + \frac{1}{y}$$

These examples show you the local nature of the procedure **subsop**. Only numbered subexpressions one level deep in the representation tree can be replaced, and all other operands are left alone. This is opposite to the global nature of **subs**, with which you can replace one or more subexpressions, irrespective of where these subexpressions occur in the given symbolic expression. If you only have to manipulate part of a symbolic expression, you can exploit the local nature of **subsop**. Another advantage of the procedure **subsop** is that you do not have to retype the perhaps very large subexpression which you want to replace. Two examples:

```
> product := ( x^2 + y^2 + 2*x*y ) * ( (x+y)^2 + 1);
```

$$product := (x^2 + y^2 + 2\ x\ y) \left((x + y)^2 + 1 \right)$$

```
> factor( product );
```

$$(x + y)^2 (x^2 + y^2 + 2\ x\ y + 1)$$

```
> subsop( 1 = factor( op(1, product) ), product );
```

$$(x + y)^2 \left((x + y)^2 + 1 \right)$$

```
> expression := (x^2 + 2*x + 1)^2 + (x^2 - 2*x +1)^2;
```

$$expression := (x^2 + 2\ x + 1)^2 + (x^2 - 2\ x + 1)^2$$

```
> factor( expression );
```

$$2\ x^4 + 12\ x^2 + 2$$

```
> subsop( 1 = factor( op(1,expression) ),
>    2 = factor( op(2,expression) ), expression );
```

$$(x + 1)^4 + (x - 1)^4$$

By the way, the latter factorization can be carried out far more easily by use of the procedure **map**.

```
> map( factor, expression );
```

$$(x + 1)^4 + (x - 1)^4$$

The command **map**(*procedure, expression*) has the following effect: apply the *procedure* to all operands of the *expression* separately, combine the results into an expression of the original data type, and carry out automatic simplification (which may change the type of the expression). In §12.5 we shall come back to the procedure **map** and describe it in another context.

Let us note that the substitution in the first of the above two examples could have been carried out as follows.

```
> subs( x+y = z, product );
```

$$(x^2 + y^2 + 2\ x\ y)\ (z^2 + 1)$$

```
> factor(");
```

$$(x + y)^2\ (z^2 + 1)$$

```
> subs( z=x+y, " );
```

$$(x + y)^2 \left((x + y)^2 + 1 \right)$$

This technique of temporary replacement of a subexpression by an unknown, manipulation of the intermediate result, and back substitution of the "frozen" subexpression, is a frequently used simplification strategy. What follows is another illustration of this method.

```
> expression := (x+y)^2 + 1/(x+y)^2;
```

$$expression := (x + y)^2 + \frac{1}{(x + y)^2}$$

We want to change this expression into one of the form $\frac{numerator}{denominator}$ without expansion of the powers $(x + y)^2$. The procedure **normal** does not quite do what we want.

```
> normal( expression );
```

$$\frac{x^4 + 6\ x^2\ y^2 + 4\ y\ x^3 + 4\ x\ y^3 + y^4 + 1}{(x + y)^2}$$

If we temporarily replace the subexpression $x + y$ in the powers by a new unknown, say z, normalize the intermediate rational function, and finally substitute back $x + y$ for z, then we get the desired result.

```
> subs( x + y = z, expression );
```

$$z^2 + \frac{1}{z^2}$$

```
> normal(");
```

$$\frac{z^4 + 1}{z^2}$$

```
> subs( z = x + y, " );
```

$$\frac{(x + y)^4 + 1}{(x + y)^2}$$

Because it is not always easy in a long Maple session to recall which variables are already in use and which substitutions have already been applied, the Maple system offers you the procedures **freeze** and **thaw** as utility functions. When you use them, Maple itself chooses new names for subexpressions and keeps track of them. The above example would look like

```
> readlib( freeze ): # load the library function
> subs( x+y=freeze(x+y), expression );
```

$$\_R0^2 + \frac{1}{\_R0^2}$$

```
> normal(");
```

$$\frac{\_R0^4 + 1}{\_R0^2}$$

```
> subs( _R0=thaw(_R0), " );
```

$$\frac{(x + y)^4 + 1}{(x + y)^2}$$

6.4 Exercises

1. Describe in detail the internal representation in Maple of the polynomial $2x(y^2+1)^2$. Draw the corresponding directed acyclic graph (DAG) sand the representation tree. Write down all subexpressions which are recognized as such by Maple. Enlarge your trust in your answer by use of the procedures **whattype**, **nops**, and **op**. By use of the procedures **addressof**, **pointto**, **disassemble**, and **assemble** you can completely check your answer.

2. Transform

$$x + y + \frac{1}{x + y}$$

   into

$$\frac{(x + y)^2 + 1}{x + y}$$

   and vice versa.

3. Explain the result of the following substitution:

```
> x^2-x+1/x-1/x^2;
```

$$x^2 - x + \frac{1}{x} - \frac{1}{x^2}$$

```
> subs(-1=1,");
```

$$x^2 + 2x + \frac{1}{x^2}$$

4. Transform
$$x^2 + 2x + 1 + \frac{1}{x^2 + 2x + 1}$$

into

$$\frac{(x+1)^2 + 1}{(x+1)^2}$$

and vice versa.

5. Transform

$$\frac{(x+1)^{10} - 2y}{(x+y)^{10}} + \frac{1}{(x+y)^9} - \frac{x}{(x+y)^{10}}$$

into

$$\frac{(x+1)^{10} - y}{(x+y)^{10}}.$$

Manipulation of Polynomials and Rational Expressions

In this chapter, we shall systematically discuss manipulations of polynomials and rational expressions. The following manipulations pass under review: expansion, factorization, normalization, collection, and sorting of polynomials and rational expressions. We shall consider manipulation of expressions which are defined over the rational numbers as well as manipulation of expressions which are defined over other domains, like finite fields, algebraic numbers, and algebraic function fields. Furthermore, we shall give a short, theoretical introduction to canonical and normal form simplification.

7.1 Expansion

Suppose that you want to transform $(x^2 - x)(x^2 + 2x + 1)$ from this factored form into the expanded canonical form $x^4 + x^3 - x^2 - x$. Then you can use the procedure **expand**, and if necessary **sort** the result. In **expand**, the factors are first multiplied out, and secondly similar terms are collected. In our example, the first step leads to $x^4 + 2x^3 + x^2 - x^3 - 2x^2 - x$, and then Maple simplifies this to $x^4 + x^3 - x^2 - x$ (or eventually to a different ordering if the polynomial was already in memory in a different form; in this case you need the procedure **sort** to rearrange terms).

```
> factored_form := (x^2-x)*(x^2+2*x+1);
          factored_form := ( x² - x ) ( x² + 2 x + 1 )

> expanded_form := expand( factored_form );
          expanded_form := x⁴ + x³ - x² - x
```

The way in which Maple distributes products over sums can be illustrated best by an easier example.

```
> factored_form := (a+b)*(c+d);
```

$$factored\_form := (a + b)(c + d)$$

```
> expanded_form := expand( factored_form );
```

$$expanded\_form := a c + a d + b c + b d$$

With the Maple procedure **expand** all products are distributed over sums
and like terms are automatically collected by Maple's simplifier. The ter-
minology *full expansion* is more appropriate. For example, in our last
example, the expansion of the factored form can be described as a two-
step mechanism: first, the factored form is transformed to the expression
$a(c+d)+b(c+d)$, and after that the intermediate expression is transformed
to the final form $ac + ad + bc + bd$. If you want to avoid this second step,
than you must specify in the call of the procedure **expand** that you want
to keep the subexpression $c + d$ intact.

```
> partially_expanded_form := expand( factored_form, c+d );
```

$$partially\_expanded\_form := (c + d) a + (c + d) b$$

The procedure **expand** also distributes powers with positive integer exponents over sums, simply by considering these powers as repeated products
and by distributing them over sums.

```
> power := (x+1)^3;
```

$$power := (x + 1)^3$$

```
> expand(");
```

$$x^3 + 3 x^2 + 3 x + 1$$

Negative powers are left untouched by **expand**.

```
> power := (x+1)^(-2);
```

$$power := \frac{1}{(x + 1)^2}$$

```
> whattype(");
```

$$\wedge$$

```
> op( power );
```

$$x + 1, \ -2$$

```
> expand( power );
```

$$\frac{1}{(x + 1)^2}$$

If you consider this expression as a rational one of which the denominator is equal to $(x+1)^2$, then you can expand the denominator separately.

```
> 1 / expand( denom(") );
```

$$\frac{1}{x^2 + 2\ x + 1}$$

Maple does not expand powers with non-integer exponents.

```
> power := (x+1)^(3/2);
```

$$power := (\ x + 1\ )^{3/2}$$

```
> expand(");
```

$$(\ x + 1\ )^{3/2}$$

The only effect of **expand** on rational expressions is that sums in the numerator are expanded.

```
> (x+1)^2 / ((x^2+x)*x);
```

$$\frac{(\ x + 1\ )^2}{(\ x^2 + x\ )\ x}$$

```
> expand(");
```

$$\frac{x}{x^2 + x} + 2\ \frac{1}{x^2 + x} + \frac{1}{(\ x^2 + x\ )\ x}$$

So far, we have only looked at expansion of polynomials and rational functions defined over the integers. When you manipulate polynomials which are defined over a finite ring, over algebraic numbers, or over algebraic function fields, then you must use the inert form of expansion, namely **Expand**. A few examples will do.

- Expansion over $\mathbb{Z}_8$.

```
> Expand( (x+1)^8 ) mod 8 ;
```

$$x^8 + 4\ x^6 + 6\ x^4 + 4\ x^2 + 1$$

- Expansion over $\mathbf{Q}(\alpha)$, where α is a root of the polynomial $z^5 + z + 1$.

```
> alias( alpha = RootOf( z^5 + z + 1, z ) ):
> (x+alpha)^5;
```

$$(\ x + \alpha\ )^5$$

```
> evala( Expand(") );
```

$$x^5 \; + \; 5 \; \alpha \; x^4 \; + \; 10 \; \alpha^2 \; x^3 \; + \; 10 \; \alpha^3 \; x^2 \; + \; 5 \; \alpha^4 \; x \; - \; \alpha \; - \; 1$$

- Expansion over $\mathbb{Z}_5(\alpha)$, where α is a root of the polynomial $z^5 + z + 1$.

```
> Expand("") mod 5;
```

$$x^5 \; + \; 4 \; \alpha \; + \; 4$$

- Expansion over the algebraic function field $\mathbf{Q}\big(\sqrt{1+y}\big)$.

  Recall that an algebraic function over $\mathbb{C}$ is a function which annihilates a univariate polynomial with coefficients in a rational function field. In our example, $\sqrt{1+y}$ is defined as a root of the polynomial $z^2 - 1 - y$ with coefficients in the rational function field $\mathbf{Q}(y)$.

```
> alias( beta = RootOf( z^2 - 1 - y, z ) ):
> (x+beta)^2;
```

$$(x \; + \; \beta)^2$$

```
> evala( Expand(") );
```

$$x^2 \; + \; 2 \; \beta \; x \; + \; 1 \; + \; y$$

7.2 Factorization

The Maple procedure **factor** is **expand**'s big brother. It computes the factorization of a polynomial over the rationals in irreducible factors. The result is unique up to ordering of factors; we speak of a *factored normal form*. The procedure also works fine for rational expressions, in that common factors in numerator and denominator are first canceled before they are factored.

In §5.1 we have already seen that Maple can factor polynomials over various domains. In case of polynomials over finite fields and algebraic function fields, you may have to use the inert form **Factor**. We give more examples.

- Factorization over $\mathbf{Q}(\sqrt{6})$.

```
> factor( 8*x^3 - 12*x, sqrt(6) );
```

$$2 \left(2 \; x \; + \; \sqrt{6} \right) \left(2 \; x \; - \; \sqrt{6} \right) x$$

- Factorization over finite fields $\mathbb{Z}_2, \mathbb{Z}_3$, and $\mathbb{Z}_5$.

```
> x^4 + 1;
```
$$x^4 + 1$$

```
> Factor(") mod 2;
```
$$(x + 1)^4$$

```
> Factor("") mod 3;
```
$$(x^2 + x + 2) \ (x^2 + 2 \ x + 2)$$

```
> Factor(""") mod 5;
```
$$(x^2 + 2) \ (x^2 + 3)$$

- Factorization over $\mathbb{Z}_7(\alpha)$, where α is a root of the polynomial $z^7 + z^3 + 1$.

```
> alias( alpha = RootOf( z^7 + z^3 + 1, z ) ):
> x^7 + 6*alpha^3 + 6;
```
$$x^7 + 6 \ \alpha^3 + 6$$

```
> Factor(") mod 7;
```
$$(x + \alpha)^7$$

- Factorization over the algebraic function field $\mathbf{Q}(\sqrt{1+y})$.

```
> alias( beta = RootOf( z^2 - 1 - y, z ) ):
> x^2 + 2*beta*x + 1 + y;
```
$$x^2 + 2 \ \beta \ x + 1 + y$$

```
> factor( x^2 + 2*beta*x + 1 + y, beta );
```
$$(x + \beta)^2$$

The extension of the field of rational numbers with the square root of six appeared more or less out of nothingness to yield the complete factorization of $8x^3 - 12x$. But Maple itself can compute the splitting field of a univariate polynomial with the procedure **split**.

```
> readlib(split):   # load the library function
> split( 8*x^3 - 12*x, x );
```
$$8 \ x \left(x - \frac{1}{2} \ RootOf(\_Z^2 - 6) \right) \left(x + \frac{1}{2} \ RootOf(\_Z^2 - 6) \right)$$

```
> convert( ", ´radical´ );
```

$$8\ x\left(x - \frac{1}{2}\sqrt{6}\right)\left(x + \frac{1}{2}\sqrt{6}\right)$$

AFactor does absolute factorization of multivariate polynomials over the complex numbers.

```
> evala( AFactor( x^3 + y^3 ) );
```

$$(x + y)\ (x + (-RootOf(\_Z^2 + \_Z + 1) - 1)\ y)$$

$$(x + RootOf(\_Z^2 + \_Z + 1)\ y)$$

```
> # select one root to come to a more common notation
> subs( RootOf(_Z^2+_Z+1) =
>    allvalues( RootOf(_Z^2+_Z+1) )[1], " );
```

$$(x + y)\left(x + \left(-\frac{1}{2} - \frac{1}{2}\ I\ \sqrt{3}\right)y\right)$$

$$\left(x + \left(-\frac{1}{2} + \frac{1}{2}\ I\ \sqrt{3}\right)y\right)$$

One of the first steps in the factorization of a polynomial by **factor** is the *square-free factorization* of the polynomial. The square-free factorization of a non-constant polynomial is defined as a decomposition of the form $c\,p_1\,p_2^2\,p_3^3\ldots$, where c is a rational constant and the polynomials p_1, p_2, p_3, $\ldots$, are relatively prime and have no multiple factors. In Maple you can compute the square-free factorization by explicit conversion or by calling the procedure **sqrfree**.

```
> x^4 + x^3 - x^2 - x;
```

$$x^4 + x^3 - x^2 - x$$

```
> convert( ", ´sqrfree´ );
```

$$(x^2 - x)\ (x + 1)^2$$

```
> sqrfree("");
```

$$[1,\ [\,[\,x^2 - x,\ 1\,],\ [\,x + 1,\ 2\,]\,]\,]$$

When you compute over the field $\mathbb{Z}_2$ with two elements, the latter polynomial has a square-free factorization equal to $x(x + 1)^3$; in Maple computed as

```
> Sqrfree(""") mod 2;
```
$$[1, [[x, 1], [x + 1, 3]]]$$

7.3 Canonical Form and Normal Form

So far the terms *canonical form* and *normal form* have appeared several times in the context of simplification or manipulation of expressions. It is worthwhile to linger a bit longer on them, even though it is a more theoretical intermezzo. A detailed survey can be found in [17].

The main problem with simplification is that a mathematical expression can be written in several equivalent forms whereas it is not always easy to recognize equivalence. For example, the third Hermite polynomial is equal to $8x^2 - 12x$, but you can easily write down four equivalent formulae:

$$x(8x^2 - 12),$$
$$4x(2x^2 - 3),$$
$$2x(2x - \sqrt{6})(2x + \sqrt{6}),$$
$$(2x)^3 - 6 \cdot (2x).$$

What is the simplest form? If we want to stress the fact that it is a polynomial in $2x$, then $2x(2x - \sqrt{6})(2x + \sqrt{6})$ and $(2x)^3 - 6 \cdot (2x)$ are good candidates. If we use the number of terms as criterion, then $8x^3 - 12x$ and $(2x)^3 - 6 \cdot (2x)$ would be our favorites.

A more clearly specified problem is the so-called *zero equivalence* problem, i.e., to recognize whether an expression is equal to zero. But even this may turn out to be a hard problem as in

$$\ln \tan(\frac{1}{2}x + \frac{1}{4}\pi) - \operatorname{arcsinh} \tan x = 0.$$

Verification of this equality is non-trivial.

In general the simplification problem can be treated as follows. Let $\mathcal{E}$ be a class of symbolic expressions (e.g., univariate polynomials over the integers) and let $\sim$ be an equivalence relation defined on $\mathcal{E}$. The problem of finding an equivalent but simpler expression can be characterized as finding a computable transformation $\mathcal{S}: \mathcal{E} \longrightarrow \mathcal{E}$ such that for any expression t in $\mathcal{E}$ we have

$$\mathcal{S}(t) \sim t \quad \text{and} \quad \mathcal{S}(t) \preceq t.$$

Here, $\preceq$ denotes some simplification concept: $s \prec t$ is our notation for "expression s is simpler in $\mathcal{E}$ than expression t," and this means e.g., "expression s has less terms than t," "s uses less memory than t," or "s is more readable than t." We say that expressions s and t are identical and denote this by $s \equiv t$, when s and t are built up in the same way from basic elements, or more precisely when they have the same directed acyclic graph (see e.g., the previous chapter for a description of Maple's internal data representation).

A *canonical simplifier* $\mathcal{S}$ on $\mathcal{E}$ is a computable procedure such that for all s and t in $\mathcal{E}$ we have

$$\mathcal{S}(t) \sim t \text{ and}$$
$$s \sim t \implies \mathcal{S}(s) \equiv \mathcal{S}(t).$$

A canonical simplifier chooses a unique representative in each equivalence class, the *canonical form.*

For univariate polynomials, the expanded canonical form can be obtained as follows:

(i) recursively distribute all products over sums,

(ii) collect terms of the same degree, and

(iii) remove superfluous terms and reorder the remaining terms in descending order of their degrees.

The requirements for canonical simplification are high and cannot always be met. A weaker form of simplification is *normal form simplification.* Suppose that there is a distinguished element, say 0, in $\mathcal{E}$. A *normal simplifier* $\mathcal{S}$ on $\mathcal{E}$ is a computable procedure such that for all s and t in $\mathcal{E}$ holds

$$\mathcal{S}(t) \sim t \text{ and}$$
$$t \sim 0 \implies \mathcal{S}(t) \equiv \mathcal{S}(0).$$

An expression t is called a *normal form* in $\mathcal{E}$ when $\mathcal{S}(t) \equiv t$. So, the normal form need not be unique in each equivalence class except for the class to which 0 belongs in $\mathcal{E}$.

For univariate polynomials, the expanded normal form, which we called collected form, can be obtained as follows:

(i) recursively distribute all products over sums,

(ii) collect terms of the same degree, and

(iii) remove superfluous terms.

Normal simplification is usually easier than canonical simplification. Other examples of normal forms of polynomials are the square-free form and the Horner form, which is a nested form often used for efficiency reasons.

```
> poly := expand( (x+y+z)^2*(x+y+1) );
```

$$poly := x^3 + 3 \ x^2 \ y + x^2 + 3 \ x \ y^2 + 2 \ x \ y + 2 \ x^2 \ z$$
$$+ \ 4 \ x \ z \ y + 2 \ x \ z + y^3 + y^2 + 2 \ y^2 \ z + 2 \ y \ z$$

$$+ z^2 x + z^2 y + z^2$$

```
> readlib(cost)( poly );
```

$$14 \; additions \; + \; 32 \; multiplications$$

```
> horner_form := convert( poly, `horner`, [x,y,z] );
```

$$horner\_form := z^2 + ((2 + z) z + (2 z + 1 + y) y) y$$

$$+ ((2 + z) z + (2 + 4 z + 3 y) y$$

$$+ (2 z + 1 + 3 y + x) x) x$$

```
> cost( horner_form );
```

$$14 \; additions \; + \; 13 \; multiplications$$

Partial fraction decomposition of rational functions is an example of a normal simplifier of rational expressions.

7.4 Normalization

The procedure **normal** provides the normal simplification for rational functions over $\mathbf{Q}$ in Maple. A rational function is converted into the so-called *factored normal form*. This is the form $\dfrac{numerator}{denominator}$, where the numerator and denominator are relatively prime polynomials with integer coefficients; the numerator and denominator are both products of expanded polynomials and during the normal simplification common factors are kept intact as much as possible.

```
> (x-1)*(x+2)/((x+1)*x) + (x-1)/(1+x)^2;
```

$$\frac{(x - 1) (x + 2)}{(x + 1) x} + \frac{x - 1}{(x + 1)^2}$$

```
> normal(");
```

$$\frac{(x - 1) (x^2 + 4 x + 2)}{(x + 1)^2 x}$$

```
> (x^2+x-2)/((x+1)*x)+(x-1)/(1+x)^2;
```

$$\frac{x^2 + x - 2}{(x + 1) x} + \frac{x - 1}{(x + 1)^2}$$

```
> normal(");
```

$$\frac{x^3 + 3\ x^2 - 2\ x - 2}{(x+1)^2\ x}$$

```
> normal( """, ´expanded´ );
```

$$\frac{x^3 + 3\ x^2 - 2\ x - 2}{x^3 + 2\ x^2 + x}$$

You specify with the keyword expanded as the last argument that you want both numerator and denominator in expanded normal form.

There exist several normal forms for rational expressions and you can produce some of them by application of the procedures **normal, expand** and **factor** upon numerator and denominator separately. Alternatives are:

```
> ratfunc := (x^4+x^3-4*x^2-4*x)/(x^3+x^2-x-1);
```

$$\ln(z) + e^z$$

- $\dfrac{\textit{factored normal form}}{\textit{factored normal form}}$

```
> factor( ratfunc );
```

$$(\ln(z) + 1)\ (e^z - 1)$$

- $\dfrac{\textit{factored normal form}}{\textit{expanded canonical form}}$

```
> factor(numer(ratfunc)) / sort(expand(denom(ratfunc)));
```

$$\frac{x\ (x-2)\ (x+2)\ (x+1)}{x^3 + x^2 - x - 1}$$

- $\dfrac{\textit{expanded canonical form}}{\textit{factored normal form}}$

```
> sort(expand(numer(ratfunc))) / factor(denom(ratfunc));
```

$$\frac{x^4 + x^3 - 4\ x^2 - 4\ x}{(x-1)\ (x+1)^2}$$

- $\dfrac{\textit{expanded canonical form}}{\textit{expanded canonical form}}$

```
> sort( normal( ratfunc, ´expanded´ ) );
```

$$\frac{x^3 - 4\,x}{x^2 - 1}$$

Above, we have applied **normal** on a rational function, but, as was already explained in §6.2, you can also normalize a generalized rational expression with this procedure. We confine ourselves to one example, which explains the recursive character of **normal**.

```
> sin(x+1/x) + 1/sin(x+1/x);
```

$$\sin\!\left(x + \frac{1}{x} \right) + \frac{1}{\sin\!\left(x + \dfrac{1}{x} \right)}$$

```
> normal(");
```

$$\frac{\sin\!\left(\dfrac{x^2 + 1}{x} \right)^2 + 1}{\sin\!\left(\dfrac{x^2 + 1}{x} \right)}$$

The procedure **normal** has a twin brother called **Normal**. This procedure is a normal simplification for various coefficient domains. We give two examples.

```
> Normal( ratfunc ) mod 3;
```

$$x$$

```
> (x^2-a)/(x-sqrt(a));
```

$$\frac{x^2 - a}{x - \sqrt{a}}$$

```
> convert( ", `RootOf` );
```

$$\frac{x^2 - a}{x - \mathrm{RootOf}(\, \_Z^2 - a\,)}$$

```
> evala( Normal(") );
```

$$x + \mathrm{RootOf}(\, \_Z^2 - a\,)$$

```
> convert( ", `radical` );
```

$$x + \sqrt{a}$$

7.5 Collection

The procedure **collect** is used to group coefficients of like terms in a polynomial. The various ways of collecting terms are best shown by examples.

```
> poly := expand( (x+y+z)^2 * (x+y+1) );
```

$$poly := x^3 + 3\ x^2\ y + x^2 + 3\ x\ y^2 + 2\ x\ y + 2\ x^2\ z$$
$$+ 4\ x\ z\ y + 2\ x\ z + y^3 + y^2 + 2\ y^2\ z + 2\ y\ z$$
$$+ z^2\ x + z^2\ y + z^2$$

This is an example of the *distributed* or *expanded form* of a polynomial in Maple. We use the notation $\mathbb{Z}[x, y, z]$ to denote the set of distributed multivariate polynomials in the unknowns x, y, and z, with integer coefficients.

Consider `poly` as a polynomial in z whose coefficients are distributed polynomials in x and y, i.e., consider `poly` as an element in $\mathbb{Z}[x, y][z]$.

```
> collect( poly, z );
```

$$(\ x + y + 1\ )\ z^2 + (\ 4\ x\ y + 2\ x + 2\ x^2 + 2\ y^2 + 2\ y\ )\ z$$
$$+ x^3 + 3\ x^2\ y + x^2 + 3\ x\ y^2 + 2\ x\ y + y^2 + y^3$$

Now consider `poly` as a polynomial in z whose coefficients are polynomials in y whose coefficients are polynomials in x with integer coefficients, i.e., consider `poly` as an element of $\mathbb{Z}[x][y][z]$.

```
> collect( poly, [z,y], ´recursive´ );
```

$$(\ x + y + 1\ )\ z^2$$
$$+ (\ 2\ y^2 + (\ 4\ x + 2\ )\ y + 2\ x + 2\ x^2\ )\ z + y^3$$
$$+ (\ 3\ x + 1\ )\ y^2 + (\ 3\ x^2 + 2\ x\ )\ y + x^3 + x^2$$

Loosely speaking, we have considered here `poly` as a polynomial in z and y with preference for the indeterminate z.

Of course you can also consider `poly` as a polynomial in z and y without giving preference to any of the two unknowns, i.e., you can consider the `poly` as an element of $\mathbb{Z}[x][y, z]$.

```
> collect( poly, [z,y], ´distributed´ );
```

$$(\ 2\ x + 2\ x^2\ )\ z + (\ 3\ x^2 + 2\ x\ )\ y + y^3 + x^3 + x^2$$
$$+ (\ 3\ x + 1\ )\ y^2 + (\ 4\ x + 2\ )\ y\ z + 2\ y^2\ z + z^2\ y$$
$$+ (\ x + 1\ )\ z^2$$

Finally, you can add as an argument to **collect** the name of a procedure which has to be applied to each coefficient separately.

```
> collect( poly, z, factor ); # recursive order by default
```

$$(x + y + 1) \; z^2 + 2 \; (x + y + 1) \; (x + y) \; z$$

$$+ \; (x + y + 1) \; (x + y)^2$$

```
> collect( poly , [z,y], 'distributed', factor );
```

$$2 \; x \; (x + 1) \; z + x \; (3 \; x + 2) \; y + y^3 + x^2 \; (x + 1)$$

$$+ \; (3 \; x + 1) \; y^2 + (4 \; x + 2) \; y \; z + 2 \; y^2 \; z + z^2 \; y$$

$$+ \; (x + 1) \; z^2$$

The main reasons for using collected forms of multivariate polynomials in Maple are readability and efficiency with respect to memory and computing time. If a polynomial is dense in some variable, it is advantageous to collect with respect to this variable because this will reduce representation space compared to the expanded form. Collecting terms is a way to overcome the length limitation of internal Maple objects. In Maple, a sum with more than 65535 $(= 2^{16} - 1)$ terms cannot be represented, and the system will print

System Error, object too large

By maintaining the expression collected in some of the indeterminates, you may be able to reduce the maximum size of the sums in the expression. In our example above, the expanded form of `poly` has 15 terms, whereas the collected form in $\mathbb{Z}[x, y][z]$ with all coefficients in factored form has only 3 terms.

Like **normal**, the procedure **collect** can be applied to generalized rational expressions.

```
> ln(x)^3/a + ln(x)^2*x/(a^2+a) + a^2*ln(x)^2*x/(a^2+a)
>    + 2*x^2/(1+a)+a*x^2/(1+a) + a^3*ln(x)/(a^2+a)
>    + 2*ln(x)*a/(a^2+a) + ln(x)/(a^2+a) + a/(a^2+a);
```

$$\frac{\ln(x)^3}{a} + \frac{\ln(x)^2 \; x}{a^2 + a} + \frac{a^2 \; \ln(x)^2 \; x}{a^2 + a} + 2 \; \frac{x^2}{1 + a}$$

$$+ \; \frac{a \; x^2}{1 + a} + \frac{a^3 \; \ln(x)}{a^2 + a} + 2 \; \frac{a \; \ln(x)}{a^2 + a} + \frac{\ln(x)}{a^2 + a}$$

$$+ \; \frac{a}{a^2 + a}$$

```
> collect( ", [x,ln(x)], `distributed`, normal );
```

$$\frac{(2 + a)\ x^2}{1 + a} + \frac{\ln(x)^2\ (a^2 + 1)\ x}{a\ (1 + a)} + \frac{\ln(x)^3}{a}$$

$$+ \frac{(a^3 + 2\ a + 1)\ \ln(x)}{a\ (1 + a)} + \frac{1}{1 + a}$$

Note that you can only collect with respect to names and function calls, but not with respect to polynomial expressions. If the first few terms of

```
> x^5 - 5*x^4*y^2 + 10*x^3*y^4 - 10*x^2*y^6 + 5*x*y^8
>    - y^10 - 2;
```

$$x^5 - 5\ x^4\ y^2 + 10\ x^3\ y^4 - 10\ x^2\ y^6 + 5\ x\ y^8 - y^{10} - 2$$

remind you of $(x - y^2)^5$, then you cannot simply collect with respect to $x - y^2$.

```
> collect( ", x - y^2 );
Error, (in collect) cannot collect, x-y^2
```

Instead, you can simplify with respect to the side relation $x - y^2 = z$.

```
> siderel := {z = x - y^2};
```

$$siderel := \{ z = x - y^2 \}$$

```
> simplify( "", siderel, [x,y,z] );
```

$$-2 + z^5$$

```
> subs( siderel, " );
```

$$(x - y^2)^5 - 2$$

See §13.7 for more examples of such polynomial simplifications.

7.6 Sorting

The procedure **sort** is used to sort polynomials in some suitable ordering. We have already described this in §5.2. Here, we only give an example of a rational function whose numerator and denominator are sorted.

```
> r := sort( (x-y)/(x+y), [x,y], `plex` );
```

$$r := \frac{x - y}{x + y}$$

```
> sort( (x-y)/(x+y), [y,x], `plex` );
```

$$\frac{-y + x}{y + x}$$

7.7 Exercises

1. Describe a canonical simplification of univariate rational functions with rational coefficients.

2. Consider the rational expression.
$$\frac{x^4 + x^3 - 4x^2 - 4x}{x^4 + x^3 - x^2 - x}$$
   Transform this expression with Maple into:

   (a) $\dfrac{x^2 - 4}{x^2 - 1}$

   (b) $\dfrac{(x - 2)(x + 2)}{x^2 - 1}$

3. Consider the rational expression.
$$2\frac{x^3 - yx^2 - yx + y^2}{x^3 - yx^2 - x + y}$$
   Transform this expression with Maple into:

   (a) $2\dfrac{x^2 - y}{x^2 - 1}$

   (b) $2\dfrac{x^2 - y}{(x - 1)(x + 1)}$

   (c) $2 - \dfrac{y - 1}{x - 1} + \dfrac{y - 1}{x + 1}$

   (d) $2 - 2\dfrac{y - 1}{x^2 - 1}$

4. Consider the polynomial $(2x^2 - x)(2x^2 + x)$.
   Transform this polynomial with Maple into:

   (a) $(-1 + 4x^2)x^2$

   (b) $x^2(2x - 1)(2x + 1)$

   (c) $(2x^3 + x^2)(2x - 1)$

5. Consider the polynomial $(x^2 + xy + x + y)(x + y)$.
   Transform this polynomial with Maple into:

   (a) $x^3 + 2x^2y + xy^2 + x^2 + 2xy + y^2$

   (b) $(x + 1)(x + y)^2$.

   (c) $y^2 + (2y + y^2)x + (1 + 2y)x^2 + x^3$

   (d) $x^3 + x^2 + (2x^2 + 2x)y + (x + 1)y^2$

Functions

In Maple, a functional relationship can be specified in two ways: as an arrow operator (similar to common mathematical notation), and as a procedure. In this chapter, we shall discuss both methods in detail. Special attention will be payed to recursively defined procedures and functions. The role of the `remember` option in defining efficient, recursive functions will be treated in detail.

This chapter is not about programming; we shall only discuss how mathematical functions can be defined in Maple. Local variables in procedures, the way these variables are evaluated, and scoping rules are a few of the programming topics that will not be treated. In this chapter, we shall focus on practical issues like "how to define a function," "how to transform a formula into a function," and "when to use anonymous functions."

8.1 Mathematical Functions

In previous chapters we have already seen some commonly used mathematical functions that are available in Maple. You can get a complete list with the instruction **?inifcns** (help about **ini**tially known **functions**). This list also contains names of less known functions such as *Lambert's W function*. This function has been introduced as the solution of the following equation in [46].

```
> f(x) * exp(f(x)) = x;
```

$$f(x) \ e^{f(x)} = x$$

```
> solve(",f(x));
```

$$W(x)$$

A more detailed description of Lambert's W function can be found in [14]. Below are two examples of computations in which this function plays a role.

```
> a*x + b^x = c;
```

$$a\,x + b^x = c$$

```
> solve(",x);
```

$$-\frac{W\!\left(\dfrac{e^{\frac{\ln(b)\,c}{a}}\ln(b)}{a}\right) - \dfrac{\ln(b)\,c}{a}}{\ln(b)}$$

```
> f(x) = solve( f(x) = x^f(x), f(x) );
```

$$f(x) = -\frac{W(-\ln(x))}{\ln(x)}$$

The latter result is nothing more than saying that the function

$$f : x \longmapsto x^{x^{x^{\cdot^{\cdot^{\cdot}}}}}$$

is equal to

$$f : x \longmapsto -\frac{W(-\ln x)}{\ln x}$$

for $x \in (0,1)$. On this interval the function looks like

```
> plot( rhs("), x=0..1, title=`graph of f(x)` );
```

graph of f(x)

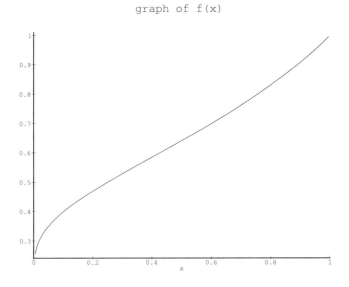

In Maple, you can specify functional relationship in two ways:

- The dependency of a quantity on variables can be specified in a formula. For example, if the temperature of a body decreases exponentially in time, then the following formula can be entered in Maple.

```
> T := T0 * exp(-c*t);
```

$$T := T0 \ e^{-c \ t}$$

To get the value of the temperature at a particular time you can replace t by some value.

```
> subs( t=1/c , T );
```

$$T0 \ e^{-1}$$

- You can introduce functions in a more mathematical way.

```
> T := t -> T0 * exp(-c*t);
```

$$T := t \rightarrow T0 \ e^{-c \ t}$$

```
> T(2/c), T(time), T(0);
```

$$T0 \ e^{-2}, \ T0 \ e^{-c \ time}, \ T0$$

Mathematical functions often come in handy, and you should be careful to distinguish in Maple between a variable which points to an expression in other unknowns and a variable whose value is a function. Referring to the above function definition of T:

```
> T;   # evaluation to the name of the function
```

$$T$$

```
> T(t);
```

$$T0 \ e^{-c \ t}$$

```
> solve( T = 100, t );
```

Maple does not show a result after the last instruction as a sign that no solution is found. If `infolevel[solve]` has a value greater than zero, then the system notifies that no solution is found.

```
> infolevel[solve] := 1:
> solve( T = 100, t );
solve:   Warning: no solutions found
```

Indeed, there is no value for t such that the *function* T is equal to the number 100. This was of course not what we intended to do; when we ask the correct question, Maple finds the answer.

```
> solve( T(t) = 100, t );
```

$$- \frac{\ln\left(100 \; \frac{1}{T0} \right)}{c}$$

8.2 Arrow Operators

In the previous section, you have seen one way of defining functions in Maple, viz., the *arrow operator* definition, which mimics the syntax for functions often used in mathematics:

$$function\_name := parameter \; -> \; expression.$$

You may be tempted to define functions as follows:

```
> T := evaln(T):   # make sure that T is a free variable
> T(t)  := T0 * exp(-c*t);
```

$$T(\; t \;) \; := \; T0 \; e^{-c \; t}$$

Maple accepts the instruction. It looks promising, but it does not really do what you think it means, as illustrated below.

```
> T(t), T(1/c), T(0);
```

$$T0 \; e^{-c \; t}, \; T\left(\frac{1}{c} \right), \; T(\; 0 \;)$$

What happened? You created a function without a function description.

```
> print(T);
  proc() options remember; ´procname(args)´ end
```

Instead, you stored in the *remember table* of the procedure T the value of the function at t. When you ask for the function value at 1/c, then Maple has no value in the remember table nor a function description. Therefore, the system can do nothing more than printing the function call; perhaps you will want to assign a function description to T later on in the session.

You have already seen the case of a function in one variable. Functions with more than one variable are defined similarly.

```
> f := (x,y) -> x^3 - 3*x*y^2;
```

$$f := (x, y) \rightarrow x^3 - 3\ x\ y^2$$

```
> f(3,2);
```

$$-9$$

```
> plot3d( f, -1..1, -1..1,
>    numpoints=2500, style=patchcontour, axes=framed );
```

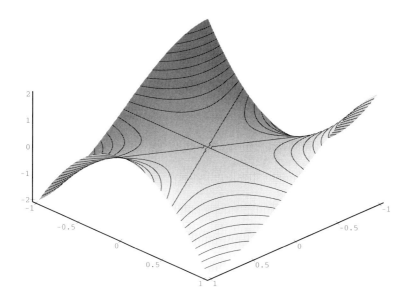

Mind the brackets around the function parameters; otherwise Maple will interpret it as

```
> f := x, ( y -> x^3 - 3*x*y^2 );
```

$$f := x,\ y \rightarrow x^3 - 3\ x\ y^2$$

i.e, you have created the expression sequence f consisting of the variable x and the anonymous function $y \longrightarrow x^3 - 3xy^2$.

The general form of a function definition with the arrow operator is

$$\textit{parameter} \ \text{->} \ [\textbf{local}\ \textit{name\_sequence;}]\ \textit{expression}$$

for functions of one parameter, and

$$(\textit{parameter\_sequence}) \ \text{->} \ [\textbf{local}\ \textit{name\_sequence;}]\ \textit{expression}$$

for functions of zero or more parameters. Examples explain this better.

```
> sqrt2 := () -> sqrt(2); # constant function sqrt(2)
```
$$sqrt2 := (\ \ ) \rightarrow sqrt(\ 2\ )$$

```
> sqrt2();
```
$$\sqrt{2}$$

```
> sqrt2(x); # no check on number of arguments
```
$$\sqrt{2}$$

```
> duplicate := (x,n) -> local j; seq( x, j=1..n );
```
$$duplicate := (\ x,\ n\ ) \rightarrow local\ j:\quad seq(\ x,\ j=1\ ..\ n\ )$$

```
> duplicate(y,5);   # 5 copies of y
```
$$y,\ y,\ y,\ y,\ y$$

The introduction of j as a *local variable*, which only has a meaning inside the function definition, is necessary to avoid side effects like

```
> DUPLICATE := (x,n) -> seq(x,j=1..n):
> DUPLICATE(y,5);   # still 5 copies of y
```
$$y,\ y,\ y,\ y,\ y$$

```
> j;   # but j has been assigned a value!
```
$$6$$

Piecewise defined functions can easily be introduced with the arrow operator notation. Let us look at a step function whose values are 1 for real numbers larger than 1, 0 at 1, and −1 otherwise

```
> step := x -> if x>1 then 1 elif x=1 then 0 else -1 fi;

step := proc(x)
        options operator,arrow;
            if 1 < x then 1 elif x = 1 then 0 else -1 fi
        end

> step(3/2), step(1), step(1/2);
```
$$1,\ 0,\ -1$$

```
> plot( step, -1..Pi,
>    title=`graph of step function`, style=line );
```

graph of step function

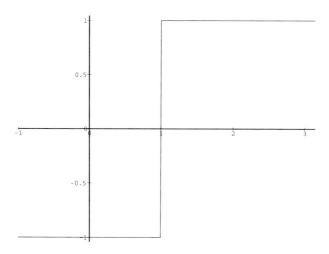

That such a function definition is already more delicate than at first sight becomes clear in the following instruction.

```
> printlevel := 2:   # make Maple more communicative
> step(Pi);

Error, (in step) cannot evaluate boolean
executing statement: if 1 < args[1] then ...
elif args[1] = 1 then ... else ... fi
step called with arguments: Pi
```

The problem here is that when Maple executes the condition

```
if 1 < Pi then ...
```

it cannot do it. Maple can only compare numbers of type *numeric*, i.e., integers, fractions, and floating-point numbers. Of course we know that 1 < Pi. There is a more powerful function in Maple called **csgn** to compute the sign of a real or complex number. With this function we can providing a better, but still not perfect, program.

```
> step := x -> if testeq(x=1) then 0 else csgn(x-1) fi;

step := proc(x)
        options operator,arrow;
            if testeq(x = 1) then 0 else csgn(x-1) fi
        end
```

```
> step(Pi), step( 2 + sqrt(2)  -  sqrt(3+2*sqrt(2)) );
```

$$1, \ 0$$

```
> step( exp(Pi/3*sqrt(163)) - 640319 ); # no simple answer
```

$$\mathrm{csgn}\Big(e^{1/3 \ \pi \ \sqrt{163}} - 640320 \Big)$$

```
> Digits := 50:  # assist Maple by raising the precision
> step( exp(Pi/3*sqrt(163)) - 640319 ); # a better answer
```

$$1$$

8.3 Maple Procedures

Look again at the output of the arrow operator definition of the step function of the previous section: it is a *procedure*. In general, the definition of a Maple procedure has the following syntax

$$\begin{aligned}
&\textbf{proc}(\textit{parameter\_sequence}) \\
&\quad [\textbf{local } \textit{name\_sequence} ;)] \\
&\quad [\textbf{options } \textit{name\_sequence} ;)] \\
&\quad \textit{statements} \\
&\textbf{end}
\end{aligned}$$

where *name_sequence* is a sequence of Maple names separated by commas. The *parameter_sequence* is in many cases a sequence of Maple names too, but when the dynamic type checking facility is used, each name may be followed by its data type (separated by a colon).

```
> sgn := proc( n:integer ) (-1)^n end:
> sgn(Pi);

Error, sgn expects its 1st argument, n,
to be of type integer, but received Pi

> sgn(-2);
```

$$1$$

The procedure **sgn** has one parameter. When it is called, Maple checks whether the given argument is of type *integer*. If not, or when no argument is supplied, the system returns an error message. Otherwise, it computes the power.

In general, the value returned by a procedure is the last value computed unless there is an explicit return. An example:

```
> MEMBER := proc( x:anything, L:list, pos:name ) local i;

>    for i to nops(l) do

>       if L[i] = x then pos := i; RETURN(true) fi

>    od:

>    false

> end:

> MEMBER( 2, [2,1,3,2], `position` );
```

$$true$$

```
> position;
```

$$1$$

```
> MEMBER( 4, [2,1,3,2] );
```

$$false$$

We give another example of a procedure definition in which a local variable is introduced to avoid interference with globally defined variables.

```
> f := proc(x) local y;

>    y := 1 + sin(x);

>    y^2 + y + 1/y + 1/y^2

> end;

f := proc(x) local y; y := 1+sin(x); y^2+y+1/y+1/y^2 end;

> f(t);
```

$$(1 + \sin(t))^2 + 1 + \sin(t) + \frac{1}{1 + \sin(t)}$$

$$+ \frac{1}{(1 + \sin(t))^2}$$

Maple V Release 2 has a *subscripted function* calling facility. For example, it is used for the log function for different bases. **log[b]** is used to specify the logarithm with base b. Here, we give only one example. It should give you an idea about the definition of subscripted functions. We extend Maple's implementation of Euler's beta function to the incomple beta function, which is defined as

$$B_x(p,q) = \int_0^x t^{p-1} (1-t)^{q-1} \, dt \, .$$

$B_1(p,q)$ becomes the regular (complete) beta function. In Maple, a rudimentary, but not foolproof implementation of $B_x(p,q)$ can be as follows.

```
> BETA := proc(p,q)

>     local x:

>     if type( procname, ´indexed´ )

>     then x := op(procname);

>             int( t^(p-1)*(1-t)^(q-1), t=0..x )

>     else Beta(p,q)

>     fi

>     end:

> BETA[1](2,3), Beta(2,3);
```

$$\frac{1}{12}, \ \frac{1}{12}$$

```
> BETA(3/2,5/2), Beta(3/2,5/2);
```

$$\frac{1}{16}\pi, \ \frac{1}{16}\pi$$

```
> BETA[1/2](3/2,5/2);
```

$$\frac{1}{24} + \frac{1}{32}\pi$$

When the procedure **BETA** is called, Maple will first have a closer look at the actual procedure name. It checks whether the variable procname inside the procedure is an indexed name of the form **BETA**[x] or not. If not, it is assumed that **BETA** is equal to the regular (complete) beta function. If an indexed name is used, the local variable x is assigned the value of the index, and the integral which defines the incomplete beta function is computed.

We end this section with two remarks:

• Dynamic type checking is only available in procedure definitions, not in arrow operator definitions.

• In contrast with arrow operators, the procedure body may consists of several statements.

8.4 Recursive Procedure Definitions

Recursive definition of a function or procedure is possible in Maple. We shall illustrate this with the computation of Lucas numbers L_n, which are defined by the linear recurrence

$$L_1 = 1, L_2 = 3, \text{ and } L_n = L_{n-1} + L_{n-2}, \text{ for } n > 2.$$

In the arrow operator notation, it can be coded directly by

```
> L := n ->
>    if not type(n,`nonnegint`)
>    then ERROR(`wrong type of arguments`)
>    elif n=1 then 1
>    elif n=2 then 3
>    else L(n-1) + L(n-2)
>    fi;

L := proc(n)
       options operator,arrow;
            if not type(n,`nonnegint`) then
                ERROR(`wrong type of arguments`)
            elif n = 1 then 1
            elif n = 2 then 3
            else L(n-1)+L(n-2)
            fi
       end
```

Here, we have used the procedure **ERROR** to generate an error message from within the function when the given argument is not a **nonneg**ative **int**eger. The standard way of defining Maple procedures is slightly more convenient.

```
> L := proc( n:nonnegint )
>    if n = 1 then 1
>    elif n = 2 then 3
>    else L(n-1)+L(n-2)
> fi
> end:
> L(6);
```

$$18$$

However, this is not an efficient way to compute the Lucas numbers. Let us have Maple count the number of procedure calls with **profile**.

```
> readlib( profile ):  # load the library function
> profile( L ):  # activate profile for L procedure
> L(6):
> showprofile();
```

```
function              depth        calls
--------------------------------------------
L:                      1            1
                        2            2
                        3            4
                        4            6
                        5            2
```

Here, we have omitted information about computer time and memory usage. The information shown becomes clear when you realize how Maple computes the Lucas numbers. To compute `L(6)`, it is necessary to compute `L(5)` and `L(4)`. For each of these Lucas numbers two more function calls are needed, and this goes on until all needed Lucas numbers have been calculated. The following picture is the graph of function calls when computing `L(6)`.

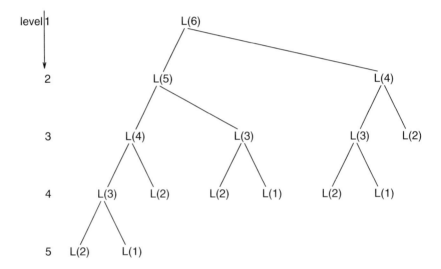

The graph is in agreement with the result of **profile** and shows clearly that, for example, `L(2)` is computed five times.

So, with the above procedure definition of **L**, it takes exponential time (2^n) to compute Lucas numbers, and we shall never be able to compute `L(100)`. However, we can do better. It is clear that we should remember the function values as they are computed so that they can be used when they are needed. Maple provides the option `remember` for this purpose.

```
> L := proc( n:nonnegint ) Lucas(n) end:

> Lucas := proc(n)

>    option remember;

>    if n = 1 then 1

>    elif n = 2 then 3
```

```
>    else Lucas(n-1) + Lucas(n-2)

> fi

> end:

> profile( Lucas ):

> L(6):

> showprofile();

function              depth        calls
---------------------------------------
L:                      1            1
                        2            2
                        3            2
                        4            2
                        5            2
```

With the new definition of **L**, time-complexity is linear $(2n)$. What happens when **L** is called is the following: the type of the argument is checked, and if valid, the recursive procedure **Lucas** is called. In this manner, we check only once the type of the argument and not over and over again during the recursive computation that follows. Each Maple procedure has an associated *remember table*. In many cases it is non-existing in the sense that the pointer to the remember table is NULL. But Maple's remember mechanism becomes activated when you add the option remember to the procedure definition. The entries of the remember table will be function values indexed by the arguments of the corresponding function calls. When, in our example, the procedure **Lucas** is called with some argument n, Maple will first look up the remember table of **Lucas** to see if the value Lucas(n) has been computed before. If it has, it returns the result from the remember table. Otherwise, it executes the code present in the procedure body of **Lucas**, and automatically stores the pair (n, Lucas(n)) in the remember table of **Lucas**. In this way, each Lucas number is computed only once. In terms of the above graph of function calls, it can be understood as: "follow the depth-first strategy of traversing the graph, compute function values only once, store the results, and use them when needed."

The remember table of a procedure is accessible as the fourth operand of the procedure structure.

```
> op( 4, eval(Lucas) );   # remember table of Lucas

    table([

        1 = 1

        6 = 18

        2 = 3
```

$$3 = 4$$

$$4 = 7$$

$$5 = 11$$

])

The remember table of a procedure can be explicitly updated by a function assignment of the form *procedure(argument) := value*. We illustrate this possibility of explicitly saving values in a remember table by using the so-called *functional assignment*.

```
> Lucas := proc(n)
>    Lucas(n) := Lucas(n-1) + Lucas(n-2)
> end:
> Lucas(1) := 1:
> Lucas(2) := 3:
> op( 4, eval(Lucas) );   # initial remember table
      table([

            1 = 1

            2 = 3

            ])

> Lucas(4);
                              7

> op( 4, eval(Lucas) );   # updated remember table
      table([

            1 = 1

            2 = 3

            3 = 4

            4 = 7

            ])
```

Maple provides the utility function **forget** to remove one or all entries from a remember table.

```
> readlib( forget ):    # load the utility function
> forget( Lucas, 3):    # forget the result of Lucas(3);
> op( 4, eval(Lucas) );   # updated remember table

    table([

        1 = 1

        2 = 3

        4 = 7

        ])
```

To empty the remember table of **Lucas**, enter

```
> forget( Lucas ):
> op( 4, eval(Lucas) );   # empty remember table

    table([

        ])
```

To remove the remember table of **Lucas** completely, enter

```
> Lucas := subsop( 4 = NULL, eval(Lucas) ):
> op( 4, eval(Lucas) );   # NULL pointer to remember table

>
```

8.5 unapply

There exists a third way of making new functions, a way that is especially convenient when you encounter, in the midst of a Maple session, a symbolic expression which you want to use as a description of a function. This is done by **unapply**. As the name implies: it is the opposite of applying a function to symbolic parameters.

```
> formula := ( b^2*x^2*sin(b*x) - 2*sin(b*x)
>     + 2*b*x*cos(b*x)*a*t ) / b^3;
```

$$formula := (b^2 \ x^2 \ \sin(b \ x) \ - \ 2 \ \sin(b \ x)$$
$$+ \ 2 \ b \ x \ \cos(b \ x) \ a \ t)/b^3$$

```
> F := unapply( formula, x, t );
```

$$F := (x, t) \rightarrow (b^2 x^2 \sin(b x) - 2 \sin(b x)$$
$$+ 2 b x \cos(b x) a t)\big/b^3$$

```
> F(0,1), F(Pi/b,5);
```

$$0, \quad -10 \frac{\pi a}{b^3}$$

Here again, you may be tempted to use other methods such as

```
> formula := ( b^2*x^2*sin(b*x) -2*sin(b*x)
>    + 2*b*x*cos(b*x)*a*t ) / b^3:
> F := (x,t) -> ";
```

$$F := (x, t) \rightarrow \text{"}$$

The problem is that the ditto operator is a so-called *environment variable*, which works locally inside the procedure **F**, but does not refer to anything outside.

```
> G := (x,t) -> formula;
```

$$G := (x, t) \rightarrow formula$$

In this case, you get what you ask for: for any argument of **G**, the value is the evaluation of `formula`. Now, you should be able to understand the result of the following command.

```
> F(u,v), G(u,v);
```

$$(b^2 x^2 \sin(b x) - 2 \sin(b x) + 2 b x \cos(b x) a t)$$
$$\big/b^3$$

None of the above methods works well; you really have to type the function description in *parameter* -> *description* form. The only alternative is to substitute the expression into the function description.

```
> H := subs( body = formula, (x,t) -> body );
```

$$H := (x, t) \rightarrow (b^2 x^2 \sin(b x) - 2 \sin(b x)$$
$$+ 2 b x \cos(b x) a t)\big/b^3$$

```
> H(u,v);
```

$$(b^2 \ u^2 \ \sin(\ b \ u \ ) \ - \ 2 \ \sin(\ b \ u \ ) \ + \ 2 \ b \ u \ \cos(\ b \ u \ ) \ a \ v)$$

$$\Big/ b^3$$

8.6 Operations on Functions

Elementary operations on functions like addition, multiplication, and composition are easily done in Maple. A few examples:

```
> f := x -> ln(x) + 1:  g := y -> exp(y) - 1:
> h := f + g:   h(z);
                        f( x ) + g( x )
> h := f*g:   h(z);
                        f( x ) g( x )
> h := f @ g:  h(z);
                      ln( e^z - 1 ) + 1
> h := g @ f:  h(z);
                      e^{ln( z ) + 1} - 1
> simplify(");
                         z e - 1
> (f@@4)(z);  # equivalent to f(f(f(f(z))))
             ln( ln( ln( ln( z ) + 1 ) + 1 ) + 1 ) + 1
```

The use of the @ operator in combination with the **macro** facility can be a powerful mechanism to introduce abbreviations in Maple. For example, suppose that we always want to apply evaluation on the result of substitution in Maple, then we can do the following:

```
> subs( n=2, Zeta(n) ); # with old version of subs
                         Zeta( 2 )
> macro( subs = eval @ subs ): # new version of subs
> subs( n=2, Zeta(n) ); # with new version of subs
```

$$\frac{1}{6} \ \pi^2$$

8.7 Anonymous Functions

You are not obliged to name a function. Such *anonymous functions* come in hand when you want to perform an operation only once and do not want to waste a name on it. Anonymous functions are used mostly in conjunction with procedures like **map** and **select**. Three examples:

```
> map( x -> x^2, a + b + c );   # square summands
```

$$a^2 + b^2 + c^2$$

```
> data := [ [1,1.0], [2,3.8], [3,5.1] ]:
> # take the logarithm of the 2nd element of each entry
> map( x -> subsop( 2=ln(op(2,x)), x ), data );
```

$$[[1, 0], [2, 1.335001067], [3, 1.629240540]]$$

```
> sum( ´x^i´, ´i´ = 0..6 );
```

$$1 + x + x^2 + x^3 + x^4 + x^5 + x^6$$

```
> select( t -> degree(t)<3, " );   # select low order terms
```

$$1 + x + x^2$$

8.8 Exercises

1. Solve the following equation in x with Maple.

$$x^3 - (a - 1)x^2 + a^2 x - a^3 = 0$$

   Make a function out of the first solution and compute the solution for $a = 0$ and for $a = 1$. Give an approximate result for $a = 2$.

2. Define a function in Maple which is 1 on the segment $[-1, 1]$, and 0 otherwise. Also plot the graph of your function.

3. Define the function

$$f: t \longmapsto \sum_{n=1}^{8} (-1)^{n+1} \frac{2}{n} \sin nt .$$

   Compute $f(\frac{\pi}{10})$ and $f(\frac{\pi}{6})$. Plot the graph of your function.

4. After the following assignments,

```
> x := 1:
> f := proc(x) 2 end:
> f(x) := 3:
```

what will be `f(1)`, `f(4)`, and `f()`?

5. Write a Maple procedure which computes the Legendre polynomials $L_n(x)$. These polynomials satisfy the recurrence relation

$L_0(x) = 1$, $L_1(x) = x$, and

$L_n(x) = \frac{n-1}{n}(xL_{n-1}(x) - L_{n-2}(x)) + L_{n-1}(x)$, for $n > 1$.

Compute $L_7(x)$, and check your answer with the Maple procedure **orthopoly[P]**. Can your procedure compute $L_{50}(x)$?

6. Write an anonymous function which selects from a set of integers those values which are between 0 and 10. Use the procedure **rand** to generate a set of one hundred integers and apply your anonymous function to this set.

7. Write an anonymous function to drop from a polynomial in two unknowns (which can be created by the procedure **randpoly**) all terms with negative coefficients.

Differentiation

In this chapter, we shall explain the procedures **diff** and **D** for computing derivatives symbolically, give examples of implicit differentiation, and
finally, briefly discuss Maple's automatic differentiation facility.

9.1 Symbolic Differentiation

With the Maple procedure **diff** you can differentiate a formula.

```
> ´diff( exp(-x^2), x )´;
```

$$\frac{\partial}{\partial x} e^{-x^2}$$

```
> ";
```

$$-2\ x\ e^{-x^2}$$

The apostrophes around the first command are to postpone computation
of the derivative and will print the input in two-dimensional layout. For
this purpose we could have also used the inert **Diff** command, which simply
returns unevaluated.

```
> Diff( ln(x/(x^2+1)), x )  =  diff( ln(x/(x^2+1)), x );
```

$$\frac{\partial}{\partial x}\ \ln\!\left(\frac{x}{x^2\ +\ 1}\right) = \frac{\left(\dfrac{1}{x^2\ +\ 1}\ -\ 2\ \dfrac{x^2}{(\ x^2\ +\ 1\ )^2}\right)(\ x^2\ +\ 1\ )}{x}$$

```
> normal(");
```

$$\frac{\partial}{\partial x}\ \ln\!\left(\frac{x}{x^2\ +\ 1}\right) = -\ \frac{x^2\ -\ 1}{x\ (\ x^2\ +\ 1\ )}$$

In a real Maple session, you will probably first use the inert procedure
Diff to check whether the formula entered is the one you had in mind.

Next, if the formula is really the one you want to differentiate, you can use worksheet facilities (or, in Maple's text-based user interface, the built-in command line editor) to change **Diff** into the "active" procedure **diff** to compute the derivative. In the examples below, we shall use **Diff** to make results clearer and better understandable.

```
> Diff( x^(x^x), x ) = diff( x^(x^x), x );
```

$$\frac{\partial}{\partial x} x^{(x^x)} = x^{(x^x)} \left(x^x \ (\ln(x) + 1) \ \ln(x) + \frac{x^x}{x} \right)$$

```
> collect( ", ln(x), simplify );
```

$$\frac{\partial}{\partial x} x^{(x^x)} = x^{(x^x + x)} \ln(x)^2 + x^{(x^x + x)} \ln(x) + x^{(x^x + x - 1)}$$

Rigorous application of differentiation rules without simplification quickly leads to incomprehensible results. Taking account of this expression swell, higher derivatives can be computed without any difficulty.

```
> Diff( exp(-x^2), x, x ) = diff( exp(-x^2), x, x );
```

$$\frac{\partial^2}{\partial x^2} e^{-x^2} = -2 \ e^{-x^2} + 4 \ x^2 \ e^{-x^2}$$

```
> Diff( exp(-x^2), x$5 ) = diff( exp(-x^2), x$5 );
```

$$\frac{\partial^5}{\partial x^5} e^{-x^2} = -120 \ x \ e^{-x^2} + 160 \ x^3 \ e^{-x^2} - 32 \ x^5 \ e^{-x^2}$$

Here, we have used the sequence operator **$** to shorten input.

```
                   diff( exp(-x^2), x$5 )
```

is equivalent to

```
                   diff( exp(-x^2), x,x,x,x,x ).
```

Differentiation of a function y of x which is implicitly defined by an equation can be done in the following, elegant way.

```
> alias( y = y ) # consider y as a function of x
> eq := x^2 + y^2 = c; # equation defining y
```

$$eq := x^2 + y^2 = c$$

```
> diff( eq, x );
```

$$2\ x\ +\ 2\ y\ \left(\frac{\partial}{\partial x}\ y\right) = 0$$

```
> dydx := solve( ", diff(y,x) ); # 1st derivative
```

$$dydx\ := \ -\ \frac{x}{y}$$

```
> diff( eq, x$2 );
```

$$2\ +\ 2\ \left(\frac{\partial}{\partial x}\ y\right)^2 +\ 2\ y\ \left(\frac{\partial^2}{\partial x^2}\ y\right) = 0$$

```
> solve( ", diff(y,x$2) ); # 2nd derivative
```

$$-\ \frac{1}{2}\ \frac{2\ +\ 2\ \left(\frac{\partial}{\partial x}\ y\right)^2}{y}$$

```
> d2ydx2 := normal( subs( diff(y,x) = dydx, " ) );
```

$$d2ydx2\ := \ -\ \frac{x^2\ +\ y^2}{y^3}$$

```
> alias( y = y(x) ): # unalias y for further usage
```

Partial derivatives cause no extra problems for **diff**. Two examples of functions in two unknowns:

```
> Diff( exp(a*x*y^2), x, y$2 ) =
>    diff( exp(a*x*y^2), x, y$2 );
```

$$\frac{\partial^3}{\partial y^2\ \partial x}\ e^{a\ x\ y^2} =$$

$$2\ a\ e^{a\ x\ y^2}\ +\ 10\ a^2\ y^2\ x\ e^{a\ x\ y^2}\ +\ 4\ a^3\ y^4\ x^2\ e^{a\ x\ y^2}$$

```
> factor(");
```

$$\frac{\partial^3}{\partial y^2\ \partial x}\ e^{a\ x\ y^2} = 2\ a\ e^{a\ x\ y^2}\ (\ 1\ +\ 5\ a\ x\ y^2\ +\ 2\ a^2\ y^4\ x^2\ )$$

```
> Diff( sin(x+y)/y^4, x$5, y$2 ) =
>    diff( sin(x+y)/y^4, x$5, y$2 );
```

$$\frac{\partial^7}{\partial y^2\ \partial x^5}\ \frac{\sin(\ x\ +\ y\ )}{y^4} = -\ \frac{\cos(\ x\ +\ y\ )}{y^4}\ +\ 8\ \frac{\sin(\ x\ +\ y\ )}{y^5}$$

$$+ 20 \; \frac{\cos (x + y)}{y^6}$$

```
> collect( ", cos(x+y), normal );
```

$$\frac{\partial^7}{\partial y^2 \; \partial x^5} \; \frac{\sin (x + y)}{y^4} =$$

$$- \; \frac{(y^2 - 20) \; \cos (x + y)}{y^6} + 8 \; \frac{\sin (x + y)}{y^5}$$

If you want to differentiate a function instead of a formula, then you can use the **D** operator. **D** works on a function and computes the derivative as a function again. This is convenient when you want to compute or specify the derivative of a function at some point.

```
> g := x -> x^n * exp(sin(x)); # the function
```

$$g := x \rightarrow x^n \; e^{\sin(x)}$$

```
> D(g); # the derivative
```

$$x \rightarrow \frac{x^n \; n \; e^{\sin(x)}}{x} + x^n \; \cos (x) \; e^{\sin(x)}$$

```
> D(g)(Pi/6); # the derivative at Pi/6
```

$$6 \; \frac{\left(\frac{1}{6} \; \pi \right)^n \; n \; e^{1/2}}{\pi} + \frac{1}{2} \left(\frac{1}{6} \; \pi \right)^n \; \sqrt{3} \; e^{1/2}$$

Basically, `D(f)` is equivalent to `unapply( diff(f(x),x), x )`.

It is essential to make a clear distinction between **diff** and **D**; **diff** differentiates a formula and returns a formula, whereas **D** differentiates a mapping and returns a mapping. A few examples:

```
> diff( cos(t), t ); # derivative of a formula
```

$$-\sin(t)$$

```
> D(cos); # derivative of a function
```

$$-\sin$$

```
> (D@@2)(cos); # 2nd derivative of a function
```

$$-\cos$$

```
> D(cos)(t); # derivative of a function at some point
```

$$-\sin(\,t\,)$$

```
> D( cos(t) );

Error, (in D) univariate operand expected
```

In the last command, Maple does not consider `cos(t)` as the cosine function, nor as the composition of the cosine function and some function `t`. For the latter purpose you must follow Maple's syntax and semantics closely and use the composition operator @.

```
D( cos @ t );
```

$$(\,-\sin\,)@t\ D(\,t\,)$$

However, if we add `t` to our list of constants, then Maple is indeed willing to consider `cos(t)` as a function, viz., as a constant function.

```
> constants := constants, t: # now, t is a constant
> D( cos(t) );
```

$$0$$

It is easier to understand this for a familiar constant number.

```
> D( cos(1) );
```

$$0$$

`cos(1)` is a number and can be considered as a constant function whose derivative is equal to the zero function.

```
> diff( cos, t );
```

$$0$$

In the last example, Maple considered `cos` as an expression in which `t` did not occur.

If you want to differentiate an implicitly defined function, it is convenient to manipulate the mapping as if it is an expression, and let **D** do the differentiation. The same example as was treated before with **diff** will be as follows in the new formalism.

```
> eq := x^2 + y^2 = c:
```

```
> D( eq );
```

$$2 \, D(x) \, x + 2 \, D(y) \, y = D(c)$$

```
> solve( ", D(y) );
```

$$-\frac{1}{2} \, \frac{2 \, D(x) \, x - D(c)}{y}$$

```
> # x is an independent variable, c is a constant
> dydx := subs( D(x)=1, D(c)=0, " );
```

$$dydx := -\frac{x}{y}$$

```
> (D@@2)( eq );
```

$$2 \, D^{(2)}(x) \, x + 2 \, D(x)^2 + 2 \, D^{(2)}(y) \, y + 2 \, D(y)^2 =$$
$$D^{(2)}(c)$$

```
> solve( ", (D@@2)(y) );
```

$$-\frac{1}{2} \left(2 \, D^{(2)}(x) \, x + 2 \, D(x)^2 + 2 \, D(y)^2 - D^{(2)}(c) \right) \Big/ y$$

```
> d2ydx2 := normal( subs( D(x)=1, (D@@2)(x)=0,
>     (D@@2)(c)=0, D(y)=dydx, " );
```

$$-\frac{x^2 + y^2}{y^3}$$

Use of the **D** operator is not restricted to univariate functions. An indexed function call to **D** will enable you to compute partial derivatives.

```
> h := (x,y,z) -> 1/(x^2+y^2+z^2)^(1/2);
```

$$h := (x, \, y, \, z) \rightarrow \frac{1}{\sqrt{x^2 + y^2 + z^2}}$$

```
> # partial derivative w.r.t. x
> `D[1](h)` = D[1](h);
```

$$D_{[1]}(h) = \left((x, \, y, \, z) \rightarrow -\frac{x}{(x^2 + y^2 + z^2)^{3/2}} \right)$$

Here, `D[1](h)` means the partial derivative of h with respect to the first argument. `D[1](h)` is equivalent to `unapply( diff( h(x,y,z), x ), x,y,z )`, but simplification differences may be present.

```
> # partial derivative w.r.t. x and y
> `D[1,2](h)` = D[1,2](h);
```

$$
D_{[1,\,2]}(h) = \left((x,\ y,\ z) \to 3\ \frac{y\ x}{(x^2 + y^2 + z^2)^{5/2}} \right)
$$

Here, `D[1,2](h)` is equivalent to `D[1](D[2](h))`.

```
> # 2nd partial derivative w.r.t. x
> `D[1,1](h)` = D[1,1](h);
```

$$
D_{[1,\,1]}(h) = \left((x,\ y,\ z) \to 3\ \frac{y\ x}{(x^2 + y^2 + z^2)^{5/2}} \right)
$$

If we compute the Laplacian $\left(\dfrac{\partial^2}{\partial x^2} + \dfrac{\partial^2}{\partial y^2} + \dfrac{\partial^2}{\partial z^2} \right) h$, limitations of the operator method, due to lack of simplification of intermediate results, emerge.

```
> L[h] := ( D[1,1] + D[2,2] + D[3,3] )(h);
```

$$
L_{[h]} := \left((x,\ y,\ z) \to \right.
$$

$$
3\ \frac{x^2}{(x^2 + y^2 + z^2)^{5/2}} - \frac{1}{(x^2 + y^2 + z^2)^{3/2}} \bigg) + \Big(
$$

$$
(x,\ y,\ z) \to
$$

$$
3\ \frac{y^2}{(x^2 + y^2 + z^2)^{5/2}} - \frac{1}{(x^2 + y^2 + z^2)^{3/2}} \bigg) + \Big(
$$

$$
(x,\ y,\ z) \to
$$

$$
3\ \frac{z^2}{(x^2 + y^2 + z^2)^{5/2}} - \frac{1}{(x^2 + y^2 + z^2)^{3/2}} \bigg)
$$

```
> normal( L[h](x,y,z) );
```

$$
0
$$

We end this section with a general example of implicit differentiation, which illustrates various Maple facilities with respect to differentiation. It is the same example as was treated with MACSYMA in section 1.5.4 of [37]. Let $g(x, y)$ be an implicit form, where y is a function of x. Below, we shall determine formulae for the first, second, and third derivative of y with respect to x, in terms of partial derivatives of g.

```
> alias( g = g(x,y(x)), y = y(x) ):
> diff(g,x);
```

$$D_{[1]}(g)(x, y) + D_{[2]}(g)(x, y)\left(\frac{\partial}{\partial x} y\right)$$

```
> dydx := solve( ", diff(y,x) ); # 1st derivative of y
```

$$dydx := -\frac{D_{[1]}(g)(x, y)}{D_{[2]}(g)(x, y)}$$

Perhaps, you are more familiar with the following notation.

```
> convert( dydx, 'diff' );
```

$$\left(-\frac{\frac{\partial}{\partial x} g(x, t1)}{\frac{\partial}{\partial t2} g(x, t2)}\right) \&\text{where} \ \{t1 = y, \ t2 = y\}$$

```
> subs( op(2,"), op(1,") ); # a commonly used notation
```

$$-\frac{\frac{\partial}{\partial x} g}{\frac{\partial}{\partial y} g}$$

Let us go on with computing higher derivatives of y.

```
> diff(g,x$2);
```

$$D_{[1, 1]}(g)(x, y) + D_{[1, 2]}(g)(x, y)\left(\frac{\partial}{\partial x} y\right) +$$

$$\left(D_{[1, 2]}(g)(x, y) + D_{[2, 2]}(g)(x, y)\left(\frac{\partial}{\partial x} y\right)\right)$$

$$\left(\frac{\partial}{\partial x} y\right) + D_{[2]}(g)(x, y)\left(\frac{\partial^2}{\partial x^2} y\right)$$

```
> solve( ", diff(y,x$2) );
```

$$-\left(D_{[\,1,\,1\,]}(g)(x,\ y) + 2\ D_{[\,1,\,2\,]}(g)(x,\ y)\left(\frac{\partial}{\partial x}\,y\right)\right.$$

$$\left. +\ D_{[\,2,\,2\,]}(g)(x,\ y)\left(\frac{\partial}{\partial x}\,y\right)^{2}\right)\Big/\left(D_{[\,2\,]}(g)(x,\ y)\right)$$

```
> d2ydx2 := normal( subs( diff(y,x) = dydx, " ) );
```

$$d2ydx2 := -\left(D_{[\,1,\,1\,]}(g)(x,\ y)\ D_{[\,2\,]}(g)(x,\ y)^{2} - 2\right.$$

$$D_{[\,1,\,2\,]}(g)(x,\ y)\ D_{[\,2\,]}(g)(x,\ y)\ D_{[\,1\,]}(g)(x,\ y)$$

$$D_{[\,2\,]}(g)(x,\ y)$$

$$\left. +\ D_{[\,2,\,2\,]}(g)(x,\ y)\ D_{[\,1\,]}(g)(x,\ y)^{2}\right)\Big/$$

$$D_{[\,2\,]}(g)(x,\ y)^{3}$$

```
> convert( ", `diff` ): subs( op(2,"), op(1,") );
```

$$-\left(\left(\frac{\partial^{2}}{\partial x^{2}}\,g\right)\left(\frac{\partial}{\partial y}\,g\right)^{2} - 2\left(\frac{\partial^{2}}{\partial y\,\partial x}\,g\right)\left(\frac{\partial}{\partial x}\,g\right)\left(\frac{\partial}{\partial y}\,g\right)\right.$$

$$\left. +\left(\frac{\partial^{2}}{\partial y^{2}}\,g\right)\left(\frac{\partial}{\partial x}\,g\right)^{2}\right)\Big/\left(\frac{\partial}{\partial y}\,g\right)^{3}$$

The computation of the third derivative of y clearly shows the advantage
of computer algebra usage over pencil and paper calculation.

```
> diff(g,x$3):
> d3ydx3 := normal(
>    subs( diff(y,x$2)=d2ydx2, diff(y,x)=dydx, " ) ):
> convert( ", `diff` ): subs( op(2,"), op(1,") );
```

$$\left(-\left(\frac{\partial^{3}}{\partial x^{3}}\,g\right)\left(\frac{\partial}{\partial y}\,g\right)^{4} + 3\left(\frac{\partial^{3}}{\partial y\,\partial x^{2}}\,g\right)\left(\frac{\partial}{\partial x}\,g\right)\left(\frac{\partial}{\partial y}\,g\right)^{3}\right.$$

$$-\ 3\left(\frac{\partial^{3}}{\partial y^{2}\,\partial x}\,g\right)\left(\frac{\partial}{\partial x}\,g\right)^{2}\left(\frac{\partial}{\partial y}\,g\right)^{2}$$

$$+\ 3\left(\frac{\partial^{2}}{\partial y\,\partial x}\,g\right)\left(\frac{\partial}{\partial y}\,g\right)^{3}\left(\frac{\partial^{2}}{\partial x^{2}}\,g\right)$$

$$- 6 \left(\frac{\partial^2}{\partial y \, \partial x} g \right)^2 \left(\frac{\partial}{\partial y} g \right)^2 \left(\frac{\partial}{\partial x} g \right)$$

$$+ 9 \left(\frac{\partial^2}{\partial y \, \partial x} g \right) \left(\frac{\partial}{\partial y} g \right) \left(\frac{\partial^2}{\partial y^2} g \right) \left(\frac{\partial}{\partial x} g \right)^2$$

$$+ \left(\frac{\partial^3}{\partial y^3} g \right) \left(\frac{\partial}{\partial x} g \right)^3 \left(\frac{\partial}{\partial y} g \right)$$

$$- 3 \left(\frac{\partial}{\partial x} g \right) \left(\frac{\partial^2}{\partial y^2} g \right) \left(\frac{\partial^2}{\partial x^2} g \right) \left(\frac{\partial}{\partial y} g \right)^2$$

$$- 3 \left(\frac{\partial}{\partial x} g \right)^3 \left(\frac{\partial^2}{\partial y^2} g \right)^2 \Bigg/ \left(\frac{\partial}{\partial y} g \right)^5$$

Finally, we compute derivatives for g equal to the function $\exp(x^2 + y^2)$.

```
> alias( g = g ):
> g := (x,y) -> exp( x^2 + y^2 );
```

$$g := (x, \ y) \to e^{x^2 + y^2}$$

```
> dydx;
```

$$- \frac{x}{y}$$

```
> normal( d2ydx2 );
```

$$- \frac{x^2 + y^2}{y^3}$$

```
> normal( d3ydx3 );
```

$$-3 \; \frac{x \ (x^2 + y^2)}{y^5}$$

The formulae are in agreement with the results obtained earlier for the function y which was implicitly defined by $x^2 + y^2 = c$.

9.2 Automatic Differentiation

In Maple V Release 2, the **D** operator has been extended to address the problem of automatic differentiation, that is, to differentiate Maple procedures. Let us start with an example of a piecewise defined function.

```
> F := x -> if x>0 then sin(x) else  arctan(x) fi;

F := proc(x)
      options operator,arrow;
            if 0 < x then sin(x) else arctan(x) fi
      end

> Fp := D(F); # 1st derivative

Fp := proc(x)
      options operator,arrow;
            if 0 < x then cos(x) else 1/(1+x^2) fi
      end

> # plot F and its first derivative
> plot( { F, Fp }, -3*Pi..3*Pi,
>    title = `graph of F and F`` );
```

graph of F and F'

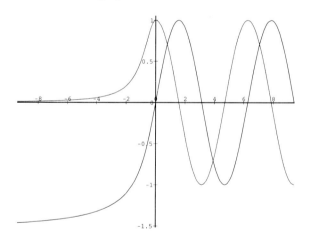

Maple can differentiate procedures that consist of more than one statement. A simple example:

```
> f := proc(x) local s,t;
>    s := ln(x);
>    t := x^2;
>    s*t+3*t
> end:
```

```
> D(f);

fp := proc(x)
      local s,t,sx,tx;
          sx := 1/x;
          s  := ln(x);
          tx := 2*x;
          t  := x^2;
          sx*t+s*tx+3*tx
      end
```

Does the procedure **fp** really compute f'? In this case, we can prove that it does by executing the procedure on symbolic parameters, in effect converting the function represented by the procedure into a formula.

```
> diff(f(x),x)  -  fp(x);
```

$$0$$

Such a check is *not* possible for procedures which contain a conditional statement involving a formal parameter (like is the case in the above function **F**). By the way, this is also one of the reasons for introducing automatic differentiation: not every function can be (conveniently) described by a formula.

How is the procedure **fp** constructed? Comparison of the source codes of **f** and **fp** gives a clue to the following general method of automatic differentiation:

> For each assignment statement $v := f(v_1, \ldots, v_n)$ that appears in the procedure, where the v_i are local variables or formal parameters, precede it by $v_x := fp(v_1, \ldots, v_n)$ where $fp(v_1, \ldots, v_n)$ is obtained by differentiating $f(v_1, \ldots, v_n)$ formally. Replace the last statement (or any RETURN value) by its derivative.

This method is called *forward differentiation*; the function and its derivative are constructed in one sweep through the procedure. This is the method implemented in Maple V Release 2. There are restrictions to what is allowed inside the procedure body: no recursive procedures, no option remember, no assignments to global variables, and only constant loop variables, are a few of the restrictions.

There exists another method, called *reverse automatic differentiation*, in which there is a forward sweep in the procedure to compute the function and a backward sweep to compute the derivative. The reverse mode of automatic differentiation is not yet implemented in Maple. For a gentle introduction to automatic differentiation we refer to [61, 62]. A good reference, in which many algorithms, implementations, and applications are described, is [63].

We end this section by illustrating another reason to use automatic differentiation. Cost-effectiveness with respect to computing time and memory space. Suppose we are interested in the iterated powers f_n recursively defined by

$$f_1 = x, \ f_n = x^{f_{n-1}} \ \text{for} \ n > 1,$$

and their derivatives. As we have seen in §9.1, the formulae for the derivatives become already quite large for small values of n. On the other hand, the derivative procedure obtained by automatic differentiation is very compact. We shall use the following iterative definition of f_n.

```
> f := proc(x,n)
>    local i,t;
>    t := 1;
>    for i to n do t := x^t od;
>    t;
> end;
```

```
f := proc(x,n)
    local i,t;
        t := 1; for i to n do   t := x^t od;
    end
```

```
> fp := D[1](f); # 1st derivative of f w.r.t. x
```

```
fp := proc(x,n)
    local i,t,tx;
    tx := 0;
    t := 1;
    for i to n do   tx := x^t*(tx*ln(x)+t/x); t := x^t od;
    tx
end
```

We shall compute the third derivative of f_{22} in two ways: by automatic differentiation, and by symbolic differentiation. There will be big differences in computing time and memory usage.

```
> # automatic differentiation
> fppp := D[1$3](f): # 3rd derivative of f w.r.t. x
> setwords := words(): # register memory usage
> settime := time(): # start timing
> fppp( 1.1, 22 );
```

$$18.23670379$$

```
> cpu_time := (time()-settime) * seconds; # computing time
```

$$cpu\_time := .933 \; seconds$$

```
> memory_used := evalf(
>    (words()-setwords) / 256 * kbytes, 4);
```

$$memory\_used := 397.6 \; kbytes$$

```
> # symbolic differentiation
> f22 := unapply( f(x,22), x );
```

$$f22 := x \rightarrow x^{x^{\cdot^{\cdot^{\cdot}}}}$$

```
> setwords := words(): # register memory usage
> settime := time(): # start timing
> (D@@3)(f22)(1.1);
```

$$18.23670379$$

```
> cpu_time := (time()-settime) * seconds; # computing time
```

$$cpu\_time := 269.900 \; seconds$$

```
> memory_used := evalf(
>    (words()-setwords) / 256 * kbytes, 4);
```

$$memory\_used := 37220. \; kbytes$$

9.3 Exercises

1. Let f, g, and h be the multivariate, real functions defined by

$$f(x,y) := \frac{\ln\left(1 + x^4 + y^4\right)}{\sqrt{x^2 + y^2}},$$

$$g(x,y,z) := \frac{1}{\sqrt{(x-a)^2 + (y-b)^2 + (z-c)^2}},$$

$$h(x,y,z) := \frac{z}{x^2 + y^2 + z^2}.$$

(a) Determine all partial derivatives of f of order 2.

(b) Check that g is a solution of the Laplace differential equation, i.e.,

$$\left(\frac{\partial^2}{\partial x^2} + \frac{\partial^2}{\partial y^2} + \frac{\partial^2}{\partial z^2}\right) g = 0.$$

(c) Check that h is a solution of the differential equation

$$\frac{\partial^2 h}{\partial x \partial y} + \left(\frac{4x}{x^2 + y^2 + z^2}\right)\frac{\partial h}{\partial y} = 0.$$

2. Compare the results of the following Maple commands:

```
> diff( f(x), x);
> convert(",`D`);
> unapply(",x);
```

3. Let the function $y(x)$ be implicitly defined by $\sqrt{x} + \sqrt{y} = 1$. Compute the derivative y' and the second derivative y''.

4. Let the bivariate function $z(x, y)$ be implicitly defined by $h(x, y, z) = 0$, for some trivariate function h. Determine formulae for $\dfrac{\partial z}{\partial x}$ and $\dfrac{\partial^2 z}{\partial x \partial y}$.
What are the results for $h = \sqrt{x} + \sqrt{y} + \sqrt{z} - 1$?

5. Consider the function f_n recursively defined by

$$f_0 = 0, \; f_1 = x, \; f_n = f_{n-1} + \sin(f_{n-2}) \text{ for } n > 1.$$

Determine (by automatic differentiation) a procedure to compute the first derivative of f_n.

Integration and Summation

Integration (both definite and indefinite), is one of the highlights in computer algebra. Maple uses non-classical algorithms such as the Risch algorithm for integrating elementary functions, instead of heuristic integration methods which are described in most mathematics textbooks. We shall briefly discuss Maple's strategy to compute integrals and give many examples so that you can get an idea of Maple's capabilities and of ways to assist the system. Examples of integral transformations like Laplace, Fourier, and Mellin transforms will also be given.

Summation, which can be seen as the discrete analogue of integration, is another important topic in calculus for which Maple uses advanced methods. A few examples will illustrate this.

10.1 Indefinite Integration

Maple has several powerful built-in algorithms for integration of functions. First, it tries traditional techniques taught at school and university: lookup-tables and pattern matching, integration by parts, change of variables, application of the chain rule, and so on. When these heuristic methods fail, then the system proceeds to deterministic methods, and in particular to the so-called Risch algorithm [104].

Let us first look at an example of indefinite integration performed by the procedure **int**.

```
> Int( x/(x^3+1), x ) =  int( x/(x^3+1), x );
```

$$\int \frac{x}{x^3 + 1}\, dx = -\frac{1}{3}\ln(x + 1) + \frac{1}{6}\ln(x^2 - x + 1)$$

$$+\frac{1}{3}\sqrt{3}\arctan\left(\frac{1}{3}(2x - 1)\sqrt{3}\right)$$

Note that Maple leaves out the constant of integration; the reason is that this is more convenient in the manipulation of the results. There is no harm in some common distrust, so let us check the answer.

```
> diff( rhs("), x );
```

$$- \frac{1}{3} \frac{1}{x+1} + \frac{1}{6} \frac{2x-1}{x^2-x+1} + \frac{2}{3} \frac{1}{1 + \frac{1}{3}(2x-1)^2}$$

```
> normal( ", ´expanded´ );
```

$$\frac{x}{x^3+1}$$

Later on in this chapter, you will see examples where such checks of integration results are not so easily done.

In the above example, we used the inert form procedure **Int** for display reasons. Henceforth we shall use **Int** to show the integrand and integration limits, and we shall use the procedure **value** to actually compute the integral.

One of the most handsome tricks you learn at school for integration of rational functions is partial fraction decomposition. It works well for the integral above. However, it becomes a more tedious and error-prone trick when you have to use it in cases like the following.

```
> Int( x/(x^5+1), x ): " = value(");
```

$$\int \frac{x}{x^5+1} \, dx = -\frac{1}{5} \ln(x+1)$$

$$-\frac{1}{20} \ln\left(2x^2 - x - \sqrt{5}\,x + 2\right)\sqrt{5}$$

$$+\frac{1}{20} \ln\left(2x^2 - x - \sqrt{5}\,x + 2\right)$$

$$+\frac{2}{5} \frac{\sqrt{5}\,\arctan\left(\dfrac{4x-1-\sqrt{5}}{\sqrt{10-2\sqrt{5}}}\right)}{\sqrt{10-2\sqrt{5}}}$$

$$+\frac{1}{20} \ln\left(2x^2 - x + \sqrt{5}\,x + 2\right)\sqrt{5}$$

$$+\frac{1}{20} \ln\left(2x^2 - x + \sqrt{5}\,x + 2\right)$$

$$-\frac{2}{5} \frac{\sqrt{5}\,\arctan\left(\dfrac{4x-1+\sqrt{5}}{\sqrt{10+2\sqrt{5}}}\right)}{\sqrt{10+2\sqrt{5}}}$$

```
> normal( diff(rhs("),x), 'expanded' ); # check the answer
```

$$\frac{x}{x^5 + 1}$$

And the trick of partial fraction decomposition does not work any more
when the integrand is only changed a little bit.

```
> infolevel[int] := 2:    # make Maple more communicative

> Int( x/(x^5+2*x+1), x ):    " = value(");
```

```
int/indef:    first-stage indefinite integration
int/ratpoly:    rational function integration
int/rischnorm:    enter Risch-Norman integrator
int/risch:    enter Risch integration
int/risch:    the field extensions are
```

$$\frac{x}{x^5 + 2 \, x + 1}$$

```
unknown:    integrand is
```

$$\frac{\_X}{\_X^5 + 2 \, \_X + 1}$$

```
int/risch/ratpoly:    integrating
```

$$\frac{\_X}{\_X^5 + 2 \, \_X + 1}$$

```
int/risch/ratpoly:    Horowitz' method yields
```

$$\int \frac{\_X}{\_X^5 + 2 \, \_X + 1} \, d\_X$$

```
int/risch/ratpoly:
starting computing subresultants at time    .866
int/risch/ratpoly:
end of subresultants computation at time    .933
int/risch/ratpoly:
Rothstein's method - factored resultant is
```

$$\left[\left[z^5 - \frac{500}{11317} z^3 + \frac{4}{11317} z + \frac{1}{11317}, \; 1\right]\right]$$

```
int/risch/ratpoly:    result is
```

$$\int \frac{x}{x^5 + 2 \, x + 1} \, dx = \sum_{\_R = \%1} \_R \, \ln\left(x + \frac{65376045600}{64828679} \_R^4\right.$$

$$\left. - \frac{4270752875}{64828679} \_R^3 - \frac{625000000}{64828679} \_R^2 + \frac{447235682}{64828679} \_R\right.$$

$$- \ \frac{21514240}{64828679} \Bigg)$$

```
%1 := RootOf( 11317 _Z⁵ - 500 _Z³ + 4 _Z + 1 )
```

```
int/risch:    exit Risch integration
```

$$\int \frac{x}{x^5 + 2\ x + 1}\ dx = \sum_{\_R = \%1} \_R\ \ln\left(x + \frac{65376045600}{64828679}\ \_R^4\right.$$

$$\left. - \ \frac{4270752875}{64828679}\ \_R^3 - \frac{625000000}{64828679}\ \_R^2 + \frac{447235682}{64828679}\ \_R \right.$$

$$\left. - \ \frac{21514240}{64828679} \right)$$

```
%1 := RootOf( 11317 _Z⁵ - 500 _Z³ + 4 _Z + 1 )
```

```
> normal( diff(rhs("),x), ´expanded´ ); # check the answer
```

$$\frac{x}{x^5 + 2\ x + 1}$$

In the above example, we have assigned infolevel[int] the value two, so that we see what method Maple actually uses. Maple's general approach for integration of rational functions is as follows.

- In what is called the "first-stage indefinite integration," Maple tries heuristic methods such as lookup-tables, "derivative-divides" (integrand of the form $\frac{p}{q}$ where q' divides p), substitutions, and partial fraction decomposition (for denominators of degree less than seven).

- If the first-stage indefinite integration fails, Maple enters the Risch algorithm. This goes as follows.

  (i) Horowitz' reduction [72] is applied to express the integral in the form $\frac{c}{d} + \int \frac{a}{b}$, where b is square-free, and degree$(a) <$ degree(b). In this form, $\frac{c}{d}$ is called the rational part because the remaining integral can be expressed only by introducing logarithms. Thus, $\int \frac{a}{b}$ is called the logarithmic part.

  (ii) The Rothstein/Trager method [105, 117] is used to express the logarithmic part in the form $\sum_i c_i \log v_i$, where c_i are nonzero constants and v_i are monic, square-free, relatively prime polynomials of positive degree. Actually, the Lazard/Rioboo/Trager improvement [85], in which algebraic extensions and factorizations are avoided in the computation of the logarithmic part, had been implemented.

Of course, you may doubt the usefulness of the above answer because it contains roots of a fifth degree polynomial which cannot be computed analytically. But the same algorithm is applied in cases like the following one taken from [116].

```
> Int( (7*x^13+10*x^8+4*x^7-7*x^6-4*x^3-4*x^2+3*x+3) /
>       (x^14-2*x^8-2*x^7-2*x^4-4*x^3-x^2+2*x+1), x ):
> " = value(");
```

$$\int (7\ x^{13} + 10\ x^8 + 4\ x^7 - 7\ x^6 - 4\ x^3 - 4\ x^2 + 3\ x + 3)\Big/$$

$$(x^{14} - 2\ x^8 - 2\ x^7 - 2\ x^4 - 4\ x^3 - x^2 + 2\ x + 1)$$

$$dx = \frac{1}{2}\ \ln\!\left(x^7 - \sqrt{2}\ x^2 + \left(-\sqrt{2} - 1\right) x - 1 \right) \sqrt{2}$$

$$+ \frac{1}{2}\ \ln\!\left(x^7 - \sqrt{2}\ x^2 + \left(-\sqrt{2} - 1\right) x - 1 \right)$$

$$+ \frac{1}{2}\ \ln\!\left(x^7 + \sqrt{2}\ x^2 + \left(\sqrt{2} - 1\right) x - 1 \right)$$

$$- \frac{1}{2}\ \ln\!\left(x^7 + \sqrt{2}\ x^2 + \left(\sqrt{2} - 1\right) x - 1 \right) \sqrt{2}$$

```
> normal( diff(rhs("),x), `expanded` ); # check the answer
```

$$(7\ x^{13} + 10\ x^8 + 4\ x^7 - 7\ x^6 - 4\ x^3 - 4\ x^2 + 3\ x + 3)\Big/($$

$$x^{14} - 2\ x^8 - 2\ x^7 - 2\ x^4 - 4\ x^3 - x^2 + 2\ x + 1)$$

The strength of the Risch algorithm [104] comes into prominence when you apply it to a larger class of functions, viz., the class of *elementary functions*. Elementary functions of x can be roughly described as follows.

- Start with a set of constants, e.g., $\mathbf{Q}, \mathbb{R}$, or $\mathbb{C}$.
- Make polynomials $p(x)$ with constant coefficients.
- Make rational functions $\dfrac{p(x)}{q(x)}$.
- Add exponentials of these (this will include the trigonometric and hyperbolic functions, and their inverses if the complex number i is one of the constants).

- Add logarithms of these (if we just go this far we have the *elementary transcendental functions*).
- Add algebraic functions, i.e., solutions of polynomial equations whose coefficients are functions of the types already introduced. (For example, add $\sqrt{x^2 + 1}$, which solves the equation $y^2 - x^2 - 1 = 0$.)

It is assumed in the construction that every step (except the choice of constants) can be iterated, so we can form a rational function of polynomials of logarithms and so on.

Risch [104] described an algorithm which given an elementary transcendental function decides whether its integral can be expressed as an elementary function, and if so, computes the integral. It is based on:

Liouville's Principle *If an elementary function $f(x)$ has an elementary integral, then it has one of the form*

$$\int f(x)\, dx = v(x) + \sum_{i=1}^{n} c_i \log(u_i(x))$$

where the c_i's are constants, and v and the u_i's involve no quantity not already in f and the c_i's.

Liouville's theorem bounds, so to speak, the search space for elementary integrals. A further generalization would be to take *Liouvillian function*, defined as elementary functions together with anything of the form $\int f(x)\, dx$ for any function $f(x)$ already in the class considered; again the constructions can be iterated. This class includes, for example, the error function erf and the exponential integral function Ei, defined by

$$\operatorname{erf}(x) = \frac{2}{\sqrt{\pi}} \int_0^x \exp(-t^2)\, dt \text{ and } \operatorname{Ei}(x) = \int_x^\infty \frac{\exp(-t)}{t}\, dt, \text{ respectively.}$$

For details about the Risch algorithm, the interested reader is referred to [9, 10, 36, 37, 51, 53, 92, 104]. Here, we only sketch Maple's general approach to integration of elementary function:

- In what is called the "first- and second-stage indefinite integration," Maple treats special forms like polynomials, rational functions, radicals such as $(\sqrt{a + bx + cx^2})^n$ and $Q(x)\left(\sqrt{a + bx + cx^2}\right)^n$, and functions of type *polynomial*·$(x) \ln x$ or *ratpoly*(x)· $\ln\big(\text{ratpoly}(x)\big)$.
- If the heuristics fail, Maple applies the Risch-Norman frontend [51] to avoid introduction of complex exponentials and logarithms for integrands in which trigonometric and hyperbolic functions are involved.
- If still no answer is found, the Risch algorithm is entered.

In the final step, the most difficult part is the integration of algebraic functions. Trager's method [118] for algebraic functions in **RootOf** notation has been implemented. But there are some restrictions in the current implementation.

- In the case where the coefficient field is not an algebraic number field, the transcendental part of the integral is not computed. In practice this means that when the integrand contains parameters, Maple may fail to find an answer even though it exists.

- The algorithm is slow.

- the integrand must contain a single **RootOf** involving the integration variable. The **evala@Primfield** procedure may be used to achieve this condition.

Let us look at some examples to get a better idea of Maple's integration capabilities.

```
> Int( ln(x-1)^3, x ):    " = value(");
```

$$\int \ln(x-1)^2 \, dx = \ln(x-1)^2 \, (x-1)$$

$$- 2 \, (x-1) \, \ln(x-1) + 2 \, x - 2$$

```
> diff( rhs("), x ); # check the answer
```

$$\ln(x-1)^3$$

```
> int( ln(x-1)^2/x, x );
```

$$\int \frac{\ln(x-1)^2}{x} \, dx$$

The first integral is computed by a table-driven integration by parts in the integrator's frontend. The Risch algorithm decides that the second integral is not elementary. In such cases Maple simply returns the input command or introduces a new function, i.e., extends the class of admissible functions (with functions such as the error function, exponential integral, sine integral, and so on).

```
> Int( exp(-x^2), x ):    " = value(");
```

$$\int e^{-x^2} \, dx = \frac{1}{2} \sqrt{\pi} \, \mathrm{erf}(x)$$

```
> Int( exp(-x)/x, x):    " = value(");
```

$$\int \frac{e^{-x}}{x} \, dx = -\mathrm{Ei}(1, x)$$

```
> Int ( 1 / ( x * (x^2+1)^(1/3) ), x ):   " = value(");
```

$$\int \frac{1}{x\ (x^2\ +\ 1\ )^{1/3}}\ dx = \int \frac{1}{x\ (x^2\ +\ 1\ )^{1/3}}\ dx$$

In this case, Maple insists on the use of radicals in **RootOf** notation. So, let us introduce α as a cube root of $x^2 + 1$.

```
> alias( alpha = RootOf( z^3 - x^2 - 1, z ) ):
> convert( "", 'RootOf' ):
```

In this notation, Maple can compute the integral.

```
> settime := time(): # start timing
> "";   # evaluation
```

$$\frac{1}{2}\ \%1\ \ln\!\left(\left(20\ -\ \%1\ -\ \%1^2\ -\ 6\ x^2\ \%1\ +\ \%1^2\ x^2\ +\ 8\ x^2\ +\ 21\ \alpha\right.\right.$$

$$\left.+\ 21\ \alpha^2\right)\!/x^2\Big)\ -\ \frac{1}{2}\ \ln\!\left(\left(20\ -\ \%1\ -\ \%1^2\ +\ 15\ x^2\right.\right.$$

$$\left.+\ 8\ x^2\ \%1\ +\ \%1^2\ x^2\ +\ 21\ \alpha\ +\ 21\ \alpha^2\right)\!/x^2\Big)\ -\ \frac{1}{2}\ \ln\!\Big(\!\Big(20$$

$$-\ \%1\ -\ \%1^2\ +\ 15\ x^2\ +\ 8\ x^2\ \%1\ +\ \%1^2\ x^2\ +\ 21\ \alpha$$

$$\left.+\ 21\ \alpha^2\right)\!/x^2\Big)\ \%1$$

$$\%1\ :=\ \mathrm{RootOf}\,(\ \_Z^2\ +\ \_Z\ +\ 1\ )$$

```
> # check the answer
> evala( Normal( diff( rhs(") , x ) - 1 / (x * alpha) ) );
```

$$0$$

```
> cpu_time := (time()-settime) * seconds; # computing time
```

$$cpu\_time\ :=\ 335.367\ seconds$$

In [36], the Chebyshev integral [28]

$$\int \frac{2x^6 + 4x^5 + 7x^4 - 3x^3 - x^2 - 8x - 8}{(2x^2 - 1)^2\sqrt{x^4 + 4x^3 + 2x^2 + 1}}$$

was computed with REDUCE. In Maple, the computation and the result are as follows.

```
> alias( beta =
>    RootOf( z^2 - x^4 - 4*x^3 - 2*x^2 - 1, z ) ):
> settime := time():
> Int( ( 2*x^6 + 4*x^5 + 7*x^4 - 3*x^3 - x^2 - 8*x - 8) /
>    ( (2*x^2-1)^2 * beta ), x):   " = value(");
```

$$\int \frac{2\ x^6 + 4\ x^5 + 7\ x^4 - 3\ x^3 - x^2 - 8\ x - 8}{(\ 2\ x^2 - 1\ )^2\ \beta}\ dx =$$

$$\frac{1}{2}\ \frac{(\ 2\ x + 1\ )\ \beta}{2\ x^2 - 1} + \frac{1}{2}\ \ln\Big(\ (\ 1025\ x^{10} + 6138\ x^9$$

$$+\ 12307\ x^8 + 10188\ x^7 + 4503\ x^6 + 3134\ x^5$$

$$+\ 1589\ x^4 + 140\ x^3 + 176\ x^2 + 2 - 4104\ \beta\ x^7$$

$$-\ 10\ \beta\ x^2 - 624\ \beta\ x^3 - 805\ \beta\ x^4 - 2182\ \beta\ x^5$$

$$-\ 5084\ \beta\ x^6 - 28\ \beta\ x - 1023\ \beta\ x^8\ )\big/(\ 2\ x^2 - 1\ )^5\Big)$$

```
> # check the answer
> evala( Normal( diff(rhs("),x) - op(1,lhs(")) ) );
```

$$0$$

```
> cpu_time := (time()-settime) * seconds; # computing time
```

$$cpu\_time := 69.033\ seconds$$

The most time-consuming part of the computation is not the reduction of the integral to algebraic and transcendental parts, nor the computation of the algebraic part; it is the expensive computation of the transcendental part.

Algebraic functions appear in the following two integrals.

```
> Int( x/(x^3 + x + a), x ):   " = value(");
```

$$\int \frac{x}{x^3 + x + a}\ dx = \sum_{\_R = \%1} \_R\ \ln\Big(x + 9\ \frac{(\ 4 + 27\ a^2\ )\ a\ \_R^2}{2 + 27\ a^2}$$

$$+\ \frac{(\ 4 + 27\ a^2\ )\ \_R}{2 + 27\ a^2} + 6\ \frac{a}{2 + 27\ a^2}\Big)$$

$$\%1\ :=\ RootOf(\ (\ 4 + 27\ a^2\ )\ \_Z^3 + \_Z + a\ )$$

```
> Int ( 1/(x^16 + a), x ):    " = value(");
```

$$\int \frac{1}{x^{16} + a} \, dx = \sum_{\_R = \%1} \_R \, \ln (x + 16 \, a \, \_R)$$

$$\%1 := RootOf (18446744073709551616 \; a^{15} \; \_Z^{16} + 1)$$

The next example, which is a parametrization of one of the previous integrals, shows that the current implementation of integration of algebraic functions is limited to cases where the coefficient field is an algebraic number field.

```
> alias ( gamma = RootOf ( z^3 - x^2 - a, z ) ):

> infolevel[int]:=1:

> int ( 1/(x*gamma), x );

int/indef:    first-stage indefinite integration
int/indef2:    second-stage indefinite integration
int/rischnorm:    enter Risch-Norman integrator
int/risch:    enter Risch integration
int/algrisch/int:
Risch/Trager´s algorithm for algebraic function
int/algrisch/int:
computation of the algebraic part: start time    4.033
int/algrisch/int:
computation of the algebraic part: end time    4.216
int/algrisch/int:
computation of the transcendental part: start time    4.350
int/algrisch/transcpar:
parametric case not handled yet
int/algrisch/int:
computation of the transcendental part: end time    4.366
int/algrisch/int:
could not find an elementary antiderivative
```

$$\int \frac{1}{x \, \gamma} \, dx$$

10.2 Definite Integration

Definite integration is also performed in Maple by **int** (and by the alias **integrate**). Again, for display reasons we shall use the inert form **Int** in combination with the procedure **value**.

```
> Int( x/(x^3+1), x = 1..a ):  " = value(");
```

$$\int_{1}^{a} \frac{x}{x^3 + 1}\, dx = -\frac{1}{3}\ln(1 + a) + \frac{1}{6}\ln(-a + 1 + a^2)$$

$$+ \frac{1}{3}\sqrt{3}\arctan\left(\frac{1}{3}\sqrt{3}(2a - 1)\right) + \frac{1}{3}\ln(2)$$

$$- \frac{1}{18}\sqrt{3}\,\pi$$

```
> Int( ln(t)/(1-t), t = 0..x ):  " = value(");
```

$$\int_{0}^{x} \frac{\ln(t)}{1 - t}\, dt = \mathrm{dilog}(x) - \frac{1}{6}\pi^2$$

```
> Int( 1/((1+x^2)*(1+2*x^2)), x = 0..1 ):
> " = value(");
```

$$\int_{0}^{1} \frac{1}{(x^2 + 1)(1 + 2x^2)}\, dx = -\frac{1}{4}\pi + \sqrt{2}\arctan\left(\sqrt{2}\right)$$

Definite integration does not compute the corresponding indefinite integral and substitute in the limits of integration as the next example, in which $\int_{0}^{1} \frac{1}{x^2}\, dx$ is computed, illustrates.

```
> Int( 1/x^2, x ):  " = value(");
```

$$\int \frac{1}{x^2}\, dx = -\frac{1}{x}$$

```
> subs( x=1, rhs(") ) - subs( x=-1, rhs(") );
```

$$-2$$

The problem here is that the analytic conditions for application of the fundamental theorem of analysis are not fulfilled: there is a non-removable singularity at $x = 0$ in the integrand within the interval $(-1, 1)$. Maple checks continuity of the integrand over the given interval and, in case of possible errors in the answer, simply returns the command. By the way, you can force continuity of the integrand over the interval by adding the keyword continuous. In the example chosen, Maple itself can prove that the definite integral diverges.

```
> Int ( 1/x^2, x = -1..1 ):  "  = value (");
```

$$\int_{-1}^{1} \frac{1}{x^2}\, dx = \infty$$

A more difficult example is

$$\int_{0}^{2\pi} \frac{1}{1 + 3\sin^2 t}\, dt$$

```
> Int ( 1/(1+3*sin(t)^2), t = 0..2*Pi ):   "  = value (");
```

$$\int_{0}^{2\,\pi} \frac{1}{1 + 3\,\sin(t)^2}\, dt = -\,\pi\,\left(-\sqrt{3}\,\sqrt{28 - 16\sqrt{3}}\right.$$

$$-\,2\,\sqrt{28 - 16\sqrt{3}} + \sqrt{3}\,\sqrt{28 + 16\sqrt{3}}$$

$$-\,2\,\sqrt{28 + 16\sqrt{3}}\,\Big)\Big/\Big(\sqrt{28 + 16\sqrt{3}}$$

$$\left.\sqrt{28 - 16\sqrt{3}}\,\right)$$

Because denesting of roots is not implemented in Maple, it is difficult to simplify this answer to π. In the next section, you will see how this answer can be obtained with Maple by applying a different method.

In many cases Maple uses lookup-tables and pattern matching [50], and differentiation of special functions with respect to a parameter to compute definite integrals.

```
> Int ( exp(-sqrt(t)) / ( t^(1/4) * (1-exp(-sqrt(t)) ),
>     t = 0..infinity ):   "  = value (");
```

$$\int_{0}^{\infty} \frac{e^{-\sqrt{t}}}{t^{1/4}\left(1 - e^{-\sqrt{t}}\right)}\, dt = \sqrt{\pi}\ \mathrm{Zeta}\!\left(\frac{3}{2}\right)$$

```
> evalf ( rhs (") );
```

$$4.630314748$$

```
> Int ( t^4 * ln(t)^2 / (1+3*t^2)^3, t = 0..infinity ):
> " = value(");
```

$$\int_0^\infty \frac{t^4 \ln(t)^2}{(1 + 3 t^2)^3} dt = \frac{1}{216} \pi \sqrt{3} + \frac{1}{576} \pi^3 \sqrt{3}$$

$$- \frac{1}{108} \pi \sqrt{3} \ln(3) + \frac{1}{576} \pi \sqrt{3} \ln(3)^2$$

These are examples of integrals of the general form

$$\int_0^\infty \frac{\exp(-u_1 t^{s_1} - u_2 t^{s_2}) t^w \ln(b t^{d_l})^m \begin{Bmatrix} \cos \\ \sin \end{Bmatrix} (c t^r)}{(a_0 + a_1 f^d)^p} dt,$$

where

$f = t$ or $\exp(t^s)$,

p and m are nonnegative integers,

$\text{signum}(a_0/a_1) > 0$,

s_1 and s_2 are nonzero real numbers,

d and d_l are any real numbers,

b, u_1, and u_2 are positive real numbers,

w is a complex number such that $\Re\left(\dfrac{w+1}{s}\right) > 0$, and

$r = 0$ or $r = s$ or $r = 2s$ or $s = 2r$.

Other types of definite integrals which are computed by pattern matching are

$$\int_0^\infty \exp(-u t^s) t^w \ln(b t^{d_l})^m \begin{Bmatrix} \text{erf} \\ \text{erfc} \end{Bmatrix} \left(f t^v + g\right) dt,$$

$$\int_0^\infty \exp(-u t^s) t^w \text{BesselJ}(b, c t^{s_p})^{k_J} \text{BesselY}(\pm b, c t^{s_p})^{k_Y} dt,$$

and

$$\int_{t_0}^{t_1} \begin{Bmatrix} \sin \\ \cos \end{Bmatrix} \left(z \begin{Bmatrix} \sin \\ \cos \end{Bmatrix} (a t)\right) \begin{Bmatrix} \sin \\ \cos \end{Bmatrix} (b t) dt.$$

Two more examples:

```
> Int ( t * exp(-t^2) * erf(2*t+1), t = 0..infinity ):
```

```
> " = value(");
```

$$\int_0^\infty t\ \mathrm{e}^{-t^2}\ \mathrm{erf}(\,2\ t\ +\ 1\,)\ dt = \frac{1}{2}\ \mathrm{erf}(\,1\,)\ +\ \frac{1}{5}\ \sqrt{5}\ \mathrm{e}^{-1/5}$$

$$-\ \frac{1}{5}\ \sqrt{5}\ \mathrm{e}^{-1/5}\ \mathrm{erf}\!\left(\frac{2}{5}\ \sqrt{5}\ \right)$$

```
> Int( x * exp(-x^2) * BesselJ(0,x) * BesselY(0,x),
>      x = 0..infinity ):   " = value(");
```

$$\int_0^\infty x\ \mathrm{e}^{-x^2}\ \mathrm{BesselJ}(\,0,\ x\,)\ \mathrm{BesselY}(\,0,\ x\,)\ dx =$$

$$-\ \frac{1}{2}\ \frac{\mathrm{e}^{-1/2}\ \mathrm{BesselK}\!\left(0,\ \dfrac{1}{2}\right)}{\pi}$$

```
> Int( sin(z*sin(x)) * sin(3*x), x = 0..Pi):
> " = value(");
```

$$\int_0^\pi \sin(\,z\ \sin(\,x\,)\,)\ \sin(\,3\ x\,)\ dx = 8\ \frac{\pi\ \mathrm{BesselJ}(\,1,\ z\,)}{z^2}$$

$$-\ 4\ \frac{\pi\ \mathrm{BesselJ}(\,0,\ z\,)}{z}\ -\ \pi\ \mathrm{BesselJ}(\,1,\ z\,)$$

Elliptic integrals of the first, second and third kinds are available in algebraic form (Jacobi's notation). The notation used in Maple follows that used in the Handbook of Elliptic Integrals by Byrd and Friedman [12]; see the list on the next page. A few examples:

```
> Int( 1/sqrt((x^2-1)*(x^2-2)), x = a..b ):
> " = value(");
```

$$\int_a^b \frac{1}{\sqrt{x^2\ -\ 1}\ \sqrt{x^2\ -\ 2}}\ dx =$$

$$\frac{1}{2}\ \mathrm{LegendreF}\!\left(\,|\ a\ |,\ \frac{1}{2}\ \sqrt{2}\ \right)\sqrt{2}$$

$$+\ \frac{1}{2}\ I\ \sqrt{2}\ \mathrm{LegendreF}\!\left(1,\ \frac{1}{2}\ \sqrt{2}\ \right)$$

$$-\frac{1}{2}\ \texttt{LegendreF}\left(\ \middle|\ b\ \middle|,\ \frac{1}{2}\ \sqrt{2}\ \right)\sqrt{2}$$

```
> Int( 1/sqrt((x-1)*(x-2)*(x-3)*(x-4)),
>    x = 4..infinity ):   " = simplify( value(") );
```

$$\int_{4}^{\infty}\frac{1}{\sqrt{x-1}\ \sqrt{x-2}\ \sqrt{x-3}\ \sqrt{x-4}}\ dx = 2$$

$$\sqrt{2\sqrt{3}-3}\ \texttt{LegendreF}\left(\frac{1}{6}\ 3^{3/4}\ \sqrt{2\sqrt{3}+3}\ ,\right.$$

$$\left. 6\ \frac{\sqrt{2}\ \sqrt{2-\sqrt{3}}}{\sqrt{2\sqrt{3}-3}\ \left(2\sqrt{3}+3\right)}\right)\middle/\sqrt{2\sqrt{3}+3}$$

Elliptic Integrals in Maple		
Description	**Definition**	**Maple function**
incomplete elliptic integral of the 1st kind	$\int_0^x \frac{1}{\sqrt{(1-t^2)(1-k^2t^2)}}\,dt$	$\text{LegendreF}(x, k)$
incomplete elliptic integral of the 2nd kind	$\int_0^x \frac{\sqrt{1-k^2t^2}}{\sqrt{1-t^2}}\,dt$	$\text{LegendreE}(x, k)$
incomplete elliptic integral of the 3rd kind	$\int_0^x \frac{1}{(1-at^2)\sqrt{(1-t^2)(1-k^2t^2)}}\,dt$	$\text{LegendrePi}(x, a, k)$
complete elliptic integral of the 1st kind	$\int_0^1 \frac{1}{\sqrt{(1-t^2)(1-k^2t^2)}}\,dt$	$\text{LegendreKc}(k)$
complete elliptic integral of the 2nd kind	$\int_0^1 \frac{\sqrt{1-k^2t^2}}{\sqrt{1-t^2}}\,dt$	$\text{LegendreEc}(k)$
complete elliptic integral of the 3rd kind	$\int_0^1 \frac{1}{(1-at^2)\sqrt{(1-t^2)(1-k^2t^2)}}\,dt$	$\text{LegendrePic}(a, k)$
associated complete elliptic integral of the 1st kind	$\int_0^1 \frac{1}{\sqrt{(1-t^2)(1-c^2t^2)}}\,dt$	$\text{LegendreKc1}(k)$
associated complete elliptic integral of the 2nd kind	$\int_0^1 \frac{\sqrt{1-c^2t^2}}{\sqrt{1-t^2}}\,dt$	$\text{LegendreEc1}(k)$
associated complete elliptic integral of the 3rd kind	$\int_0^1 \frac{1}{(1-at^2)\sqrt{(1-t^2)(1-c^2t^2)}}\,dt$	$\text{LegendrePic1}(a, k)$

Here, $0 < k < 1$, and $c = \sqrt{1-k^2}$.

10.3 Numerical Integration

A computer algebra system aims at getting exact results, but Maple also
has several numerical facilities, e.g., numerical integrators.

```
> int( exp( arcsin(x) ), x = 0..1 );
```

$$\int_0^1 e^{\arcsin(x)} \ dx$$

```
> evalf(");
```

$$1.905238690$$

```
> Int( exp(-2*t) * t * ln(t), t = 0..infinity ):
> " = value(");
```

$$\int_0^\infty e^{-2\ t}\ t\ \ln(\ t\ )\ \ dt = -\ \frac{1}{4}\ \ln(\ 2\ )\ +\ \frac{1}{4}\ -\ \frac{1}{4}\ \gamma$$

```
> evalf(");
```

$$-.06759071137 = -.0675907114$$

```
> evalf( "", 20 );
```

$$-.067590711365369542506 = -.06759071136536954251$$

The default integration method is Clenshaw-Curtis quadrature, but
when convergence is slow (due to nearby singularities) the system tries
to remove the singularities or switches to an adaptive double-exponential
quadrature method. An adaptive Newton-Cotes method is available when
low precision (e.g., `Digits <= 15`) suffices. The optional fourth argument
of the call to **evalf/int** indicates the preferred integration method.

```
> readlib(`evalf/int`)( 1/sqrt(x), x = 0..1, 10, _Dexp );
```

$$1.999998825$$

By the way, generalized series expansions and variable transformations are
two of the techniques used in the Maple procedure **evalf/int** to deal with
singularities in an analytic integrand. The interested reader is referred to
[48, 52].

10.4 Integral Transforms

In this section, we shall give examples of integral transformations such as
Laplace transforms, Fourier transforms, and Mellin transforms. In general,

the integral transform $\mathcal{T}(f)$ of a function f with respect to the kernel K is defined by

$$\mathcal{T}(f)(s) = \int_a^b f(t)\, K(s,t)\, dt,$$

at least when this integral exists. The Laplace, Fourier, and Mellin transforms are the most popular ones, with kernels e^{-ist}, e^{-st}, and t^{s-1}, respectively.

Integral Transforms		
Transform	**Definition**	**Maple function**
Laplace	$\int_0^\infty f(t)e^{-st}\, dt$	laplace$(f(t), t, s)$
Fourier	$\int_{-\infty}^\infty f(t)e^{-ist}\, dt$	fourier$(f(t), t, s)$
Mellin	$\int_0^\infty f(t)t^{s-1}\, dt$	mellin$(f(t), t, s)$

Expressions in the form of sums of rational expressions of polynomials or certain functions like the **Dirac** function, the **Heaviside** function, or Bessel functions can be transformed to their Laplace transform the Maple procedure **laplace**. The corresponding inverse Laplace transform can be computed with **invlaplace**.

```
> (cosh(3*t) - 3*t*sinh(3*t) - 1) / t^2;
```

$$\frac{\cosh(3\,t)\; -\; 3\,t\,\sinh(3\,t)\; -\; 1}{t^2}$$

```
> laplace(",t,s);
```

$$\frac{1}{2}\ln(s+3)\,s + \frac{1}{2}\ln(s-3)\,s - \ln(s)\,s$$

```
> invlaplace(",s,t);
```

$$\frac{1}{2}\frac{e^{-3\,t}}{t^2} + \frac{3}{2}\frac{e^{-3\,t}}{t} + \frac{1}{2}\frac{e^{3\,t}}{t^2} - \frac{3}{2}\frac{e^{3\,t}}{t} - \frac{1}{t^2}$$

```
> convert(",´trig´);
```

$$\frac{1}{2}\frac{\cosh(3\,t)\; -\; \sinh(3\,t)}{t^2}$$
$$+ \frac{3}{2}\frac{\cosh(3\,t)\; -\; \sinh(3\,t)}{t}$$

$$+ \frac{1}{2} \frac{\cosh(3\ t)\ +\ \sinh(3\ t)}{t^2}$$

$$- \frac{3}{2} \frac{\cosh(3\ t)\ +\ \sinh(3\ t)}{t} - \frac{1}{t^2}$$

```
> normal(");
```

$$- \frac{-\cosh(3\ t)\ +\ 3\ t\ \sinh(3\ t)\ +\ 1}{t^2}$$

```
> combine(");  # get rid of the minus sign
```

$$\frac{\cosh(3\ t)\ -\ 3\ t\ \sinh(3\ t)\ -\ 1}{t^2}$$

The next example shows that integral transforms can be used to enlarge the class of integration problems that can be solved through Maple.

```
> integrate( BesselJ(1,x), x = 0..t );
```

$$\int_0^t BesselJ(1,\ x)\ dx$$

```
> laplace(",t,s);
```

$$\frac{\sqrt{s^2\ +\ 1}\ -\ s}{s\ \sqrt{s^2\ +\ 1}}$$

```
> invlaplace(",s,t);
```

$$1\ -\ BesselJ(0,\ t)$$

```
> eval(subs(t=0,"));  # check constant
```

$$0$$

The main application of Laplace transforms is in the field of differential equations and integral equations.

```
> int_eqn := integrate( exp(a*x) * f(t-x), x = 0..t )
>    + b*f(t) = t;
```

$$int\_eqn := \int_0^t e^{a\ x}\ f(t\ -\ x)\ dx\ +\ b\ f(t) = t$$

```
> laplace(",t,s);
```

$$\frac{laplace(\,f(\,t\,),\ t,\ s\,)}{s\ -\ a}\ +\ b\ laplace(\,f(\,t\,),\ t,\ s\,) = \frac{1}{s^2}$$

```
> readlib(isolate)( ", laplace(f(t),t,s) );
```

$$laplace(\,f(\,t\,),\ t,\ s\,) = \frac{1}{s^2\left(\dfrac{1}{s\ -\ a}\ +\ b\right)}$$

```
> invlaplace(",s,t);
```

$$f(\,t\,) = \frac{1}{b^2\ a^2\ -\ 2\ b\ a\ +\ 1}\ +\ \frac{a\ t}{b\ a\ -\ 1}$$

$$+\ \frac{b\ e^{\frac{(\,b\,a\,-\,1\,)\ t}{b}}}{-b^3\ a^2\ +\ 2\ b^2\ a\ -\ b}$$

Let us check the answer.

```
> f := unapply( rhs("), t );
```

$$f\ :=\ t \rightarrow \frac{1}{b^2\ a^2\ -\ 2\ b\ a\ +\ 1}\ +\ \frac{a\ t}{b\ a\ -\ 1}$$

$$+\ \frac{b\ e^{\frac{(\,b\,a\,-\,1\,)\ t}{b}}}{-b^3\ a^2\ +\ 2\ b^2\ a\ -\ b}$$

```
> normal( int_eqn, ´expanded´ );
```

$$t = t$$

The Maple procedure **fourier** can transform expressions in the form of sums of rational functions of polynomials to their Fourier transforms.

```
> 1/(1+t^3);
```

$$\frac{1}{1\ +\ t^3}$$

```
> fourier(",t,omega);
```

$$\frac{1}{3}\ I\ e^{I\ \omega}\ \pi\ -\ \frac{2}{3}\ I\ e^{I\ \omega}\ \pi\ Heaviside(\,\omega\,)\ -\ \frac{2}{9}\ \pi\ \sqrt{3}$$

$$e^{-\,1/2\ I\ \omega}\left(\frac{1}{2}\ I\ \sqrt{3}\ \left(e^{1/2}\ \sqrt{3}\ \omega\ Heaviside(\,-\omega\,)\right.\right.$$

$$\left.\left.-\ e^{-\,1/2}\ \sqrt{3}\ \omega\ Heaviside(\,\omega\,)\right)\right)$$

$$- \frac{3}{2} \; e^{-\,1/2\,\sqrt{3}\,\omega} \; \text{Heaviside}(\,\omega\,)$$

$$\left. - \frac{3}{2} \; e^{1/2\,\sqrt{3}\,\omega} \; \text{Heaviside}(\,-\omega\,) \right)$$

We can check the answer by computing the inverse Fourier transform with
invfourier.

```
> invfourier(",omega,t);
```

$$\frac{1}{2}\left(\frac{2}{3} \; I \; \pi^2 \; \text{Dirac}(\,-t\,-\,1\,) \right.$$

$$- \frac{2}{3} \; I \; \pi \left(\pi \; \text{Dirac}(\,-t\,-\,1\,) \; - \; \frac{I}{-t\,-\,1} \right) - \frac{2}{9} \; \pi \sqrt{3}$$

$$\left(-\frac{1}{2} \; \frac{I \sqrt{3}}{-\frac{1}{2}\sqrt{3}\,+\,I\left(-t\,+\,\frac{1}{2}\right)} \right.$$

$$-\frac{1}{2} \; \frac{I \sqrt{3}}{\frac{1}{2}\sqrt{3}\,+\,I\left(-t\,+\,\frac{1}{2}\right)}$$

$$-\frac{3}{2} \; \frac{1}{\frac{1}{2}\sqrt{3}\,+\,I\left(-t\,+\,\frac{1}{2}\right)}$$

$$\left.\left.\left. +\frac{3}{2} \; \frac{1}{-\frac{1}{2}\sqrt{3}\,+\,I\left(-t\,+\,\frac{1}{2}\right)} \right) \right/ \pi \right)$$

```
> normal(",´expanded´);
```

$$\frac{1}{1\,+\,t^3}$$

Maple can also apply convolution methods, look-up tables, and definite
integration to handle special functions such as trigonometric functions, the
Dirac and Heaviside functions, and Bessel functions.

```
> fourier( sin(t^2), t, omega );
```

$$\sqrt{\pi}\ \sin\!\left(\frac{1}{4}\ \omega^2\ +\ \frac{1}{4}\ \pi\right)$$

```
> fourier( BesselJ(0,t), t, omega );
```

$$2\ \frac{\text{Heaviside}(\omega\ +\ 1)\ -\ \text{Heaviside}(\omega\ -\ 1)}{\sqrt{1\ -\ \omega^2}}$$

```
> fourier( BesselJ( 0, sqrt(t^2+1) ), t, omega );
```

$$2\ e^{I\ \omega}\ \cos\!\left(-1\ +\ \omega^2\right)$$

$$\left.(\text{Heaviside}(\omega\ +\ 1)\ -\ \text{Heaviside}(\omega\ -\ 1))\middle/\right.$$

$$\sqrt{1\ -\ \omega^2}$$

You can define Fourier transforms for your own functions. For example, Maple does not know the Fourier transform of $x/\sinh x$. When you give this function a name, say F, then you can add it to the look-up table by

```
> `fourier/F` := proc(t,w,u)

>    2/Pi * exp(Pi*w) / (1 + exp(Pi*w))^2

> end:

> fourier( F(x), x, omega );
```

$$2\ \frac{e^{\pi\ \omega}}{\pi\ (1\ +\ e^{\pi\ \omega})^2}$$

```
> fourier( x^2 * F(x), x, omega );
```

$$I\left(2\ \frac{I\ \pi\ e^{\pi\ \omega}}{(1\ +\ e^{\pi\ \omega})^2}\ -\ 12\ \frac{I\ (e^{\pi\ \omega})^2\ \pi}{(1\ +\ e^{\pi\ \omega})^3}\ +\ 12\ \frac{I\ (e^{\pi\ \omega})^3\ \pi}{(1\ +\ e^{\pi\ \omega})^4}\right)$$

```
> simplify(");
```

$$-2\ \frac{\pi\ (e^{\pi\ \omega}\ -\ 4\ e^{2\ \pi\ \omega}\ +\ e^{3\ \pi\ \omega})}{(1\ +\ e^{\pi\ \omega})^4}$$

fourier and **invfourier** are procedures for computing symbolic Fourier transforms and their inverses. The procedures **FFT** and **iFFT** are meant for numerical **F**ast **F**ourier **T**ransforms and their inverses. Recall the definition of the Fourier transform $X = [X_0, X_1, \cdots, X_{N-1}]$ for a list of data $x = [x_0, x_1, \cdots, x_N]$ of lenght N.

$$X[k] = \sum_{j=0}^{N-1} x_j e^{-2\pi ijk/N} \, ,$$

for $0 \leq k \leq N-1$. For N equal to a power of two, the so-called Fast Fourier Transform Method [35] has been implemented. In the first example below, we take $N = 2^3$, and compute the fast Fourier transform of the sequence of real numbers $[-1, -1, -1, -1, 1, 1, 1, 1]$.

```
> readlib( FFT ): # load the procedure FFT
> # the real parts of the data
> x := array( [-1,-1,-1,-1,1,1,1,1] ):
> # the imaginary parts of the data
> y := array( [0,0,0,0,0,0,0,0] ):
> FFT(3,x,y):
> # the real parts of the transformed data
> print(x); # note that the array x has been updated
    [ 0   -2.000000001   0   -1.999999999   0   -1.999999999   0

        -2.000000001 ]

> # the imaginary parts of the transformed data
> print(y);
    [ 0    4.828427122   0    .828427124   0   -.828427124   0

        -4.828427122 ]

> iFFT(3,x,y): # check results
> print(x);
    [ -1.000000000   -.9999999990   -.9999999995

        -.9999999985   1.000000000   .9999999990

        .9999999995   .9999999985 ]

> print(y);
    [ 0    .2500000000 10^{-9}   0   -.2500000000 10^{-9}   0

        -.2500000000 10^{-9}   0   .2500000000 10^{-9} ]
```

The procedure **zip** is handy when you want to write the complex numbers in a more conventional way.

```
> zip( (a,b) -> a+b*I, x, y ):  convert(",´list´);

   [ -1.000000000, -.9999999990 + .2500000000 10⁻⁹ I,

        -.9999999995, -.9999999985 - .2500000000 10⁻⁹ I,

        1.000000000, .9999999990 - .2500000000 10⁻⁹ I,

        .9999999995, .9999999985 + .2500000000 10⁻⁹ I ]
```

A common and important application of fast Fourier transforms is doing convolutions in data smoothing. Below is a simple, but artificial example. It is presented without comments, but all data types and procedures used will be dealt with later on in this book.

First, we load the random number generator for a normal distribution from the *stats* package.

```
> random := stats[RandNormal](0,1):
```

Next, we generate data; in particular, we generate the real and imaginary parts of the data separately.

```
> re_data := array( [ seq( sin(0.0625*k) + 0.1*random(),
>    k=1..2^8) ] ):
> im_data := array( [ seq( 0, k=1..2^8) ] ):
```

To get an idea of what data we have in hand, we plot the data points. By construction it will look like the sine function.

```
> xcoords := array( [ seq( 0.0625*k, k=1..2^8) ] ):
> plotdata := convert( zip( (a,b) -> [a,b], xcoords,
>    re_data ), ´list´ ):
> plot( plotdata, style = POINT );
```

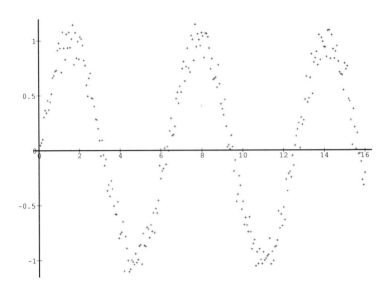

We shall use the kernel function $t \rightarrow \exp(-\frac{100}{256}t)$ for smoothing the data.

```
> re_kernel := array( [ seq( exp( -100.0 * (k/2^8)^2 ),
>   k=1..2^8 ) ] ):
> im_kernel := array( [ seq( 0, k=1..2^8) ] ):
```

We compute the fast Fourier transforms of the data and kernel and write them as arrays of complex numbers.

```
> FFT( 8, re_data, im_data ):
> FFT( 8, re_kernel, im_kernel ):
> data := zip( (a,b) -> (a+b*I), re_data, im_data ):
> kernel := zip( (a,b) -> (a+b*I), re_kernel, im_kernel ):
> newdata := zip( (a,b) -> a*b, data, kernel ):
> new_re_data := map( Re, newdata ):
> new_im_data := map( Im, newdata ):
```

Finally, we compute the inverse fast Fourier transform of the product of Fourier transforms of data and kernel. Up to a scalar, this is a smooth version of the original data. A plot shows this best.

```
> iFFT( 8, new_re_data, new_im_data ):
> plotdata := convert( zip( (a,b) -> [a,b], xcoords,
```

```
>    new_re_data), 'list' ):
> plot( plotdata, style=POINT );
```

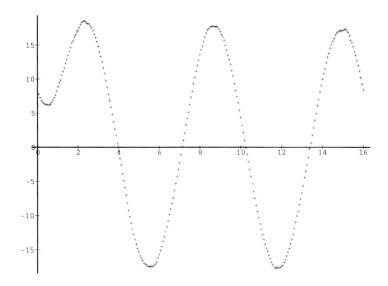

We end this section on integral transform with two examples of the Mellin transform. The Maple procedure to compute this transform is called **mellin**. Basically, it follows a lookup-table approach, and you can add your own Mellin transforms to the lookup-table (enter **?mellintable** for details).

```
> mellin( 1/(1+t), t, s );
```

$$\frac{\pi}{\sin(\pi\,s)}$$

```
> mellin( ln(1+t), t, s );
```

$$-\frac{\pi}{\sin(\pi\,(s+1))\,s}$$

10.5 Assisting Maple's Integrator

In this section, we shall look at some integration problems where Maple cannot find a solution all by itself, but with some assistance actually can solve the problem. Human assistance is quite often needed when non-elementary functions are involved or when parameters must satisfy certain conditions.

The first integration problem involves a parameter which must satisfy a certain condition in order that the integral can be solved analytically.

```
> Int( exp(-c*x^2), x = 0..infinity ):   " = value(");
```

$$\lim_{x \to \infty^-} \frac{1}{2} \frac{\sqrt{\pi} \ \mathrm{erf}\left(\sqrt{c} \ x\right)}{\sqrt{c}}$$

A common mistake in thought: you may think of c as a positive real constant, but Maple does not start from this assumption! From the above answer it is clear that Maple at least knows the indefinite integral. If you want to get further with the computation of the definite integral you must **assume** that c is a positive real constant; for non-positive values the integral diverges.

```
> assume( c>0 ):

> Int( exp(-c*x^2), x = 0..infinity ):   " = value(");
```

$$\int_0^\infty e^{-c\sim \ x^2} \ dx = \frac{1}{2} \sqrt{\frac{\pi}{c\sim}}$$

Another option to overcome the problem of insufficient information is to specify c as a square number or to use absolute values.

```
> c := p^2:

> Int( exp(-c*x^2), x = 0..infinity ):   " = value(");
```

$$\int_0^\infty e^{-p^2 \ x^2} \ dx = \frac{1}{2} \frac{\sqrt{\pi}}{p}$$

```
> c := abs(p):

> Int( exp(-c*x^2), x = 0..infinity ):   " = value(");
```

$$\int_0^\infty e^{-|p| \ x^2} \ dx = \frac{1}{2} \sqrt{\frac{\pi}{|p|}}$$

Sometimes you must delineate a method, e.g., a change of variables or integration by parts. This is conveniently done through the *student* package in Maple.

```
> with(student): # load the package

Warning: new definition for   value

> integrate( 1/sqrt(1-1/4*sin(x)^2), x = 0..Pi/2 );
```

$$\int_0^{1/2\,\pi} \frac{1}{\sqrt{1 - \dfrac{1}{4}\,\sin(x)^2}}\ dx$$

```
> changevar( sin(x)=y, ", y );
```

$$\mathrm{LegendreF}\left(1,\ \frac{1}{2}\right)$$

```
> integrate( x*exp(-a^2*x^2)*erf(b*x), x );
```

$$\int x\ e^{-a^2\ x^2}\ \mathrm{erf}(\ b\ x\ )\ dx$$

```
> intparts( ", erf(b*x) ):    "" = value(");
```

$$\int x\ e^{-a^2\ x^2}\ \mathrm{erf}(\ b\ x\ )\ dx =$$

$$-\ \frac{1}{2}\ \frac{\mathrm{erf}(\ b\ x\ )\ e^{-a^2\ x^2}}{a^2}\ +\ \frac{1}{2}\ \frac{b\ \mathrm{erf}\left(\sqrt{b^2 + a^2}\ x\right)}{a^2\ \sqrt{b^2 + a^2}}$$

In §10.2 we promised to show that

$$\int_0^{2\pi} \frac{1}{(1 + 3\sin t)^2}\ dt = \pi.$$

We shall find the result by the well-known method of contour integration and use Maple as a computational tool. First, we write the integrand as a rational function in $z = e^{it}$.

```
> alias( z = exp(sqrt(-1)*t) ):
```

Note the use of `sqrt(-1)`. It is used because you cannot define new aliases in terms of existing ones.

```
> 1/(1+3*sin(t)^2);
```

$$\frac{1}{1 + 3\ \sin(\ t\ )^2}$$

```
> convert(",exp);
```

$$\frac{1}{1 - \dfrac{3}{4}\left(z - \dfrac{1}{z}\right)^2}$$

```
> factor(");
```

$$-4 \; \frac{z^2}{(3 \; z^2 \; - \; 1 \;) \; (\; z^2 \; - \; 3 \;)}$$

From

```
> diff(z,t);
```

$$I \; z$$

follows that our original integration problem is transformed into the contour integral over the unit circle with integrand

```
> ""/";
```

$$4 \; \frac{I \; z}{(\; 3 \; z^2 \; - \; 1 \;) \; (\; z^2 \; - \; 3 \;)}$$

The answer to the definite integral is $2\pi i \sum$ *residues inside unit circle*. Therefore we search for the roots of the denominator that lie in the unit circle and compute their residues.

```
> solve( denom("), z );
```

$$\frac{1}{3} \; \sqrt{3} \;, \; -\frac{1}{3} \; \sqrt{3} \;, \; \sqrt{3} \;, \; -\sqrt{3}$$

```
> readlib( residue ): # enable computation of residues
> subs( z=Z, """ );   # introduce an unknown for z=exp(i*t)
```

$$4 \; \frac{I \; Z}{(\; 3 \; Z^2 \; - \; 1 \;) \; (\; Z^2 \; - \; 3 \;)}$$

```
> residue( ", Z=1/3*sqrt(3) );
```

$$-\frac{1}{4} \; I$$

```
> residue( "", Z=-1/3*sqrt(3) );
```

$$-\frac{1}{4} \; I$$

```
> 2*Pi*I*(" + "");
```

$$\pi$$

Usual tricks such as differentiation with respect to parameters prior to integration are performed easily in Maple. An example:

```
> assume(a>0):
> int( tanh(a*x/2) / (x*cosh(a*x)) , x = 0..infinity );
```

$$\int_0^\infty \frac{\tanh\left(\dfrac{1}{2} a{\sim} x\right)}{x \cosh(a{\sim} x)}\, dx$$

```
> diff(",a);
```

$$0$$

So, the definite integral does not depend on the parameter a.

10.6 Summation

Finite sums of numbers can be easily computed with the procedure **sum**, or with the inert form **Sum** in combination with the procedure **value**.

```
> Sum( k^7, k = 1..20 ):   " = value(");
```

$$\sum_{k=1}^{20} k^7 = 3877286700$$

Indefinite summation is also possible. Given a sequence

$$a_1, a_2, \ldots$$

or more precisely, an expression generating this sequence, we want to find an expression S_j, in which the summation sign has been eliminated and such that

$$S_j = \sum_{i=1}^{j} a_i .$$

This is the discrete analogue of indefinite integration. Having obtained S_j we then have

$$\sum_{i=m}^{n} a_i = S_n - S_{m-1},$$

where $S_0 = 0$. Maple uses the following methods to find S_j.

- Polynomials are summed using a formula based on Bernoulli polynomials:

$$\sum_{k=0}^{n-1} k^m = \frac{1}{m+1} \sum_{k=0}^{m} \binom{m+1}{k} B_k n^{m+1-k},$$

  where the Bernoulli numbers are defined by the implicit recurrence relation

$$B_0 = 1 \quad \text{and} \quad \sum_{k=0}^{m} \binom{m+1}{k} B_k = 0, \quad \text{for all } m \geq 0.$$

- Moenck's method [91] is used for summing rational functions of the summation index. The result is a rational function plus a sum of terms involving the Polygamma function Psi and its derivatives.

- Gosper's decision procedure [59] is the discrete analogue of the Risch algorithm. It is used to sum expressions containing factorials (including binomial coefficients) and powers.

- Hypergeometric identities are used for infinite sums.

A few examples:

```
> # Method of Bernoulli polynomials
> Sum( k^7, k = 1..n ):   " = value(");
```

$$\sum_{k=1}^{n} k^7 = \frac{1}{8} (n + 1)^8 - \frac{1}{2} (n + 1)^7 + \frac{7}{12} (n + 1)^6$$

$$- \frac{7}{24} (n + 1)^4 + \frac{1}{12} (n + 1)^2$$

```
> factor(");
```

$$\sum_{k=1}^{n} k^7 = \frac{1}{24} n^2 (3 n^4 + 6 n^3 - n^2 - 4 n + 2) (n + 1)^2$$

```
> # Moencks method
> Sum( 1/(k^2+k)^3, k = 1..n ):   " = value(");
```

$$\sum_{k=1}^{n} \frac{1}{(k^2 + k)^3} = - \frac{-2 + 6 (n + 1)^2 - 3 n}{(n + 1)^3}$$

$$+ 6 \Psi(1, n + 2) + 10 - \pi^2$$

```
> map( limit, ", n = infinity );
```

$$\lim_{n \to \infty} \sum_{k=1}^{n} \frac{1}{(k^2 + k)^3} = 10 - \pi^2$$

```
> Sum( 1/(k^2 - 4) , k = 3..infinity ):   " = value(");
```

$$\sum_{k=3}^{\infty} \frac{1}{k^2 - 4} = \frac{25}{48}$$

```
> Sum( 1/(3*k+1)/(3*k+2)/(3*k+3)/(3*k+4),
>    k = 0..infinity ):   " = value(");
```

$$\sum_{k=0}^{\infty} 1/((3\ k + 1)\ (3\ k + 2)\ (3\ k + 3)\ (3\ k + 4)) =$$

$$\frac{1}{6} + \frac{1}{36}\ \pi\ \sqrt{3} - \frac{1}{4}\ \ln(3)$$

```
> # Gosper´s method + hypergeometric summation theorems
> Sum( (-1)^(n-k) * binomial(2*n,k)^2, k = 0..2*n ):
> " = value(");
```

$$\sum_{k=0}^{2\ n} (-1)^{(n-k)}\ \text{binomial}(2\ n,\ k)^2 =$$

$$\frac{(-1)^{n}\ \sqrt{\pi}}{2^{(-2\ n)}\ \Gamma(1 + n)\ \Gamma\left(\frac{1}{2} - n\right)}$$

10.7 Exercises

1. Compute the following indefinite integrals and check the answers by differentiation and simplification.

   (a) $\int \sqrt{e^x - 1}\, dx$

   (b) $\int \frac{x}{(2ax - x^2)^{3/2}}\, dx$

   (c) $\int \sqrt{x^2 - a^2}\, dx$

(d) $\displaystyle\int \frac{1}{x\sqrt{1+x^2}}\,dx$

(e) $\displaystyle\int \sec^3 x\,dx$

(f) $\displaystyle\int \frac{1}{1+\sin x + \cos x}\,dx$

2. (a) Compute $\displaystyle\int_0^1 \left(\int_0^1 \frac{x-y}{(x+y)^3}\,dy\right)dx$.

   (b) Compute $\displaystyle\int_0^1 \left(\int_0^1 \frac{x-y}{(x+y)^3}\,dx\right)dy$.

   (c) Compare the results of (a) and (b). Does Maple make a mistake or is there something else going on?

3. Compute the following integrals.

   (a) $\displaystyle\int_1^{10} \frac{4x^4 + 4x^3 - 2x^2 - 10x + 6}{x^5 + 7x^4 + 16x^3 + 10x^2}\,dx$

   (b) $\displaystyle\int_0^{\pi/2} x^4 \sin x \cos x\,dx$

   (c) $\displaystyle\int_{1/7}^{1/5} \frac{1}{x\sqrt{5x^2 - 6x + 1}}\,dx$

   (d) $\displaystyle\int_{-2}^{-1} \frac{1}{x}\,dx$

4. Compute the following definite integrals:

   (a) $\displaystyle\int_0^1 \frac{1}{\sqrt{1-x^2}}\,dx$

   (b) $\displaystyle\int_0^1 x \arctan x\,dx$

   (c) $\displaystyle\int_0^\infty e^{-ax} \cos^2(bx)\,dx$, for positive real number a

   (d) $\displaystyle\int_0^\infty \frac{\sin x}{x}\,dx$

   (e) $\displaystyle\int_0^\infty e^{-x} \ln x\,dx$

   (f) $\displaystyle\int_0^\infty \frac{e^{-ax} \ln x}{\sqrt{x}}\,dx$, for positive real number a

(g) $\displaystyle \int_0^\infty \frac{e^{-\sqrt{t}}}{t^{1/4}\left(1 - e^{-\sqrt{t}}\right)}\, dt$

5. Let F be the function defined by $F(T) := \displaystyle \int_1^T \frac{\exp(-u^2 T)}{u}\, du$.

   (a) Define the corresponding Maple function F and determine a numerical approximation of $F(2)$.

   (b) Compute the derivative F' (by $\mathbf{D}$) and compute $F'(2)$.

6. Let A be the area $\{(x, y) \in \mathbb{R}^2 \mid 1/2 \le xy \le 2, 1 \le x \le 3\}$.

   Compute $\displaystyle \iint_A \frac{\exp(\frac{1}{xy})}{y^2(x+1)^2}\, dx\, dy$.

7. In this exercise, we shall keep track of the Risch algorithm and prove that the integral

$$\int \frac{\ln^2(x-1)}{x}\, dx$$

does not exist in the class of elementary functions. In the first place, Liouville's principle implies the following representation of the integral, when it exists as an elementary function:

$$B_3(x)\ln^3(x-1) + B_2(x)\ln^2(x-1) + B_1\ln(x-1) + B_0(x),$$

where $B_3(x)$, $B_2(x)$, and $B_1(x)$ are rational functions and only $B_0(x)$ may contain new logarithmic extensions.

   (a) Determine the differential equations satisfied by $B_0(x), \dots, B_3(x)$.

   (b) Show that $B_3(x)$ is a rational constant.

   (c) Prove that the differential equation for $B_2(x)$ cannot be solved in terms of rational functions. This proves that $\dfrac{\ln^2(x-1)}{x}$ cannot be integrated in terms of elementary functions.

8. Show by the method of residues that

$$\int_0^{2\pi} \frac{d\theta}{a^2 \cos^2\theta + b^2 \sin^2\theta}\, d\theta = \frac{2\pi}{ab},$$

   for a, b real and nonzero, and $\left|\frac{b-a}{b+a}\right| < 1$.

9. Solve the following integral equation by Laplace transforms.

$$\sin t = \int_0^t J_0(t-\theta) f(\theta)\, d\theta$$

10. Solve the integral equation $f(t) = 1 + \displaystyle \int_0^t (t-\theta) f(\theta)\, d\theta$.

11. Compute $\displaystyle\int_0^\infty \frac{x}{1+x^2}\sin\omega^2 x\,dx$.

12. Compute $\displaystyle\int_0^1 \frac{x^a - 1}{\ln x}\,dx$, for nonnegative a.

13. Compute $\displaystyle\int_0^\infty \frac{\ln x}{(x+a)(x-1)}\,dx$, for positive a.

14. Compute $\displaystyle\int \frac{\ln(x^2 + 1)}{x^2 + 1}\,dx$.

15. Compute $\displaystyle\int \frac{x^2}{\sqrt{x^6 + 1}}\,dx$.

16. Compute $\displaystyle\int \tan\left(\frac{1}{3}\arctan(x)\right)\,dx$.

17. Compute $\displaystyle\int \arcsin^2(x/a)\,dx$.

18. Compute $\displaystyle\int \frac{1}{\sqrt{a\sqrt{x}+b}}\,dx$.

19. Compute the following infinite sums.

(a) $\displaystyle\sum_{k=0}^\infty \frac{2k+3}{(k+1)(k+2)(k+3)}$

(b) $\displaystyle\sum_{k=1}^\infty \frac{k^2 + k - 1}{(k+2)!}$

(c) $\displaystyle\sum_{k=2}^\infty \frac{k}{(k-1)^2(k+1)^2}$

(d) $\displaystyle\frac{1}{4} + \sum_{k=1}^\infty \frac{3n+2}{n^3(n+1)(n+2)}$

20. Compute $\displaystyle\sum_{j=0}^n \binom{2n}{2j}(-3)^j$.

21. Compute the product of the first 32 prime numbers.

22. Compute the product $\displaystyle\prod_{k=2}^\infty 1 - 1/k^2$.

(Hint: find a closed formula for the product with k running from 2 to N and then compute with **limit** the limit for N going to infinity.)

Truncated Series Expansions, Power Series, and Limits

Three topics from calculus will be examined in this chapter: series expansion, power series, and limits. From the examples it will be clear that various series expansions such as Taylor series, Laurent series, Puisseux series, and Chebychev series are available in Maple. Padé and Chebychev-Padé are supported as well. When appropriate, these series expansions are used in computing limits [49].

11.1 Truncated Series Expansions

Taylor series expansions of univariate functions are easily and quickly computed computed with Maple. For example, in a very short time you can compute the Taylor series of $\sin(\tan x) - \tan(\sin x)$ about $x = 0$ up to order twenty-five.

```
> taylor( sin(tan(x)) - tan(sin(x)), x=0, 25 );
```

$$-\frac{1}{30} x^7 - \frac{29}{756} x^9 - \frac{1913}{75600} x^{11} - \frac{95}{7392} x^{13} - \frac{311148869}{54486432000}$$

$$x^{15} - \frac{10193207}{4358914560} x^{17} - \frac{1664108363}{1905468364800} x^{19} -$$

$$\frac{2097555460001}{7602818775552000} x^{21} - \frac{374694625074883}{6690480522485760000} x^{23} +$$

$$O(x^{25})$$

You only have to specify the function, the variable, the expansion point, and the truncation order in the call to the procedure **taylor**. The order symbol $O(x^{25})$ indicates that Maple has a special internal data structure for series expansions.

```
> whattype(");
```
$$series$$

The data type is also the name of a corresponding procedure **series**. This procedure can be used for more general truncated series expansions, e.g., for computing a Laurent series.

```
> series( GAMMA(x), x=0, 2 );
```

$$x^{-1} - \gamma + \left(\frac{1}{12} \pi^2 + \frac{1}{2} \gamma^2 \right) x + O(x^2)$$

The truncation order to which the Taylor series expansion is computed can be obtained by inspection of the order symbol or by the procedure **order**.

```
> order(");
```

$$2$$

The third argument of the **series** procedure may be left out. Maple then uses the value of the environment variable Order to determine the truncation order. Its default value is equal to six.

```
> Order;
```

$$6$$

```
> Order := 3: series( f(x), x=a );
```

$$f(a) + D(f)(a) (x - a) + \frac{1}{2} D^{(2)}(f)(a) (x - a)^2$$

$$+ O\left((x - a)^3 \right)$$

```
> series( f(x)/(x-a)^2, x=a );
```

$$f(a) (x - a)^{-2} + D(f)(a) (x - a)^{-1} +$$

$$\frac{1}{2} D^{(2)}(f)(a) + O(x - a)$$

```
> series( 1/(cos(x)-sec(x)), x=0 );
```

$$2$$

The last example illustrates that the "truncation order of a Laurent series" is only the order used by Maple during the series computation; fewer terms may be present in the final answer. It is like loosing precision in numerical arithmetic. The opposite can happen as well in series expansions.

```
> series( 1/(1-x^2), x=0, 5 );
```

$$1 + \frac{1}{2}\, x^2 + \frac{13}{24}\, x^4 + O(\,x^6\,)$$

Although we only ask for the series expansion up to order 5, Maple decides on its own that the fifth order term is equal to zero, and it informs you about this. In most cases the reason is that through the `remember` option Maple keeps track of previously computed expansions of larger order. For example, after the command `series( cos(x), x=0, 25 )`, the expansion of the cosine function will always be at least up to twenty-five terms.

If you want to restrict yourself to Laurent series, use the procedure **laurent** from the *numapprox* package. Otherwise, Maple may yield more general series such as Puisseux series.

```
> 1 / ( x * (1+sqrt(x)) );
```

$$\frac{1}{x\left(1 + \sqrt{x}\,\right)}$$

```
> series(",x);
```

$$\frac{1}{x} - \frac{1}{\sqrt{x}} + 1 - \sqrt{x} + x - x^{3/2} + x^2 - x^{5/2} + O(\,x^3\,)$$

Sometimes Maple chooses coefficients in a series expansion which depend on the main variable.

```
> series( x^(x^x), x=0, 5 );
```

$$x + \ln\!\left(\frac{1}{x}\right)^2 x^2 + \left(-\frac{1}{2}\ln\!\left(\frac{1}{x}\right)^3 + \frac{1}{2}\ln\!\left(\frac{1}{x}\right)^4\right) x^3 +$$

$$\left(\frac{1}{6}\ln\!\left(\frac{1}{x}\right)^4 - \frac{1}{2}\ln\!\left(\frac{1}{x}\right)^5 + \frac{1}{6}\ln\!\left(\frac{1}{x}\right)^6\right) x^4 + O(\,x^5\,)$$

```
> series( dilog(x), x=0, 3 );
```

$$\frac{1}{6}\,\pi^2 + \left(-\ln\!\left(\frac{1}{x}\right) - 1\right) x + \left(-\frac{1}{2}\ln\!\left(\frac{1}{x}\right) - \frac{1}{4}\right) x^2 + O(\,x^3\,)$$

The growth of a coefficient in such *generalized series expansions* [49] must be less than the polynomial in x.

A nice feature of Maple is that it can compute a truncated series expansion of a function which is only defined by an integral. An example:

```
> integrate( ln(1+s*t)/(1+t^2), t=0..infinity );
```

$$\int_0^\infty \frac{\ln(1 + s\,t)}{1 + t^2}\,dt$$

```
> series( ", s=0, 5 );
```

$$\left(\ln\left(\frac{1}{s}\right) + 1\right) s + \frac{1}{4}\,\pi\,s^2 + \left(-\frac{1}{3}\ln\left(\frac{1}{s}\right) - \frac{1}{9}\right) s^3 - \frac{1}{8}\,\pi\,s^4$$

$$+\ O(s^5)$$

The above series expansion is computed in three steps:

- differentiate the integrand with respect to s and integrate it,
- compute the series expansion of the intermediate result at $s = 0$, and
- integrate the terms of the series expansion and determine the correct integration constant.

The order symbol vanishes in the case of polynomials — at least when the truncation order of the series expansion is high enough.

```
> polynomial := a*x^3+b*x^2+c*x+d;
```

$$polynomial := a\,x^3 + b\,x^2 + c\,x + d$$

```
> taylor_series := series( polynomial, x, 4 );
```

$$taylor\_series := d + c\,x + b\,x^2 + a\,x^3$$

```
> convert( (x+y)^6, ´series´, x ); # infinite order
```

$$y^6 + 6\,y^5\,x + 15\,y^4\,x^2 + 20\,y^3\,x^3 + 15\,y^2\,x^4 + 6\,y\,x^5 +$$

$$x^6$$

Although a series expansion looks like a polynomial, certainly in the last examples, the internal data structure is completely different.

```
> whattype( polynomial );
```

$$+$$

```
> op( polynomial );
```

$$a\,x^3,\ b\,x^2,\ c\,x,\ d$$

```
> whattype( taylor_series );
```

$$series$$

```
> op( taylor_series );
```

$$d, \ 0, \ c, \ 1, \ b, \ 2, \ a, \ 3$$

```
> op( 0, taylor_series );   # the main variable
```

$$x$$

Objects of type *series* are dealt with differently in Maple; all kinds of operations allowed for polynomials do not work for series expansions.

```
> sin_series := series( sin(x), x=0, 6 );
```

$$sin\_series := x - \frac{1}{6} x^3 + \frac{1}{120} x^5 + O(x^6)$$

```
> subs( x=2,  sin_series );
Error, invalid substitution in series
> sin_series * sin_series;
```

$$\left(x - \frac{1}{6} x^3 + \frac{1}{120} x^5 + O(x^6) \right)^2$$

```
> expand(");
```

$$\left(x - \frac{1}{6} x^3 + \frac{1}{120} x^5 + O(x^6) \right)^2$$

```
> series(",x);
```

$$x^2 + O(x^4)$$

Some of these difficulties have been removed with the procedure **mtaylor**, fit for multivariate Taylor series expansions. The reason is that the result type of **mtaylor** is not a series but an ordinary polynomial.

However, you normalize series expansions with **normal** and extract coefficients with respect to the main variable with **coeff**.

```
> F := (3*x*y-2*y^2)*(3*x+y)/(6*x^2-6*y);
```

$$F := \frac{(3 \ x \ y \ - \ 2 \ y^2) \ (3 \ x \ + \ y)}{6 \ x^2 \ - \ 6 \ y}$$

```
> series( F, x=0, 4 );
```

$$\frac{1}{3} y^2 + \frac{1}{2} y \ x - \frac{1}{6} \frac{9 \ y \ - \ 2 \ y^2}{y} x^2 + \frac{1}{2} x^3 + O(x^4)$$

```
> normal(");
```

$$\frac{1}{3} y^2 + \frac{1}{2} y x + \left(-\frac{3}{2} + \frac{1}{3} y\right) x^2 + \frac{1}{2} x^3 + O(x^4)$$

```
> coeff( ", x^2 );
```

$$-\frac{3}{2} + \frac{1}{3} y$$

You can only extract coefficients in the main variable.

```
> coeff( "", y^2 );
```

```
Error, unable to compute coeff
```

With the procedure **coeftayl**, you can compute a coefficient in a Taylor series expansion without actually computing the series. Instead,

$$\textbf{coeftayl}(f, x = x_0, k)$$

computes the coefficient of $(x - x_0)^k$ in the series expansion of f about $x = x_0$ as

$$\lim_{x \to x_0} \frac{\frac{d^k f}{d x^k}(x)}{k!} \ .$$

```
> readlib(coeftayl)( F, x=0, 20 );
```

$$-\frac{3}{2} \frac{1}{y^9} + \frac{1}{3} \frac{1}{y^8}$$

You can also differentiate and integrate a series.

```
> sin_series;
```

$$x - \frac{1}{6} x^3 + \frac{1}{120} x^5 + O(x^6)$$

```
> diff( sin_series, x);
```

$$1 - \frac{1}{2} x^2 + \frac{1}{24} x^4 + O(x^5)$$

```
> integrate( sin_series, x);
```

$$\frac{1}{2} x^2 - \frac{1}{24} x^4 + \frac{1}{720} x^6 + O(x^7)$$

Series reversion can be done with the Maple procedure **solve**.

```
> solve( y = sin_series, x );
```

$$y + \frac{1}{6}\, y^3 + \frac{3}{40}\, y^5 + O(\,y^6\,)$$

```
> arcsin_series := series( arcsin(y), y=0, 6 );
```

$$arcsin\_series := y + \frac{1}{6}\, y^3 + \frac{3}{40}\, y^5 + O(\,y^6\,)$$

A problem in applied mathematics, which can be solved as a problem of series reversion, is the computation of the series expansion of the solution for Kepler's equation (q.v., [4]). We are interested in the series expansion of the solution for E, as a function of u and e, of the implicit equation

$$E = u + e\sin E\,,$$

where e is to be regarded as a small quantity, typically the eccentricity of an elliptic orbit.

Note that we cannot use the variable E in Maple as it is reserved for the base of the natural logarithm. Therefore we shall consider the equation $A = u + e\sin A$. We shall also write the coefficients in the expansion as linear combinations of trigonometric functions.

```
> series( A - u - e*sin(A), A=u );
```

$$- e\,\sin(u) + (1 - e\,\cos(u))\,(A - u) +$$

$$\frac{1}{2}\,e\,\sin(u)\,(A - u)^2 + \frac{1}{6}\,e\,\cos(u)\,(A - u)^3 -$$

$$\frac{1}{24}\,e\,\sin(u)\,(A - u)^4 - \frac{1}{120}\,e\,\cos(u)\,(A - u)^5$$

$$+ O\!\left((A - u)^6\right)$$

```
> solve( ", A-u );
```

$$\sin(u)\,e + \cos(u)\,\sin(u)\,e^2 +$$

$$\left(- \frac{1}{2}\,\sin(u)^3 + \cos(u)^2\,\sin(u)\right)e^3 +$$

$$\left(- \frac{5}{3}\,\cos(u)\,\sin(u)^3 + \cos(u)^3\,\sin(u)\right)e^4 + \Bigg($$

$$\frac{13}{24} \sin(u)^5 - \frac{11}{3} \cos(u)^2 \sin(u)^3$$

$$+ \cos(u)^4 \sin(u) \bigg) e^5 + O(e^6), \quad - \frac{e}{-1 + e} u -$$

$$\frac{1}{6} \frac{e}{(-1 + e)^4} u^3 - \frac{1}{120} \frac{e(1 + 9e)}{(-1 + e)^7} u^5 + O(u^6)$$

```
> # simplify the expansion of A in e
> u + map( combine, "[1], ´trig´ );
```

$$u + \bigg(\sin(u) \, e + \frac{1}{2} \sin(2\,u) \, e^2 +$$

$$\bigg(\frac{3}{8} \sin(3\,u) - \frac{1}{8} \sin(u) \bigg) e^3 +$$

$$\bigg(\frac{1}{3} \sin(4\,u) - \frac{1}{6} \sin(2\,u) \bigg) e^4 +$$

$$\bigg(\frac{125}{384} \sin(5\,u) - \frac{27}{128} \sin(3\,u) + \frac{1}{192} \sin(u) \bigg) e^5$$

$$+ O(e^6) \bigg)$$

In many computations it is convenient to convert series expansions into polynomials. This is a simple matter.

```
> sin_series;
```

$$x - \frac{1}{6} x^3 + \frac{1}{120} x^5 + O(x^6)$$

```
> convert( sin_series, ´polynom´ );
```

$$x - \frac{1}{6} x^3 + \frac{1}{120} x^5$$

Padé approximations and continued fraction series expansions, i.e., approximations by rational functions, are also available in Maple. You can use the procedure **convert** or the procedures **pade** and **confracform** from the *numapprox* package (if you don't want to compute a series expansion first).

```
> convert( sin_series, ´ratpoly´ );
```

$$\frac{-\dfrac{7}{60}\,x^3 + x}{1 + \dfrac{1}{20}\,x^2}$$

```
> convert( sin_series, `ratpoly`, 1, 3);
```

$$\frac{x}{1 + \dfrac{1}{6}\,x^2}$$

```
> convert( sin_series, `confrac` );
```

$$\frac{x}{1 + \dfrac{x^2}{6 - \dfrac{7}{10}\,x^2}}$$

These approximations can be used in conjunction with the so-called Chebyshev series expansion.

```
> Digits := 5:
> chebyshev( sin(x), x); # Chebyshev expansion
```

$$.88010\ T(\,1,\ x\,)\ -\ .039127\ T(\,3,\ x\,)$$

$$+\ .00049952\ T(\,5,\ x\,)\ -\ .30152\ 10^{-5}\ T(\,7,\ x\,)$$

```
> convert( ", `ratpoly` );
```

$$\frac{.89083\ T(\,1,\ x\,)\ -\ .027887\ T(\,3,\ x\,)}{T(\,0,\ x\,)\ +\ .025529\ T(\,2,\ x\,)}$$

```
> with( orthopoly, T ):   "";
```

$$\frac{.97449\ x\ -\ .11155\ x^3}{.97447\ +\ .051058\ x^2}$$

Maple is liberal with respect to conversion to polynomials.

```
> series( sin(x+a)/x^2, x, 4 );
```

$$\sin(\,a\,)\ x^{-2}\ +\ \cos(\,a\,)\ x^{-1}\ -\ \frac{1}{2}\,\sin(\,a\,)\ -\ \frac{1}{6}\,\cos(\,a\,)\ x\ +$$

$$O(\,x^2\,)$$

```
> convert ( ", `polynom` );
```

$$\frac{\sin(a)}{x^2} + \frac{\cos(a)}{x} - \frac{1}{2}\sin(a) - \frac{1}{6}\cos(a)\ x$$

But some conversions are too much for Maple.

```
> series( sqrt(x*(1-x)) , x=0 , 2 );
```

$$\sqrt{x} - \frac{1}{2}\ x^{3/2} + O(\ x^{5/2}\ )$$

```
> convert (", `polynom` );
```

$$\sqrt{x} - \frac{1}{2}\ x^{3/2} + O(\ x^{5/2}\ )$$

Here, Maple keeps the order symbol in the conversion. The reason is that Maple represents a Puisseux series internally not as an object of type series but as an object of type `+`.

```
> whattype(""), whattype(");
```

$$+,\ +$$

This is lack of consistency in Maple. But we can assist the system in this case.

```
> eval( subs( O=0, "" ) );
```

$$\sqrt{x} - \frac{1}{2}\ x^{3/2}$$

The same inconsistency in data representation occurs in the case of an asymptotic series expansion.

```
> (a*x^3+b*x^2)/(x^2+1);
```

$$\frac{a\ x^3 + b\ x^2}{x^2 + 1}$$

```
> asympt (",x,8);
```

$$a\ x + b - \frac{a}{x} - \frac{b}{x^2} + \frac{a}{x^3} + \frac{b}{x^4} - \frac{a}{x^5} - \frac{b}{x^6} + \frac{a}{x^7}$$

$$+\ O\!\left(\frac{1}{x^8}\right)$$

```
> whattype(");
```

$$+$$

The second last command is equivalent to

```
> taylor( (a*x^3+b*x^2)/(x^2+1) , x=infinity, 8 );
```

$$a\ x\ +\ b\ -\ \frac{a}{x}\ -\ \frac{b}{x^2}\ +\ \frac{a}{x^3}\ +\ \frac{b}{x^4}\ -\ \frac{a}{x^5}\ -\ \frac{b}{x^6}\ +\ \frac{a}{x^7}$$

$$+\ O\!\left(\frac{1}{x^8}\right)$$

Essentially, the asymptotic expansion is computed in three steps:

- if x is the main variable, substitute $\dfrac{1}{x}$ for x,
- compute the series expansion at $x = 0$, and
- substitute again $\dfrac{1}{x}$ for x.

Stirling's formula is an example of an asymptotic series expansion of more general type.

```
> asympt( ln(GAMMA(x)), x, 4 );
```

$$(\ \ln(\ x\ )\ -\ 1\ )\ x\ +\ \ln\!\left(\sqrt{2}\ \sqrt{\pi}\ \right)\ -\ \frac{1}{2}\ \ln(\ x\ )\ +\ \frac{1}{12}\ \frac{1}{x}$$

$$+\ O\!\left(\frac{1}{x^3}\right)$$

```
> simplify(",´ln´); # simplification of logarithmic terms
```

$$(\ \ln(\ x\ )\ -\ 1\ )\ x\ +\ \frac{1}{2}\ \ln(\ 2\ )\ +\ \frac{1}{2}\ \ln(\ \pi\ )\ -\ \frac{1}{2}\ \ln(\ x\ )$$

$$+\ \frac{1}{12}\ \frac{1}{x}\ +\ O\!\left(\frac{1}{x^3}\right)$$

11.2 Power Series

The *powseries* package provides facilities for manipulation of formal power series. As with all Maple library packages it must be loaded first with the command

```
> with( powseries );
```

$$[\ add,\ compose,\ evalpow,\ inverse,\ multconst,$$

$$multiply,\ negative,\ powcreate,\ powdiff,\ powexp,$$

$$powint,\ powlog,\ powpoly,\ powsolve,\ quotient,$$

$$reversion,\ subtract,\ tpsform\ ]$$

You learn best about this package by example. Henceforth we shall consider the power series

$$\exp(ax) = \sum_{n=0}^{\infty} \frac{a^n}{n!} x^n \quad \text{and} \quad \ln(1+x) = \sum_{n=1}^{\infty} \frac{(-1)^{n+1}}{n} x^n$$

First, we define the two power series.

```
> powcreate( f(n)=a^n/n! ):
> powcreate( g(n)=(-1)^(n+1)/n, g(0)=0 ):
```

We have now specified the rules to compute coefficients in the power series. Let us ask for the first five terms with **tpsform** (truncated **power** series **form**).

```
> f_series := tpsform( f, x, 5 );
```

$$f\_series :=$$

$$1 + a\ x + \frac{1}{2}\ a^2\ x^2 + \frac{1}{6}\ a^3\ x^3 + \frac{1}{24}\ a^4\ x^4 + O(\ x^5\ )$$

```
> g_series := tpsform( g, x, 5 );
```

$$g\_series := x - \frac{1}{2}\ x^2 + \frac{1}{3}\ x^3 - \frac{1}{4}\ x^4 + O(\ x^5\ )$$

Let us do some manipulations with these power series: addition, multiplication, inversion with respect to multiplication, and composition, respectively.

```
> s := add(f,g): tpsform(s,x,3);
```

$$1 + (\ a + 1\ )\ x + \left(\frac{1}{2}\ a^2 - \frac{1}{2} \right) x^2 + O(\ x^3\ )$$

```
> p := multiply(f,g): tpsform(p,x,4);
```

$$x + \left(-\frac{1}{2} + a \right) x^2 + \left(\frac{1}{3} - \frac{1}{2} a + \frac{1}{2} a^2 \right) x^3 + O(x^4)$$

```
> i := inverse(f): tpsform(i,x,5);
```

$$1 - a\ x + \frac{1}{2} a^2\ x^2 - \frac{1}{6} a^3\ x^3 + \frac{1}{24} a^4\ x^4 + O(x^5)$$

```
> p := multiply(i,f): tpsform(p,x,10);
```

$$1 + O(x^{10})$$

```
> c := compose(f,g): tpsform(c,x,4);
```

$$1 + a\ x + \left(-\frac{1}{2} a + \frac{1}{2} a^2 \right) x^2 + \left(\frac{1}{3} a - \frac{1}{2} a^2 + \frac{1}{6} a^3 \right) x^3 +$$

$$O(x^4)$$

```
> a := 1: # special case, which may take a while
> c := compose(f,g): eval( tpsform(c,x,25) );
```

$$1 + x + O(x^{25})$$

The last result could have been obtained much more efficiently by

```
> c := powexp(g): tpsform(c,x,25);
```

$$1 + x + O(x^{25})$$

You can also apply the logarithmic function to a power series.

```
> a := ´a´: # reset a to a free variable
> r := powlog(f): tpsform(r,x,30);
```

$$a\ x + O(x^{30})$$

Other computations are differentiation and integration.

```
> d := powdiff(f): tpsform(d,x,4);
```

$$a + a^2\ x + \frac{1}{2} a^3\ x^2 + \frac{1}{6} a^4\ x^3 + O(x^4)$$

```
> i := powint(f): tpsform(i,x,4);
```

$$x + \frac{1}{2} a\ x^2 + \frac{1}{6} a^2\ x^3 + O(x^4)$$

Reversion of a power series with respect to composition is also easily done in Maple. We shall use the power series expansion of the function $\ln(1 + x)$ as our example; the reverse power series should be of the series expansion of $\exp(x) - 1$.

```
> r := reversion(g): tpsform(r,x,5);
```

$$x + \frac{1}{2} x^2 + \frac{1}{6} x^3 + \frac{1}{24} x^4 + O(x^5)$$

```
> c := compose(g,r): tpsform(c,x,5);
```

$$x + O(x^5)$$

```
> c := compose(r,g): tpsform(c,x,5);
```

$$x + O(x^5)$$

We end this section with the popular example of the computation of the "f and g series," which are used in certain expansions of elliptic motion in celestial mechanics (q.v., [44]). The coefficients of the series expansions are defined by the following recurrences.

$$f_n = -\mu g_{n-1} - \sigma(\mu + 2\epsilon)\frac{\partial f_{n-1}}{\partial \epsilon} + (\epsilon - 2\sigma^2)\frac{\partial f_{n-1}}{\partial \sigma} - 3\mu\sigma\frac{\partial f_{n-1}}{\partial \mu}, \quad f_0 = 1,$$

$$g_n = f_{n-1} - \sigma(\mu + 2\epsilon)\frac{\partial g_{n-1}}{\partial \epsilon} + (\epsilon - 2\sigma^2)\frac{\partial g_{n-1}}{\partial \sigma} - 3\mu\sigma\frac{\partial g_{n-1}}{\partial \mu}, \quad g_0 = 0.$$

First we define the coordinate functions.

```
> mu := (mu,sigma,epsilon) -> mu:
> sigma := (mu,sigma,epsilon) -> sigma:
> eps:= (mu,sigma,epsilon) -> epsilon:
```

Using the **D** operator, we can define the recurrence relations.

```
> with(powseries):
> powcreate( f(n) = -mu*g(n-1) - sigma*(mu+2*epsilon)
>     *D[3](f(n-1)) + (epsilon-2*sigma^2)*D[2](f(n-1))
>     - 3*mu*sigma*D[1](f(n-1)), f(0) = 1 ):
> powcreate( g(n) = f(n-1) - sigma*(mu+2*epsilon)
>     *D[3](g(n-1)) + (epsilon-2*sigma^2)*D[2](g(n-1))
>     - 3*mu*sigma*D[1](g(n-1)), g(0) = 0 ):
```

and compute the first terms of the series expansion.

```
> tpsform(f,T,5);
```

$$1 - \mu \ T^2 + 3 \ \mu \ \sigma \ T^3 + \left(\mu^2 + 3 \left(\varepsilon - 2 \ \sigma^2\right) \mu - 9 \ \mu \ \sigma^2\right) T^4$$
$$+ \ O(\ T^5\ )$$

There is a drawback. You would probably prefer to expand intermediate results, but when you define the recurrence relations in the **powcreate** command, there is no easy way to specify this. After the computation of the series you can simplify it.

```
> map(factor,");
```

$$1 - \mu \ T^2 + 3 \ \mu \ \sigma \ T^3 + \mu \left(\mu + 3 \ \varepsilon - 15 \ \sigma^2\right) T^4 + O(\ T^5\ )$$

The only trick to expanding intermediate results is based on the implementation details of the *powseries* package: before computing any truncated series expansion add the following statements.

```
> f(_k) := ´expand´( f(_k) ):   g(_k) := ´expand´( g(_k) ):
```

11.3 Limits

Internally, Maple often uses generalized series expansion for the computation of limits [49, 57]. For example, from the asymptotic series expansion

```
> ln(x) - ln(x+exp(-x));
```

$$\ln(\ x\ ) - \ln(\ x + e^{-x}\ )$$

```
> asympt(",x,3);
```

$$- \frac{1}{x \ e^x} + \frac{1}{2} \frac{1}{x^2 \ (e^x)^2} + \frac{1}{(e^x)^3} + O\left(\frac{1}{x^3}\right)$$

it is clear that

```
Limit( "", x=infinity ):   " = value(");
```

$$\lim_{x \to \infty} \ln(\ x\ ) - \ln(\ x + e^{-x}\ ) = 0$$

Here, we have used the **value** procedure to evaluate the call to the inert **Limit** procedure. What you see is that you don't have to worry much about details but only have to use the procedure **limit**.

You may specify some options to **limit**: `left`, `right`, `real`, and `complex`. An example:

```
> Limit( cos(x)^(1/x^3), x=0 ):    " = value(");
```

$$\lim_{x \to 0} \cos(x)^{\left(\frac{1}{x^3}\right)} = undefined$$

```
> Limit( cos(x)^(1/x^3), x=0, 'right' ):    " = value(");
```

$$\lim_{x \to 0+} \cos(x)^{\left(\frac{1}{x^3}\right)} = 0$$

```
> Limit( cos(x)^(1/x^3), x=0 , 'left' ):    " = value(");
```

$$\lim_{x \to 0-} \cos(x)^{\left(\frac{1}{x^3}\right)} = \infty$$

If the direction is not specified in **limit**, the limit is the real bidirectional limit (except in the case where the limit point is $+\infty$ or $-\infty$, in which case the limit is from the left and the right, respectively).

In some cases Maple needs more information. For example:

```
> y := exp(a*x)*cos(b*x);
```

$$y := e^{a\,x} \cos(b\,x)$$

```
> limit( y, x = -infinity );
```

$$\lim_{x \to (-\infty)} e^{a\,x} \cos(b\,x)$$

Of course Maple did not presume that we had in mind a positive value of a. We can assist Maple for the generic case by using a^2.

```
> y := exp(a^2*x)*cos(b*x);
```

$$y := e^{a^2\,x} \cos(b\,x)$$

```
> limit( y, x = -infinity );
```

$$0$$

But more elegantly, we could also have added the assumption

```
> assume( a>0 ):
```

before the computation of the limit.

```
> limit(  exp(a*x)*cos(b*x), x = -infinity );
```

$$0$$

11.4 Exercises

1. Compute the following limits and check the answers.

(a) $\displaystyle\lim_{x\to 0} \frac{\sin x}{x}$

(b) $\displaystyle\lim_{x\to 0} (\sin x)^{1/x}$

(c) $\displaystyle\lim_{x\to 0} \frac{1-\cos x}{x}$

(d) $\displaystyle\lim_{x\to\infty} (1+\frac{\pi}{x})^x$

(e) $\displaystyle\lim_{x\to 0} x^{\sin x}$

(f) $\displaystyle\lim_{x\to\infty} (2^x + 3^x)^{1/x}$

2. Compute the following limits.

(a) $\displaystyle\lim_{x\to\infty} \frac{\ln x}{x}$

(b) $\displaystyle\lim_{x\to\infty} \frac{\ln x}{e^x}$

(c) $\displaystyle\lim_{x\to\infty} \frac{x^2 + \sin x}{2x^2 + \cos 4x}$

(d) $\displaystyle\lim_{x\downarrow 0} \frac{2}{1+e^{-1/x}}$

(e) $\displaystyle\lim_{x\to\infty} \sinh(\tanh x) - \tanh(\sinh x)$

3. In a fresh Maple session or after the **restart** command, compute the Taylor series expansion of $x^3 - 1 - 4x^2 + 5x$ about $x = 1$ up to order 10. We do want you to enter the terms in the polynomial in the above ordering. Of what data type is the obtained expression? To what order does Maple think that the series expansion goes?

4. What is the asymptotic expansion of $\binom{2n}{n}$?

5. What is the power series expansion of Lambert's W function?

6. (a) Compute the Taylor series expansion of $\dfrac{1 - t^2}{1 - 2xt + t^2}$ about $x = 0$
   and $t = 0$ up to degree 8.

   (b) The Chebyshev polynomials $T_n(x)$ of the first kind are defined
   by the generating function

   $$\frac{1 - t^2}{1 - 2xt + t^2} = \sum_{n=0}^{\infty} \epsilon_n T_n(x) t^n \,,$$

   where $\epsilon_0 = 1$ and $\epsilon_n = 2$ for $n \geq 1$.
   Compute $T_2(x)$ and $T_{10}(x)$. Check your answer with the built-in
   command **orthopoly[T]**.

7. Find the Taylor series expansion up to order 25 of the solution for
   Kepler's equation $E = u + \sin E$ by use of the **RootOf** procedure.
   Compare the efficiency with the method described in the first section
   of this chapter.

8. When you study Josephson's junction circuit you may need the series
   expansion of the function ptan defined as

   $$\mathrm{ptan}(s) = p, \text{ if } p - \tan p = s\,.$$

   Compute the series expansion of this function.

Composite Data Types

Active knowledge of Maple data types is quite often needed even when using Maple interactively as a symbolic calculator. Recall the elementary data types *polynom* and *ratpoly*, and the simplification and manipulation of such expressions. This chapter will introduce you to *composite data types* like *sequence, set, list,* and *array*, which are built from elementary data types and used for grouping objects together.

12.1 Sequence

You have seen objects of type *exprseq* (*expr*ession *seq*uence) before. For example, the result of the **op** function is in most cases a sequence — objects separated by commas.

```
> polynomial := x^3 - 6*x^2 + 11*x - 6;
```
$$polynomial := x^3 - 6\ x^2 + 11\ x - 6$$

```
> sequence := op( polynomial );
```
$$sequence := x^3,\ -6\ x^2,\ 11\ x,\ -6$$

Sequences are frequently used in Maple. Below, not only the result of the command `solve( polynomial, x )` is a sequence, but also the arguments of the function call form a sequence.

```
> arguments := polynomial, x;
```
$$arguments := x^3 - 6\ x^2 + 11\ x - 6,\ x$$

```
> whattype( arguments );
```
$$exprseq$$

```
> solve( arguments );
```
$$1,\ 2,\ 3$$

Note that a sequence is one object: internally it is represented by one data vector, viz.,

exprseq	↑ expr1	↑ expr2	↑ expr3	↑ expr4	. . . .

Here, the symbols ↑expr1, ↑expr2, ... indicate pointers to the data vectors which correspond to the expressions expr1, expr2, and so on. The components of an expression sequence are not necessarily of the same type.

```
> seq1 := H, e, c, k:  # author´s name
> seq2 := 72, 101, 99, 107: # author´s name in ASCII code
> `concatenated sequence` := seq1, seq2;

  concatenated sequence := H, e, c, k, 72, 101, 99, 107
```

Maple uses the special name NULL to denote the empty sequence.

```
> `empty sequence`:= NULL;

                    empty sequence :=

> 1, 2, `empty sequence`, 2, 1;

                        1, 2, 2, 1
```

Sequences can also be generated by the **seq** function.

```
> # generate the first nine odd prime numbers
> seq( ithprime(i), i = 2..10 );

            3, 5, 7, 11, 13, 17, 19, 23, 29
```

A function call of the form **seq(** $f(i)$, $i = m \ldots n$ **)** generates the sequence $f(m)$, $f(m+1)$, $f(m+2)$, ..., $f(n)$. Alternatively, Maple provides the sequence operator **$**.

```
> x$4;

                    x, x, x, x
```

Except for the above use in combination with a function call of **diff**, the sequence operator **$** is of limited use. It may even be dangerous to use.

```
> (´[k,l] $ k=1..2´) $ l=3..4;

        [ 1, 3 ], [ 2, 3 ], [ 1, 4 ], [ 2, 4 ]
```

In this example, the quotes are absolutely necessary to prevent premature evaluation, and more quotes would be needed if the sequence indices k and l had been assigned values before. In the worst case, you would have had to enter a horrible command like

```
> (´[´k´,´l´] $ ´k´=1..2´) $ ´l´=3..4:
```

Instead, you would certainly prefer the command

```
seq( seq( [i,j], i = 1..2 ), j = 3..4 ):
```

The call **seq**($f(i)$, $i = expression$) generates a sequence by applying f to each operand of the *expression*.

```
> seq( i^2, i = { 1, 2, 3, 4, 5 } );
```
$$1, \ 4, \ 9, \ 16, \ 25$$
```
> seq( i^2, i = x + y + z );
```
$$x^2, \ y^2, \ z^2$$

You select an element of a sequence by the selection operator [].

```
> "[2];
```
$$y^2$$

You can also select more than one element of a sequence at the same time.

```
> sequence := v, w, x, y, z:   sequence[ 2..4 ];
```
$$w, \ x, \ y$$

You may consider the last command as an abbreviation of

```
> seq( sequence[i], i = 2..4 );
```
$$w, \ x, \ y$$

Such abbreviations also occur at other places, e.g., when you want to generate a sequence of names *p1*, *p2*, ... with

```
> p.( 1..5 );
```
$$p1, \ p2, \ p3, \ p4, \ p5$$

```
> seq( p.i, i = 1..5 );
```
$$p1, \ p2, \ p3, \ p4, \ p5$$

We end this section with a short remark on the subexpression of the form

$$left\_expression \ .. \ right\_expression$$

It is a regular Maple expression of type *range*. You have already seen such expressions being used as range specifications for integration and summation. You may choose any Maple expression as *left_* and *right_expression*, but in most cases it should evaluate to a numerical value. By the way, you may use more than two dots as the range operator; but remember that *one dot* is used as the concatenation operator.

12.2 Set

You use objects of type *set* most fequently when you try to solve systems of equations with the Maple procedure **solve**. The arguments of this procedure are a set of equations and a set of unknowns, and the solution is in general a sequence of objects of type *set*.

Maple uses the common mathematical notation of a set: a sequence between braces. Data do not occur more than once in a set. As a user you have almost no control on the ordering of the elements of a set, because the system uses internal address ordering.

```
> { 1, 3, 5, 2, 4 }; # used earlier in increasing ordering
```
$$\{\, 1,\ 2,\ 3,\ 4,\ 5\, \}$$

```
> { x, x, x*y, x*(x-1), y*x, x^2-x };
```
$$\{\, x,\ x\,y,\ x\,(\,x\,-\,1\,),\ x^2\,-\,x\, \}$$

```
> `empty set` := {};
```
$$empty\ set := \{\quad\}$$

Internally a set is represented by

The entries in the expression sequence are sorted in increasing address order. In this way, it can be assured that no duplicates are present.

For objects of type *set* the usual operators are present: **union, minus,** and **intersect**.

```
> {0,1,2,3} union {0,2,4,6};
```
$$\{\, 0,\ 1,\ 2,\ 3,\ 4,\ 6\, \}$$

```
> {0,1,2,3} minus {0,2,4,6};
```
$$\{\, 1,\ 3\, \}$$

```
> {0,1,2,3} intersect {0,2,4,6};
```

$$\{\ 0,\ 2\ \}$$

You can ask whether a certain Maple object is an element of a set, and if so, find its position in the set.

```
> member( 2, {0,1,2,3}, ´pos´ );
```

true

```
> pos;
```

3

You can select an element of a set by the selection operator [ ] or by the function **op**.

```
> # generate all subsets of {1,2,3}
> collection := combinat[powerset](3);
```

collection := { { }, { 1, 2, 3 }, { 1 }, { 1, 3 },

{ 2, 3 }, { 3 }, { 2 }, { 1, 2 } }

```
> nops( collection ); # number of elements in the set
```

8

```
> collection[4];
```

{ 1, 3 }

```
> collection[6..8]; ▪
```

{ 3 }, { 2 }, { 1, 2 }

```
> op( 8, collection );
```

{ 1, 2 }

If you want to select elements of a set which meet some criterion, then the Maple function **select** is helpful. A few examples:

```
> die := rand(-10..10):
> numberset := { ´die()´ $ 10 };
```

numberset := { -4, -5, -6, 6, 7, -8, 8, 10 }

```
> select( isprime, numberset ); # select prime numbers
```

{ 7 }

```
> # select nonnegative integers
```

```
> select ( type, numberset, ´nonnegint´ );
```

$$\{ 6, 7, 8, 10 \}$$

```
> select ( x -> x > -5, numberset ); # select numbers > -5
```

$$\{ -4, 6, 7, 8, 10 \}$$

The general format is

select(*criterion, set, extra arguments*).

The selection criterion should always return a boolean value *true* or *false*. Extra arguments of the selection criterion are always added after the set from which elements will be selected.

12.3 List

You can construct an object of type *list* by enclosing a sequence in square brackets. You have already seen such objects being used as arguments in **collect** to specify the ordering of variables in polynomials.

```
> 1 + x + y^2 + z^3 + x^2*y^2 + x^2*z^3 + y^3*z^3;
```

$$1 + x + y^2 + z^3 + x^2 \; y^2 + x^2 \; z^3 + y^3 \; z^3$$

```
> collect ( ", [ x, y, z ] );
```

$$(y^2 + z^3) \; x^2 + x + 1 + y^2 + z^3 + y^3 \; z^3$$

```
> collect ( ", [ z, y, x ] );
```

$$(x^2 + 1 + y^3) \; z^3 + (x^2 + 1) \; y^2 + x + 1$$

Important differences between objects of type *list* and *set* are that in a list the same objects may occur more than once and that the ordering of the elements of a list is preserved.

```
> [ x, x, x*y, x*(x-1), y*x, x^2-x ];
```

$$[x, \; x, \; x \; y, \; x \; (x - 1), \; x \; y, \; x^2 - x]$$

```
> sort ("); # sort by machine address
```

$$[x, \; x, \; x \; y, \; x \; y, \; x \; (x - 1), \; x^2 - x]$$

```
> convert (", ´set´);
```

$$\{ x, \; x \; y, \; x \; (x - 1), \; x^2 - x \}$$

```
> [ x$5 ];   # list of five x´ses
```

$$[x, \ x, \ x, \ x, \ x]$$

```
> `empty list` := [];
```

$$empty \ list := [\quad]$$

The internal structure of a list is similar to that of a set.

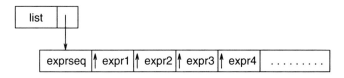

Below, the most frequently used operations on lists are listed and examples show how they can be carried out in Maple.

- Find the length of a list.

```
> cl := [ black, red, green, yellow, blue, white ]:
> nops( cl );   # number of colors
```

$$6$$

- Search for an element in a list.

```
> member( indigo, cl );
```

$$false$$

```
> member( blue, cl, ´pos´ );
```

$$true$$

```
> pos;
```

$$5$$

- Select one or more elements.

```
> cl[5];
```

$$blue$$

```
> op(5,cl);
```

$$blue$$

```
> cl[3..6];
```

$$green, \ yellow, \ blue, \ white$$

```
> # special cases: drop the first or the last element:
```

```
> [ cl[ 2 .. nops(cl) ] ];
```
> > [*red*, *green*, *yellow*, *blue*, *white*]

```
> subsop( 1 = NULL, cl );
```
> > [*red*, *green*, *yellow*, *blue*, *white*]

```
> [ cl[ 1 .. nops(cl)-1 ] ];
```
> > [*black*, *red*, *green*, *yellow*, *blue*]

```
> subsop( nops(cl) = NULL, cl );
```
> > [*black*, *red*, *green*, *yellow*, *blue*]

- Prepend, append, and insert elements.

```
> [ crimson, op(cl) ];
```
> [*crimson*, *black*, *red*, *green*, *yellow*, *blue*, *white*]

```
> [ op(cl), crimson ];
```
> [*black*, *red*, *green*, *yellow*, *blue*, *white*, *crimson*]

```
> [ cl[1..3], crimson, cl[4..nops(cl)] ];
```
> [*black*, *red*, *green*, *crimson*, *yellow*, *blue*, *white*]

- Concatenate lists.

```
> cl2 := [ crimson, indigo ]:  [ op(cl), op(cl2) ];
```
> > [*black*, *red*, *green*, *yellow*, *blue*, *white*, *crimson*,
> > > *indigo*]

- Replace one element in a list.

```
> subsop( 5 = indigo, cl );
```
> > [*black*, *red*, *green*, *yellow*, *indigo*, *white*]

- Replace all specified elements in a list.

```
> subs( blue = crimson, cl ); # replace every color blue
```
> > [*black*, *red*, *green*, *yellow*, *crimson*, *white*]

- Rearrange lists.

```
> # sort the list (in lexicographic ordering)
> sort( cl, `lexorder` );  # variable cl is not changed
```
        [*black*, *blue*, *green*, *red*, *white*, *yellow*]

```
> # reverse the list
> [ seq( cl[ nops(cl)-i+1 ], i=1..nops(cl) ) ];
```
        [*white*, *blue*, *yellow*, *green*, *red*, *black*]

```
> # rotate the list one position to the left or right
> [ cl[2..nops(cl)], cl[1] ];
```
        [*red*, *green*, *yellow*, *blue*, *white*, *black*]

```
> [ cl[nops(cl)], cl[1..nops(cl)-1] ];
```
        [*white*, *black*, *red*, *green*, *yellow*, *blue*]

Using a few basic Maple functions and constructs you can carry out most operations on lists so easily that the designers of Maple have chosen not to waste function names for these operations. If you wish, you can easily transcribe the above examples into Maple procedures. For example, the last two operations could be transcribed into procedures in the following way.

```
> rotateleft := proc(l:list)
>    [ l[2..nops(l)], l[1] ]
> end:
> rotateright := proc(l:list)
>    [ l[nops(l)], l[1..nops(l)-1] ]
> end:
> rotateleft( cl );
```
        [*red*, *green*, *yellow*, *blue*, *white*, *black*]

```
> rotateright( cl );
```
        [*white*, *black*, *red*, *green*, *yellow*, *blue*]

```
> (rotateright@@3)( cl ); # rotate 3 places to the right
```
        [*yellow*, *blue*, *white*, *black*, *red*, *green*]

```
> (rotateleft@rotateright)( cl ); # do nothing

      [ black, red, green, yellow, blue, white ]
```

12.4 Array

This section is a short introduction to the data type *array*, and related objects like *vectors* and *matrices*. In §17.2 we shall describe in more detail how tables and arrays are evaluated. In this section, we restrict ourselves to the construction of these data structures.

Like conventional programming languages, Maple has a data structure for one-, two-, or multi-dimensional arrays. Below is an example of an object of type *array*.

```
> array( -1..1, 0..1,

>    [ (-1,0)=a,  (-1,1)=b,  (0,0)=c,  (0,1)=d ] );

    array(-1 .. 1, 0 .. 1, [

            ( -1,  0 ) = a

            ( -1,  1 ) = b

            ( 0,  0 ) = c

            ( 0,  1 ) = d

            ( 1,  0 ) = ?[ 1, 0 ]

            ( 1,  1 ) = ?[ 1, 1 ]

            ])
```

Firstly, the ranges of the indices of the two-dimensional array are specified. Secondly, some, but not necessarily all, array elements are assigned values. Be careful not to mess up the round and square brackets: this is a little bit confusing, as selection of array elements is done by square brackets.

The data type *array* is actually a special case of the data type *table*, which is frequently used by Maple itself (e.g., remember tables of procedures). Characteristic of the data type *array* is the use of a Cartesian product of segments of contiguous integers as the set of allowed indices.

At first sight, the data type *array* is similar to the data type *list*. This is reflected in the way objects of type *array* can be constructed from

objects of type *list*. Below, a one-, two- and three-dimensional array are
constructed.

```
> v := array( [1+a,2+b,3+c] );
```
$$v := [\, 1 + a \quad 2 + b \quad 3 + c \,]$$

```
> type( v, 'list' );
```
$$false$$

```
> type( v, 'array' );
```
$$true$$

```
> M := array( [ [1-p,2-q], [1-r,2-s] ] );
```
$$M := \begin{bmatrix} 1 - p & 2 - q \\ 1 - r & 2 - s \end{bmatrix}$$

```
> d := array( [ [ [1,2], [3,4] ], [ [5,6], [8,9] ],
>    [ [10,11], [12,13] ] ] );
```

$$d := array(1 \,..\, 3, \, 1 \,..\, 2, \, 1 \,..\, 2, \, [$$

$$(1, \ 1, \ 1) = 1$$

$$(1, \ 1, \ 2) = 2$$

$$(1, \ 2, \ 1) = 3$$

$$(1, \ 2, \ 2) = 4$$

$$(2, \ 1, \ 1) = 5$$

$$(2, \ 1, \ 2) = 6$$

$$(2, \ 2, \ 1) = 8$$

$$(2, \ 2, \ 2) = 9$$

$$(3, \ 1, \ 1) = 10$$

$$(3, \ 1, \ 2) = 11$$

$$(3, \ 2, \ 1) = 12$$

$$(3, \ 2, \ 2) = 13$$

$$])$$

By entering the array elements through lists (or lists of lists) a lot of typing
is avoided. Furthermore, if you leave out the ranges of indices, Maple

determines the index ranges from the lengths of the lists, assuming that the ranges start at one. You can see this in the example of a three-dimensional array — the index range is explicitly mentioned in the output. One- and two-dimensional arrays whose index ranges start at one are most frequently used as vectors and matrices, respectively. Hence, the typical vector- and matrix-notation is used.

```
> type( v, ´vector´ ),   type( M, ´matrix´ );
```

$$true, \ true$$

When you start working with vectors and matrices it is important to know that, although they are printed horizontally, Maple considers vectors as column vectors. In this respect it is somewhat incongruous that Maple considers a matrix as a list of row vectors when we enter the matrix elements, i.e., Maple uses like most programming languages row major order.

You could also have constructed the above matrix M and vector v by the commands **matrix** and **vector** from the *linalg* package.

```
> with( linalg ):
Warning: new definition for    norm
Warning: new definition for    trace
> M := matrix( [ [ 1-p, 2-q ], [ 1-r, 2-s ] ] );
```

$$M := \begin{bmatrix} 1-p & 2-q \\ 1-r & 2-s \end{bmatrix}$$

```
> v := vector( [ 1+a, 2+b, 3+c ] );
```

$$v := [\, 1+a \quad 2+b \quad 3+c \,]$$

Sometimes you just want to declare a vector without specifying the elements. This is no problem in Maple.

```
> vec := vector(100);
```

$$vec := array(\, 1 \ .. \ 100, \ [\ \ ] \,)$$

```
> vec := array(-1000..1000, [] );
```

$$vec := array(\, -1000 \ .. \ 1000, \ [\ \ ] \,)$$

Furthermore, matrices can be conveniently constructed with the help of index functions. For example, a 4×4 Hilbert matrix can be made by

```
> h := (i,j) -> 1/(i+j-x); # index function
```

$$h := (i, j) \rightarrow \frac{1}{i + j - x}$$

```
> matrix( 4, 4, h );
```

$$\begin{bmatrix} \dfrac{1}{2-x} & \dfrac{1}{3-x} & \dfrac{1}{4-x} & \dfrac{1}{5-x} \\ \dfrac{1}{3-x} & \dfrac{1}{4-x} & \dfrac{1}{5-x} & \dfrac{1}{6-x} \\ \dfrac{1}{4-x} & \dfrac{1}{5-x} & \dfrac{1}{6-x} & \dfrac{1}{7-x} \\ \dfrac{1}{5-x} & \dfrac{1}{6-x} & \dfrac{1}{7-x} & -\dfrac{1}{8-x} \end{bmatrix}$$

In this case, you could also have used the built-in function **linalg[hilbert]**. Another example is the construction of a zero matrix.

```
> matrix( 3, 3, 0 );
```

$$\begin{bmatrix} 0 & 0 & 0 \\ 0 & 0 & 0 \\ 0 & 0 & 0 \end{bmatrix}$$

In this function call, 0 means the zero function.

The procedure **array** has options available for matrices of special form.

```
> M := array( symmetric, 1..2, 1..2 ):   M[1,2]:=1:
> print(M);
```

$$\begin{bmatrix} M_{[1,\ 1]} & 1 \\ 1 & M_{[2,\ 2]} \end{bmatrix}$$

```
> v := array( sparse, 1..10):   v[1]:=1:   v[5]:=-1:
> print(v);
```

$$[1\quad 0\quad 0\quad 0\quad -1\quad 0\quad 0\quad 0\quad 0\quad 0]$$

Other options are antisymmetric, identity, and diagonal. Only one option can be specified, and only in the function **array** — not in **matrix** or **vector**. The role of these options is to indicate how matrix entries can be computed so that actual values do not have to be stored in the internal data structure.

Evaluation of variables which point to data of type *array* is different from the usual *full evaluation*, which applies to variables that point to formulae or lists. In §17.2 evaluation of these data types and the consequences will be explained in full. Here, we only look at certain aspects.

```
> vec := vector( [ 1+a, 2+b, 3+c ] );
```
$$vec := [1 + a \quad 2 + b \quad 3 + c]$$
```
> vec;
```
$$vec$$

Evaluation of the variable vec does not show the array. You must force full evaluation.

```
> eval( vec );
```
$$[1 + a \quad 2 + b \quad 3 + c]$$

Use **op** or **lprint** if you want to see the index range too.

```
> op( eval(vec) );
```
$$1 \ .. \ 3, \quad [2 = 2 + b, \ 3 = 3 + c, \ 1 = 1 + a]$$
```
> lprint( eval(vec) );
array(1 .. 3,[(2)=2+b,(1)=1+a,(3)=3+c])
```

Important differences between objects of type *list* and objects of type *array* are replacement and selection of elements. Array components can be changed, but list elements cannot be changed without complete reconstruction of the list.

```
> xlist := [ x.(1..5) ];
```
$$xlist := [x1, \ x2, \ x3, \ x4, \ x5]$$
```
> xvec := convert( xlist, `array` );
```
$$xvec := [x1 \quad x2 \quad x3 \quad x4 \quad x5]$$
```
> # selection in list and array
> op(4,xlist), xlist[4];
```
$$x4, \ x4$$
```
> xvec[4];
```
$$x4$$

```
> # replacement in list and array
> # first some unsuccessful attempts for the list
> xlist[4] := X;
Error, cannot assign to a list
> op(4,xlist) := X ;
Error, invalid left hand side in assignment
> subsop( 4=X, xlist );
```
$$[\ x1,\ x2,\ x3,\ X,\ x5\ ]$$

```
> xlist;   # list unchanged
```
$$[\ x1,\ x2,\ x3,\ x4,\ x5\ ]$$

```
> xlist := subsop( 4=X, xlist ); # explicit assignment
```
$$xlist := [\ x1,\ x2,\ x3,\ X,\ x5\ ]$$

```
> xvec[4] := X:  print(xvec); # immediate replacement
```
$$[\ x1\quad x2\quad x3\quad X\quad x5\ ]$$

Array access and update are of constant time, whereas list access and update depend on the length of the list. An example to illustrate this:

```
> L1 := [ x $ 2^13 ]:   # list of x´ses
> L2 := [ x $ 2^17-2 ]: # list of x´ses of maximal length
> # access-time to short list
> time(): L1[1]: time():  cpu_time := ("-""") * second;
```
$$cpu\_time := .034\ second$$

```
> # access-time to long list
> time(): L2[1]: time():  cpu_time = ("-""") * second;
```
$$cpu\_time =\ .417\ second$$

```
> time(): L2[2^17-2]: time():
> cpu_time = ("-""") * second;
```
$$cpu\_time =\ .416\ second$$

```
> V1 := convert( L1, ´array´ ):  # array of x´ses
> V2 := convert( L2, ´array´ ):  # "long" aray of x´ses
```

```
> # access-time to "short" array
> time():  V1[1]:  time():  cpu_time = ("-""") * second;
                        cpu_time =  0

> time():  V2[1]:  time():  cpu_time = ("-""") * second;
                        cpu_time =  0

> time():  V2[2^17-2]:  time():
> cpu_time = ("-""") * second;
                        cpu_time =  0
```

In all three examples of access to an array component, the access time is neglectable. The difference in computing time can be easily explained: a list is evaluated as a whole even if you only want to access one element. The data type *array* has a special internal representation (using hash tables) which allows constant-time array access.

12.5 convert and map

You have already seen how to convert a sequence into a set or list: simply surround the object by braces or square brackets, respectively. Objects of type *set* or *list* can be converted through the function **op**. Maple also provides some explicit conversion routines for sets and lists. Below are a few examples which summarize these conversion possibilities.

```
> sequence := a, b, p, q;
                   sequence := a, b, p, q
> [ sequence ];
                     [ a, b, p, q ]
> { sequence };
                     { q, p, b, a }
> op( [ sequence ] );
                      a, b, p, q
> op( { sequence } );
                      q, p, b, a

> convert( { sequence }, `list` );
                     [ q, p, b, a ]
```

```
> convert ( [ sequence ], ´set´ );
```
$$\{ q, \ p, \ b, \ a \}$$

Such explicit conversion routines can also be used for conversions between lists and arrays.

```
> convert ( linalg[vector] ( [a,b,c] ), ´list´ );
```
$$[a, \ b, \ c]$$

```
> convert ( linalg[matrix] ( [ [a,b], [c,d] ] ),
>    ´listlist´ );
```
$$[[a, \ b], \ [c, \ d]]$$

```
> convert ( [a,b,c], ´vector´ );
```
$$[a \quad b \quad c]$$

```
> convert ( [ [a,b], [c,d] ], ´matrix´ );
```
$$\begin{bmatrix} a & b \\ c & d \end{bmatrix}$$

You can use these conversions to change the shape of lists.

```
> L := [ 1, 2, 3, 4, 5, 6, 7, 8, 9, 10, 11, 12 ]:
> convert ( linalg[matrix] ( 2, 6, L ), ´listlist´ );
```
$$[[1, \ 2, \ 3, \ 4, \ 5, \ 6], \ [7, \ 8, \ 9, \ 10, \ 11, \ 12]]$$

```
> convert ( linalg[matrix] ( 6, 2, L ), ´listlist´ );
```
$$[[1, \ 2], \ [3, \ 4], \ [5, \ 6], \ [7, \ 8], \ [9, \ 10],$$
$$[11, \ 12]]$$

```
> op (");
```
$$[1, \ 2], \ [3, \ 4], \ [5, \ 6], \ [7, \ 8], \ [9, \ 10],$$
$$[11, \ 12]$$

```
> map (op,");
```
$$[1, \ 2, \ 3, \ 4, \ 5, \ 6, \ 7, \ 8, \ 9, \ 10, \ 11, \ 12]$$

Here again you see an example of mapping a function to each operand of

an expression by the procedure **map**. The same function can be used for
data of type *array*. In the following example, **map** does not work on the
operands of the expression, but on the array entries themselves.

```
> linalg[matrix]( [ [a,b], [c,d] ] );
```

$$\begin{bmatrix} a & b \\ c & d \end{bmatrix}$$

```
> cos(");
```

$$\cos\left(\begin{bmatrix} a & b \\ c & d \end{bmatrix}\right)$$

```
> map(cos,"");
```

$$\begin{bmatrix} \cos(a) & \cos(b) \\ \cos(c) & \cos(d) \end{bmatrix}$$

Be warned that this does not always work as expected for matrices with
special index functions.

```
> Id := array( identity, 1..2, 1..2 );
```

$$Id := array(\ identity,\ 1\ ..\ 2,\ 1\ ..\ 2,\ [\quad]\ )$$

```
> map( cos, Id );
```

$$\begin{bmatrix} 1 & 0 \\ 0 & 1 \end{bmatrix}$$

```
> M := array( symmetric, 1..2, 1..2 ):  M[1,2]:= a:
> eval(M);
```

$$\begin{bmatrix} ?_{[\ 1,\ 1\ ]} & a \\ a & ?_{[\ 2,\ 2\ ]} \end{bmatrix}$$

```
> map( cos, M );
```

$$\begin{bmatrix} ?_{[\ 1,\ 1\ ]} & \cos(a) \\ \cos(a) & ?_{[\ 2,\ 2\ ]} \end{bmatrix}$$

The reason for this is that first the function **cos** is applied to matrix entries
to which values have been assigned. Hereafter, the index functions are used
to generate values for the remaining matrix entries.

12.6 Exercises

1. Let U be the set of the first ten prime numbers. Let V be the set of the first twenty natural numbers of the form $2^n - 1$.
   (a) Generate the sets U and V in Maple.
   (b) Compute $U \cup V$ and $U \cap V$.

2. (a) Generate a list of 100 integers between -10 and 10.
   (b) Remove all duplicate entries from this list.
   (c) Select from the list obtained in (b) all numbers which can be divided by 2 or 3.
   (d) Pick out from the list obtained in (b) all numbers greater than 5.
   (e) For each number in the list obtained in (d) compute the number of occurrences in the original list of random numbers.

3. You know of course how many solutions the equation $x^{50} - x^{20} = 0$ has over the complex numbers. When you use the procedure **solve** to solve equations, so many equations scroll over the terminal screen that it is difficult to count the number of solutions found by Maple. Use the procedures **nops** and **map** for the above mentioned equation to count the number of solutions and to check the answers by back substitution. (Advice: in order to be able to use **map** in combination with **subs** you had better consider the equation as a system of one equation in one variable.)

4. Create the 3×3 matrix M defined by
   $$M_{ij} = x^{\gcd(i+1,j+1)} + 1,$$
   and write it as a matrix with factored entries.

5. Create the 5×5 matrix M defined by
   $$M_{ij} = 10^{-(i^2+j^2)},$$
   and use the procedure **fnormal** to normalize small matrix entries into zero.

6. Create the 7×7 lower-triangular matrix M with all nonzero entries equal to one. Convert it into a list of integers using the row major order.

Simplification

In §7, we discussed manipulation of polynomials and rational functions. Manipulations such as normalization, collection, sorting, factorization, and expansion passed under review. Characteristic of these manipulations is that they are carried out on expressions as a whole. However, in computations which involve mathematical functions, you frequently want to apply simplification rules that are known for these mathematical functions. For example, in computations which involve trigonometric functions you want to apply the equality $\sin^2 + \cos^2 = 1$. In this chapter, we shall describe how simplifications of expressions containing mathematical functions can be performed.

After a short introduction to automatic simplification, the procedures **expand**, **combine**, **simplify**, and **convert** will be described one after the other. One of Maple's specialities is that the system itself finds out which mathematical functions are involved and which transformation rules are available. This is another example of Maple's *hybrid algorithmic structure*.

For each simplification procedure we shall look at its effect on trigonometric functions, exponential function and logarithm, powers, and other functions, respectively. In the last two sections, extra attention will be paid to trigonometric simplification and simplification of expressions with respect to side relations. At the end of this chapter an overview of possible simplifications is given in tabular form.

13.1 Automatic Simplification

Let us first look at some automatic simplifications in Maple.

```
> arcsin(1/2), Zeta(2), GAMMA(1/2), Psi(1/2);
```
$$\frac{1}{6}\,\pi,\;\; \frac{1}{6}\,\pi^2,\;\; \sqrt{\pi},\;\; -\gamma\,-\,2\,\ln(\,2\,)$$

```
> min( 3, Pi, cos(1)*3 );
```
$$3\,\cos(\,1\,)$$

```
> signum( exp(1) + exp(x) ); # sign of expression
```

$$1$$

```
> tan( arctan(x) ),   arctan( tan(x) );
```

$$x, \ arctan(\ tan(\ x\ )\ )$$

```
> x * sqrt(x*y);
```

$$x^{3/2} \sqrt{y}$$

```
> ´abs( abs(x) )´ = abs( abs(x) );
```

$$\Big|\ \big|\ x\ \big|\ \Big| = \big|\ x\ \big|$$

```
> ´abs(-Pi*x)´ = abs(-Pi*x);
```

$$\Big|\ -\pi\ x\ \Big| = \pi\ \Big|\ x\ \Big|$$

```
> ´cos(-x)´ = cos(-x), ´cos(Pi/2+x)´ = cos(Pi/2+x);
```

$$\cos(\ -x\ ) = \cos(\ x\ ), \ \cos\!\left(\frac{1}{2}\ \pi\ +\ x\ \right) = -\sin(\ x\ )$$

```
> ´exp(3*ln(x))´ = exp(3*ln(x));
```

$$e^{3\ \ln(\ x\ )} = x^3$$

```
> ln(exp(x));
```

$$\ln(\ e^x\ )$$

```
> assume( x, ´real´ );
> ln( exp(x) );
```

$$x\sim$$

In §1.3 you have already been warned that not all automatic simplifications are valid in full generality; sometimes they only work for the
generic case. For example, the automatic simplifications $0 * x \longrightarrow 0$ and
$(x - x) \longrightarrow 0$ are desirable (if only for efficiency reasons) but incorrect
when x is undefined or infinity. The automatic simplification of $0^k \longrightarrow 0$,
for all k, has the following side effect in Maple.

```
> sum( a[k]*x^k, k = 0..n );
```

$$\sum_{k=0}^{n} a_{[k]} \, x^k$$

```
> eval(subs( x=0, " ));
```

$$0$$

The above examples show a tradeoff between usability and efficiency on the one hand and mathematical correctness on the other hand. Be aware that Maple like most, if not all, computer algebra systems performs automatic simplifications which are not 100% safe.

Automatic simplifications of multiple-valued functions represented by principal values are another source of problems for many systems. Maple V Release 2 can still not be called an expert in complex multiple-valued functions. In particular, the square root function causes many problems. You may run into trouble when automatic simplifications like $\sqrt{\frac{1}{z}} \longrightarrow \frac{1}{\sqrt{z}}$ take place regardless of whether z is negative or not.

```
> sqrt(1/(-1)) = subs( z=-1, sqrt(1/z) );
```

$$I = -I$$

Another notorious automatic simplification in Maple is $\sqrt{z^2} \longrightarrow z$ regardless of whether $-\pi/2 < \Im(z) \le \pi/2$ or not. It is a special case of the buggy automatic simplification rule $\sqrt{zw} \longrightarrow \sqrt{z}\sqrt{w}$.

```
> subs( z=-1, sqrt(z^2) ) = subs( z=-1, ´sqrt(z^2)´ );
```

$$-1 = \text{sqrt}(\, 1 \,)$$

```
> ";
```

$$-1 = 1$$

A correct simplification rule would be

$$\sqrt{z^2} \longrightarrow \text{csgn}(z)z,$$

where

$$\text{csgn}(z) = \begin{cases} 1 & \text{if } \Im(z) > 0 \text{ or } (\Im(z) = 0 \text{ and } \Re(z) > 0); \\ 1 & \text{if } z = 0; \\ -1 & \text{elsewhere.} \end{cases}$$

This simplification rule is actually applied in Maple V Release 2 for numeric complex values of z.

The lesson to be learned from the above examples is that you should be very cautious when you transform symbolic expressions containing multiple-valued functions and afterwards substitute numerical values. If you are still not convinced that caution in use of software is needed you should look at [78, 113], where similar surprising results are described.

13.2 expand

In general, the procedure **expand** does credit to its name and works out an expression. For mathematical functions, this often means that sum rules are applied.

- Trigonometric Functions

```
> cos(2*x):   " = expand(");
```
$$\cos(2\ x) = 2\ \cos(x)^2 - 1$$

```
> cos(5*x):   " = expand(");
```
$$\cos(5\ x) = 16\ \cos(x)^5 - 20\ \cos(x)^3 + 5\ \cos(x)$$

```
> cos(x+y):   " = expand(");
```
$$\cos(x + y) = \cos(x)\ \cos(y) - \sin(x)\ \sin(y)$$

```
> cos(x+2*y):   " = expand(");
```
$$\cos(x + 2\ y) = 2\ \cos(x)\ \cos(y)^2 - \cos(x)$$
$$- 2\ \sin(x)\ \sin(y)\ \cos(y)$$

```
> cos(x*(y+z)):   " = expand(");
```
$$\cos(x\ (y + z)) =$$
$$\cos(x\ y)\ \cos(x\ z) - \sin(x\ y)\ \sin(x\ z)$$

The procedure **expand** works out a trigonometric function over a sum or a multiple. The above examples illustrate again that expansion of trigonometric functions is done as far as possible. A partial expansion like $\cos 5x \longrightarrow \cos x \cos 4x - \sin x \sin 4x$ cannot be done so easily with **expand**. You will have to make do with tricks like

```
> cos(5*x);
```
$$\cos(5\ x)$$

```
> subs( 5*x = x + y, " );
```

$$\cos(x + y)$$

```
> expand(");
```

$$\cos(x)\ \cos(y)\ -\ \sin(x)\ \sin(y)$$

```
> subs( y = 4*x, " );
```

$$\cos(4\ x)\ \cos(x)\ -\ \sin(x)\ \sin(4\ x)$$

Or you must, on the basis of the following source code of **expand/cos**,

```
> interface( verboseproc=2 ):
> print( `expand/cos` );

proc(x)
local n,y;
options `Copyright 1991 by the University of Waterloo`;
    y := expand(x);
    if type(y,`+`) then
        n := op(1,y);
        y := y-n;
        expand(cos(n)*cos(y)-sin(n)*sin(y))
    elif type(y,`*`) then
        n := op(1,y);
        if type(n,numeric) and n < 0 then expand(cos(-y))
        elif type(n,integer) and 0 < n and n < 100 then
            y := y/n;
            expand(2*cos((n-1)*y)*cos(y)-cos((n-2)*y))
        else cos(y)
        fi
    else cos(y)
    fi
end:
```

re-program this expansion procedure.

- exp, ln

```
> exp(x+y):   " = expand(");
```

$$e^{x\ +\ y} = e^x\ e^y$$

```
> ln(x*y):   " = expand(");
```

$$\ln(x\ y) = \ln(x)\ +\ \ln(y)$$

```
> ln(x^y):   " = expand(");
```

$$\ln(x^y) = y\ \ln(x)$$

```
> ln(x/y):    " = expand(");
```

$$\ln\left(\frac{x}{y}\right) = \ln(x) - \ln(y)$$

```
> exp(x*(y+z)):    " = expand(");
```

$$e^{x(y+z)} = e^{xy} e^{xz}$$

The responsibility for whether a transformation rule is valid or not is shifted to you yourself: e.g., the transformation $\ln(xy) \longrightarrow \ln x + \ln y$ is not valid in general (see what happens when you substitute $x = y = -1$), but the system is always willing to do the transformation when asked to.

- Powers

```
> x^(y+z):    " = expand(");
```

$$x^{(y+z)} = x^y x^z$$

```
> (x*y)^z:    " = expand(");
```

$$(x\ y)^z = x^z\ y^z$$

```
> (-x)^y:    " = expand(");
```

$$(-x)^y = (-1)^y\ x^y$$

```
> (x/y)^z:    " = expand(");
```

$$\left(\frac{x}{y}\right)^z = \frac{x^z}{y^z}$$

```
> (x^y)^z:    " = expand(");
```

$$(x^y)^z = x^{(yz)}$$

```
> x^(1/3*y):    " = expand(");
```

$$x^{(1/3\ y)} = (x^y)^{1/3}$$

- Other simplifications with **expand** are expansion of factorized natural numbers, expansion of factorials, binomial coefficients and the Gamma function, and simplifications of determinants of products and powers of matrices. Some examples:

```
> (n+1)!:    " = expand(");
```

$$(n+1)! = n!\ (n+1)$$

```
> binomial(n+1,k+1):   " = expand(");
```

$$\texttt{binomial}(\,n\,+\,1,\ k\,+\,1\,) = \frac{(\,n\,+\,1\,)\ \texttt{binomial}(\,n,\ k\,)}{k\,+\,1}$$

```
> binomial(n-1,k-1) + binomial(n-1,k);
```

$$\texttt{binomial}(\,n\,-\,1,\ k\,-\,1\,) \,+\, \texttt{binomial}(\,n\,-\,1,\ k\,)$$

```
> expand(");
```

$$\frac{k\ \texttt{binomial}(\,n,\ k\,)}{n} \,+\, \frac{(\,n\,-\,k\,)\ \texttt{binomial}(\,n,\ k\,)}{n}$$

```
> normal(");
```

$$\texttt{binomial}(\,n,\ k\,)$$

```
> ifactor(123456789):   " = expand(");
```

$$(\,3\,)^2\ (\,3803\,)\ (\,3607\,) = 123456789$$

```
> Psi(2*x):   " = expand(");
```

$$\Psi(\,2\ x\,) = \ln(\,2\,) \,+\, \frac{1}{2}\ \Psi(\,x\,) \,+\, \frac{1}{2}\ \Psi\!\left(\,x\,+\,\frac{1}{2}\,\right)$$

```
> Zeta(50):   " = expand(");
```

$$\texttt{Zeta}(\,50\,) = 39604576419286371856998202/285258771\ \backslash$$

$$4575467644633636352523744141 8325436523437\ \backslash$$

$$5\ \pi^{50}$$

```
> dilog(1/x):   " = expand(");
```

$$\texttt{dilog}\!\left(\frac{1}{x}\right) = -\texttt{dilog}(\,x\,) \,-\, \frac{1}{2}\ \ln(\,x\,)^2$$

```
> M := array(1..4,1..4):
> det(M^3):   " = expand(");
```

$$\det(\,M^3\,) = \det(\,M\,)^3$$

```
> det(3*M):   " = expand(");
```

$$\det(\,3\ M\,) = 81\ \det(\,M\,)$$

In the example of partial trigonometric expansion we already touched upon the subject that you can program your own expansion rules for functions. For a function, say **F**, you only have to define the procedure **expand/F**. Henceforth, when you apply **expand** to an expression containing **F**, Maple applies to each function call of **F** the expansion as defined in the procedure **expand/F**. An example of an additive function **F**:

```
> `expand/F` := proc(x)

>    local y,i:

>    y := expand(x):

>    if type(y,`+`) then sum( F(op(i,y)), i=1..nops(y) ) fi

> end:

> f(p+q) + F(r+s):   " = expand(");
```

$$f(\,p \,+\, q\,) \,+\, F(\,r \,+\, s\,) = f(\,p \,+\, q\,) \,+\, F(\,r\,) \,+\, F(\,s\,)$$

```
> F(p*(q+r)):    " = expand(");
```

$$F(\,p\,(\,q \,+\, r\,)\,) = F(\,p\ q\,) \,+\, F(\,p\ r\,)$$

What remains to be told is how you can prevent expansions of particular non-rational functions in an expression. This is important because more than one mathematical function may be part of a symbolic expression, but you may not want all functions expanded. For example, suppose that you only want to expand the exponential function in the expression $\sin(x + y) + \exp(x + y)$. When you apply **expand** with the expression as the sole parameter, the effect will be that the expression is fully expanded. Only when you add the keyword `sin` as an extra argument in the function call is this trigonometric function left intact.

```
> expression := sin(x+y) + exp(x+y);
```

$$expression := \sin(\,x \,+\, y\,) \,+\, e^{x\,+\,y}$$

```
> expand( expression );
```

$$\sin(\,x\,)\ \cos(\,y\,) \,+\, \cos(\,x\,)\ \sin(\,y\,) \,+\, e^{x}\ e^{y}$$

```
> expand( expression, sin );
```

$$\sin(\,x \,+\, y\,) \,+\, e^{x}\ e^{y}$$

If you want to avoid expansion of *all* non-rational functions, then you can use the Maple procedure **frontend**.

```
> frontend( expand, [expression] );
```

$$\sin (x + y) + e^{x + y}$$

When you know beforehand that you will not need expansion of certain non-rational functions for some time, then you can inform Maple with the procedure **expandoff**.

```
> expand( expandoff() ):   # enable library function
> expandoff( sin ):   # turn off expansion of sin
> expression := sin(p+q) + exp(p+q);
```

$$expression := \sin (p + q) + e^{p + q}$$

```
> expand( expression );
```

$$\sin (p + q) + e^{p} \, e^{q}$$

Perhaps you wonder why we have rewritten the previous expression in x and y in new unknowns p and q. Well, if we had not done this, Maple would have remembered that the command expand(expression) had been entered before, and consequently would have picked up the previous result from the remember table of **expand** instead of recomputing it. See for yourself.

```
> expandon( sin ):   # turn on expansion of sin
> expand( expression );
```

$$\sin (p + q) + e^{p} \, e^{q}$$

13.3 combine

When a computer algebra system provides facilities to expand expressions you may expect the existence of a procedure to do the opposite, i.e., to combine expressions. When you use the Maple procedure **combine**, you must specify which terms in an expression should be combined. This is done by options such as trig, exp, ln, power, and Psi. Otherwise, Maple only collects similar terms in sums, products, and powers into a single term.

```
> x^z * y^z:   " = combine(");
```

$$x^z \, y^z = (x \, y)^z$$

```
> sqrt(x-y) * sqrt(x+y):   " = combine(");
```

$$\sqrt{x - y} \, \sqrt{x + y} = \sqrt{x^2 - y^2}$$

```
> Int ( f(x), x ) + Int ( g(x), x ):    " = combine (");
```

$$\int f(x)\ dx + \int g(x)\ dx = \int f(x) + g(x)\ dx$$

- Trigonometric Functions

combine transforms a polynomial in sines and cosines into the finite Fourier form by successive application of the rules

$$\begin{aligned}
\sin x\ \sin y &\longrightarrow & 1/2\cos(x-y) - 1/2\cos(x+y),\\
\sin x\ \cos y &\longrightarrow & 1/2\sin(x-y) + 1/2\sin(x+y),\\
\cos x\ \cos y &\longrightarrow & 1/2\cos(x-y) + 1/2\cos(x+y).
\end{aligned}$$

Similar transformations hold for hyperbolic trigonometric functions.

```
> 2*sin(x)*cos(x):    " = combine (", ´trig´);
```

$$2\ \sin(x)\ \cos(x) = \sin(2\ x)$$

```
> sin(x)^2:    " = combine (", ´trig´);
```

$$\sin(x)^2 = \frac{1}{2} - \frac{1}{2}\cos(2\ x)$$

```
> cosh(x)^5:    " = combine (", ´trig´);
```

$$\cosh(x)^5 = \frac{1}{16}\cosh(5\ x) + \frac{5}{16}\cosh(3\ x) + \frac{5}{8}\cosh(x)$$

- exp, ln

combine combines expressions in which the exponential function and logarithm occur according to the rules

$$\begin{aligned}
\exp x\ \exp y &\longrightarrow & \exp(x+y),\\
\exp(x+n\ln y) &\longrightarrow & y^n\exp(x),\ \text{for}\ n\in\mathbb{Z},\\
(\exp x)^y &\longrightarrow & \exp(x\,y),\\
a\ln x &\longrightarrow & \ln(x^a),\\
\ln x + \ln y &\longrightarrow & \ln(x\,y).
\end{aligned}$$

```
> exp(x)*exp(y)^n:    " = combine (", exp);
```

$$e^x\ (e^y)^n = e^{x+y\,n}$$

```
> a*ln(x+1) + 2*ln(y):    " = combine (", ln);
```

$$a\ \ln(x+1) + 2\ \ln(y) = \ln\left((x+1)^a\ y^2\right)$$

```
> ln(x) - ln(y):   " = combine(",ln);
```

$$\ln(x) - \ln(y) = \ln\left(\dfrac{x}{y}\right)$$

```
> expression := exp( x + a*ln(y) );
```

$$expression := e^{x + a\ \ln(y)}$$

```
> combine( expression, exp );
```

$$e^{x + a\ \ln(y)}$$

```
> combine( expression, ln );
```

$$e^{x + \ln(y^a)}$$

```
> combine(",exp);
```

$$y^a\ e^x$$

```
> combine( expression, [ln,exp] );
```

$$y^a\ e^x$$

The last example illustrates that the second argument of a call to **combine** may be a list of keywords, and that the system applies the procedure recursively.

- Powers

The two most important **combine** rules for powers are:

$$x^y x^z \longrightarrow x^{y+z},$$
$$(x^y)^z \longrightarrow x^{yz}.$$

```
> x^y / x^(2/3):   " = combine(",`power`);
```

$$\dfrac{x^y}{x^{2/3}} = x^{(y - 2/3)}$$

```
> (1/x^2)^y:   " = combine(",`power`);
```

$$\left(\dfrac{1}{x^2}\right)^y = x^{(-2\ y)}$$

13.4 simplify

simplify is Maple's general purpose simplification routine.

- Trigonometric Functions

Rational expressions in which trigonometric functions and hyperbolic trigonometric functions occur are normalized by **simplify** according to the rules

$$\sin^2 x \quad \longrightarrow \quad 1 - \cos^2 x,$$
$$\sinh^2 x \quad \longrightarrow \quad \cosh^2(x) - 1,$$
$$\tan x \quad \longrightarrow \quad \frac{\sin x}{\cos x},$$
$$\tanh x \quad \longrightarrow \quad \frac{\sinh x}{\cosh x}.$$

More precisely, powers of sines and hyperbolic sines with exponent greater than one are simplified by the above rules as much as possible.

```
> cosh(x)^2 - sinh(x)^2:   " = simplify(");
```

$$\cosh(x)^2 - \sinh(x)^2 = 1$$

```
> sinh(x)^3:   " = simplify(");
```

$$\sinh(x)^3 = \sinh(x)\,\cosh(x)^2 - \sinh(x)$$

```
> 2*cos(x)^3+sin(x)*sin(2*x):   " = simplify(");
```

$$2\,\cos(x)^3 + \sin(x)\,\sin(2\,x) = 2\,\cos(x)$$

```
> 2*tan(x) / ( 1 + tan(x)^2 ):   " = simplify(");
```

$$2\,\frac{\tan(x)}{1 + \tan(x)^2} = 2\,\sin(x)\,\cos(x)$$

If you prefer the rule $\cos^2 x \to 1 - \sin^2 x$ to the rule $\sin^2 x \to 1 - \cos^2 x$, then you should simplify with respect to side relations. We shall discuss simplification with respect to side relations in detail in §13.7.

```
> sin(x)^3 + cos(x)^3;
```

$$\sin(x)^3 + \cos(x)^3$$

```
> simplify(");
```

$$\cos(x)^3 - \sin(x)\,\cos(x)^2 + \sin(x)$$

```
> simplify( "", {cos(x)^2+sin(x)^2=1}, [sin(x),cos(x)] );
```

$$\cos(x)^3 - \sin(x)\,\cos(x)^2 + \sin(x)$$

```
> simplify( """, {cos(x)^2+sin(x)^2=1}, [cos(x),sin(x)] );
```

$$\sin(x)^3 - \cos(x)\,\sin(x)^2 + \cos(x)$$

- exp, ln

For the exponential function and the logarithm, **simplify** does the same as **expand** with one exception, viz., $\exp x \exp y \longrightarrow \exp(x + y)$.

```
> exp(x) * exp(y):   " = simplify(");
```

$$e^x\,e^y = e^{x + y}$$

```
> expand( rhs(") );
```

$$e^x\,e^y$$

```
> exp(x)^2:   " = simplify(");
```

$$\left(e^x\right)^2 = e^{2\,x}$$

- Powers

simplify does the same as **expand** for most powers, with the important exception $x^y x^z \longrightarrow x^{y+z}$ and, as you will see below, simplification of powers with fractions as exponents.

```
> x^y * x^z:   " = simplify(");
```

$$x^y\,x^z = x^{(y + z)}$$

```
> expand( rhs(") );
```

$$x^y\,x^z$$

```
> (x^y)^z:   " = simplify(");
```

$$\left(x^y\right)^z = x^{(y\,z)}$$

```
> (x/y)^z:   " = simplify(");
```

$$\left(\frac{x}{y}\right)^z = x^z\,y^{(-z)}$$

```
> (-x)^y:   " = simplify(");
```

$$(-x)^y = (-1)^y\,x^y$$

For powers with fractional exponents, the procedure **simplify** differs a lot from **expand**. In this case, **simplify** is in fact the procedure **radsimp** (**rad**ical **simp**lification). The procedure **radsimp** is especially designed to simplify expressions in which square roots and powers with other fractional exponents occur. Such simplifications are often difficult and time-consuming. When you mention the keyword radical in a call of **simplify** then Maple knows that you only want simplification of this type and nothing else.

```
> (2/27)^(1/2):    " = simplify(");
```

$$\frac{1}{27}\sqrt{2}\sqrt{27} = \frac{1}{9}\sqrt{2}\sqrt{3}$$

```
> ( cos(x)^2 - 2 )^(3/2) /
>     ( cos(x)^4 - 4*cos(x)^2 + 4 )^(1/4) + sin(x)^2;
```

$$\frac{\left(\cos(x)^2 - 2\right)^{3/2}}{\left(\cos(x)^4 - 4\cos(x)^2 + 4\right)^{1/4}} + \sin(x)^2$$

```
> simplify( ", ´radical´ );
```

$$\cos(x)^2 - 2 + \sin(x)^2$$

```
> "" = simplify( "" );
```

$$\frac{\left(\cos(x)^2 - 2\right)^{3/2}}{\left(\cos(x)^4 - 4\cos(x)^2 + 4\right)^{1/4}} + \sin(x)^2 = -1$$

• Furthermore, Maple knows many rules for functions like the Gamma function, the Riemann zeta function, the hypergeometric function, and a lot more. Two examples:

```
> GAMMA(n+1/2)/GAMMA(n-1/2):    " = simplify(");
```

$$\frac{\Gamma\left(n + \frac{1}{2}\right)}{\Gamma\left(n - \frac{1}{2}\right)} = n - \frac{1}{2}$$

```
> readlib( hypergeom ):
> hypergeom([-n/2,-(n-1)/2],[1/2],z^2/t^2);
```

$$\text{hypergeom}\left(\left[-\frac{1}{2}n, \ -\frac{1}{2}n + \frac{1}{2}\right], \left[\frac{1}{2}\right], \frac{z^2}{t^2}\right)$$

```
> simplify(");
```

$$\frac{1}{2}\ (t\ +\ z\ )^n\ t^{(-n)}\ +\ \frac{1}{2}\ (t\ -\ z\ )^n\ t^{(-n)}$$

If you do not want to apply all possible simplifications provided for, then you must explicitly mention, in the call to **simplify**, those mathematical functions for which simplification should be carried out (as in the above example where the keyword radical was added). Note that this is the opposite to the way in which expansion of functions is suppressed.

```
> exp(x)*exp(y) + cos(x)^2 + sin(x)^2;
```

$$e^x\ e^y\ +\ \cos(\ x\ )^2\ +\ \sin(\ x\ )^2$$

```
> simplify(");
```

$$e^{x\ +\ y}\ +\ 1$$

```
> simplify("",exp);
```

$$e^{x\ +\ y}\ +\ \cos(\ x\ )^2\ +\ \sin(\ x\ )^2$$

```
> simplify(""",´trig´);
```

$$e^x\ e^y\ +\ 1$$

13.5 convert

Expressions in which (hyperbolic) trigonometric functions and their inverses occur can be explicitly transformed into different forms with **convert**. Some examples:

• Conversion of (hyperbolic) trigonometric functions into exponential form and the reverse conversion.

```
> cos(x):   " = convert(",exp);
```

$$\cos(\ x\ ) = \frac{1}{2}\ e^{I\ x}\ +\ \frac{1}{2}\ \frac{1}{e^{I\ x}}$$

```
> map( convert, ", ´trig´ );
```

$$\cos(\ x\ ) =$$

$$\frac{1}{2}\ \cos(\ x\ )\ +\ \frac{1}{2}\ I\ \sin(\ x\ )\ +\ \frac{1}{2}\ \frac{1}{\cos(\ x\ )\ +\ I\ \sin(\ x\ )}$$

```
> simplify(");
```

$$\cos(x) = \cos(x)$$

```
> cosh(x):   " = convert(",exp);
```

$$\cosh(x) = \frac{1}{2} e^x + \frac{1}{2} \frac{1}{e^x}$$

```
> map( convert, ", 'trig' );
```

$$\cosh(x) =$$

$$\frac{1}{2} \cosh(x) + \frac{1}{2} \sinh(x) + \frac{1}{2} \frac{1}{\cosh(x) + \sinh(x)}$$

```
> simplify(");
```

$$\cosh(x) = \cosh(x)$$

- Conversion of inverse (hyperbolic) trigonometric functions into logarithmic expressions.

```
> arcsin(x):   " = convert(",ln);
```

$$\arcsin(x) = -I \ln\left(\sqrt{1 - x^2} + I x\right)$$

```
> arcsinh(x):   " = convert(",ln);
```

$$\text{arcsinh}(x) = \ln\left(x + \sqrt{x^2 + 1}\right)$$

The above conversions of (hyperbolic) trigonometric functions and their inverses can be combined into one conversion by the keyword expln.

- Conversions of trigonometric functions into expressions with only tangents.

```
> sin(x):   " = convert(",tan);
```

$$\sin(x) = 2 \frac{\tan\left(\frac{1}{2} x\right)}{1 + \tan\left(\frac{1}{2} x\right)^2}$$

- Conversions of trigonometric functions into expressions with only sines and cosines, and conversions of hyperbolic trigonometric functions into expressions with only exponential functions.

```
> tan(x):   " = convert(",´expsincos´);
```

$$\tan(x) = \frac{\sin(x)}{\cos(x)}$$

```
> tanh(x):   " = convert(",´expsincos´);
```

$$\tanh(x) = \frac{(e^x)^2 - 1}{(e^x)^2 + 1}$$

- Furthermore, Maple provides conversions of factorials and binomial coefficients into Gamma functions.

```
> n!;
```

$$n!$$

```
> " = convert(",GAMMA);
```

$$n! = \Gamma(n + 1)$$

```
> rhs(") = convert( rhs("), factorial );
```

$$\Gamma(n + 1) = \frac{(n + 1)!}{n + 1}$$

```
> binomial(n,k):   " = convert(",GAMMA);
```

$$\mathrm{binomial}(n, k) = \frac{\Gamma(n + 1)}{\Gamma(k + 1)\ \Gamma(n - k + 1)}$$

```
> multinomial(n,a,b,c,d):   " = convert(",GAMMA);
```

$$\mathrm{multinomial}(n, a, b, c, d) =$$

$$\frac{\Gamma(n + 1)}{\Gamma(a + 1)\ \Gamma(b + 1)\ \Gamma(c + 1)\ \Gamma(d + 1)}$$

13.6 Trigonometric Simplification

Substitution of trigonometric expressions plays a special role in Maple. The computer algebra system provides an extra facility: for simple expressions it can suggest equivalent ones. The Maple procedure is called **trigsubs** and should first be loaded from the library. A few examples:

```
> readlib(trigsubs):
```

```
> trigsubs( sin(2*x) );
```

$$
\left[\sin(2\ x),\ \sin(2\ x),\ 2\sin(x)\cos(x), \right.
$$

$$
\frac{1}{\csc(2\ x)},\ \frac{1}{\csc(2\ x)},\ 2\ \frac{\tan(x)}{1+\tan(x)^2},
$$

$$
\left. -\frac{1}{2}\ I\ (e^{2\ I\ x}-e^{-2\ I\ x}) \right]
$$

```
> convert( trigsubs( tan(x)^2 ), 'set' );
```

$$
\left\{ \sec(x)^2-1,\ \frac{\sin(x)^2}{\cos(x)^2},\ \frac{\sin(2\ x)^2}{(1+\cos(2\ x))^2}, \right.
$$

$$
4\ \frac{\tan\left(\dfrac{1}{2}\ x\right)^2}{\left(\left(1-\tan\left(\dfrac{1}{2}\ x\right)^2\right)\right)^2},\ \frac{1}{\cot(x)^2},
$$

$$
4\ \frac{\cot\left(\dfrac{1}{2}\ x\right)^2}{\left(\cot\left(\dfrac{1}{2}\ x\right)^2-1\right)^2},\ 4\ \frac{1}{\left(\cot\left(\dfrac{1}{2}\ x\right)-\tan\left(\dfrac{1}{2}\ x\right)\right)^2},
$$

$$
\left. -\frac{(e^{I\ x}-e^{-I\ x})^2}{(e^{I\ x}+e^{-I\ x})^2},\ \frac{(1-\cos(2\ x))^2}{\sin(2\ x)^2},\ \tan(x)^2 \right\}
$$

```
> trigsubs( sin(x) + sin(y) );
```

$$
\left[2\sin\left(\frac{1}{2}\ x+\frac{1}{2}\ y\right)\cos\left(-\frac{1}{2}\ x+\frac{1}{2}\ y\right) \right]
$$

Do not expect miracles; many trigonometric equivalences are not recognized by Maple via **trigsubs**. In the case where trigonometric substitution is desired, **trigsubs** can also be used as an alternative for the substitution procedure **subs**, with the extra feature that the trigonometric equality in the first argument is verified via the knowledge base.

```
> trigsubs( cos(2*x) = cos(x)^2 - sin(x)^2,
>    cos(2*x) + sin(x)^2 + 1);
```

$$\cos(x)^2 + 1$$

13.7 Simplification w.r.t. Side Relations

Let us consider the following problem from the Dutch Mathematics Olympiad of September 6th, 1991.

Let a, b, c be real numbers such that

$$a + b + c = 3, \quad a^2 + b^2 + c^2 = 9, \quad a^3 + b^3 + c^3 = 24.$$

Compute $a^4 + b^4 + c^4$.

Maple's solution is the following:

```
> siderels := { a+b+c=3, a^2+b^2+c^2=9, a^3+b^3+c^3=24 };
```

$$siderels :=$$

$$\{ a^2 + b^2 + c^2 = 9, \ a^3 + b^3 + c^3 = 24, \ a + b + c = 3 \}$$

```
> simplify( a^4+b^4+c^4, siderels );
```

$$69$$

In order to understand how Maple computes this result you must have some notion of what a *Gröbner basis* is and how it is used. In this section, only the idea behind a Gröbner basis is described; for a more mathematically oriented introduction the interested reader is referred to [18, 19, 33].

First, Maple considers the set of polynomials which specify the side relations as pure polynomials rather than equations.

```
> polys := map( lhs - rhs, siderels );
```

$$polys := \{$$

$$a^2 + b^2 + c^2 - 9, \ a^3 + b^3 + c^3 - 24, \ a + b + c - 3$$

$$\}$$

Next, Maple computes the minimal, monic Gröbner basis with respect to the pure lexicographic ordering. Roughly speaking, a Gröbner basis is a set of polynomials which generates the same ideal as the original set of polynomials, with some extra properties imposed on the basis. The Maple package for computing this basis is called *grobner*. The command in this package which does the work is **gbasis**.

```
> with( grobner );  # load the Groebner basis package

    [ addpairs, crit1, expnum, finduni, finite, gbasis,

        grob, gsolve, hcoeff, head, hred, hterm,

        iascend, insert, leadmon, lsort, minor, newbas,

        nf, normalf, plexity, redall, reduce, reorder,

        seln, solvable, sp, spoly, sred, termlcm,

        univar, vorder ]

> G := gbasis( polys, [a,b,c], `plex` );

    G := [ a + b + c - 3, b² + c² + b c - 3 b - 3 c,

        1 - 3 c² + c³ ]
```

The Gröbner basis depends on the ordering of monomials in a, b, and c. Here, the pure lexicographic ordering with $a \succ b \succ c$ is used (cf. §5.2). A Gröbner basis is characterized by:

Characterization of Gröbner bases. *A finite set G of polynomials is a Gröbner basis iff each element of the ideal generated by G reduces to zero by application of "reductions" w.r.t. the ordering $\succ$.*

What is meant by "reductions" can best be explained via the example. From the first polynomial comes the reduction with respect to a,

$$a \longrightarrow 3 - b - c.$$

From the second polynomial the "easiest" reduction with respect to pure lexicographic ordering is that the largest monomial is eliminated via

$$b^2 \longrightarrow -b c + 3b - c^2 + 3c.$$

($b c$ is the biggest monomial occurring on the right-hand side.) From the third polynomial the "easiest" reduction is to eliminate the highest-degree term

$$c^3 \longrightarrow 3c^2 - 1.$$

When these reductions are applied to a polynomial until they can be applied no longer, then a so-called *normal form* of the given polynomial is reached. A Gröbner basis G can also be characterized by the property that zero is the unique normal form of every element of the ideal generated by G. In other words, in a Gröbner basis G it is guaranteed that the result of successive applications of these reductions on a polynomial in the ideal generated by G will be zero.

A Gröbner basis G is a minimal, monic basis when each element g of G has a leading coefficient equal to 1 and is in normal form with respect to $G \backslash g$. For a minimal, monic Gröbner basis the normal form of any polynomial is unique: it is a "canonical form" in the sense that two polynomials are equivalent when their normal forms are the exact same polynomial.

Maple provides the procedure **normalf** for computing the normal form. Let us determine the normal form of $a^4 + b^4 + c^4$ with respect to the computed Gröbner basis.

```
> normalf( a^4+b^4+c^4, G, [a,b,c], `plex` );
```

$$69$$

Hence, simplification with respect to polynomial side relations is nothing but the computation of the normal form of a polynomial with respect to the minimal, reduced Gröbner basis of the ideal generated by the side relations in some term ordering. On a rational expression, simplification with respect to polynomial side relations is applied separately to the numerator and denominator of the normalized quotient. If no variables are specified or if indeterminates are specified as a set, then total degree ordering is chosen. If variables are specified as a list, then induced pure lexicographic ordering is chosen. (For the definition of these term orderings we refer to §5.2.) In order to control the outcome of simplification with respect to side relations, it is often prudent to specify variables in the ordering needed.

```
> simplify( x^3 + y^3, {x^2 + y^2 = 1}, [x,y] );
```

$$y^3 - x \, y^2 + x$$

```
> simplify( x^3 + y^3, {x^2 + y^2 = 1}, [y,x] );
```

$$x^3 - y \, x^2 + y$$

```
> simplify( (x^3-y^3) / (x^3+y^3), {x^2 + y^2 = 1} );
```

$$\frac{x^3 + y \, x^2 - y}{x^3 - y \, x^2 + y}$$

Compare this simplification with

```
> siderel := {sin(x)^2 + cos(x)^2 = 1};
```

$$siderel := \left\{ \cos(x)^2 + \sin(x)^2 = 1 \right\}$$

```
> eqn := cos(x)^3 + sin(x)^3;
```

$$eqn := \cos(\,x\,)^3 + \sin(\,x\,)^3$$

```
> simplify( eqn, siderel, [cos(x),sin(x)] );
```

$$\sin(\,x\,)^3 - \cos(\,x\,)\,\sin(\,x\,)^2 + \cos(\,x\,)$$

```
> simplify( eqn, siderel, [sin(x),cos(x)] );
```

$$\cos(\,x\,)^3 - \sin(\,x\,)\,\cos(\,x\,)^2 + \sin(\,x\,)$$

From this it should be clear how simplification with side relations works for generalized rational expressions.

Simplification with respect to side relations is a powerful tool. Consider, for example, the simplification of the polynomial f defined as

```
> f;
```

$$y^3\,x^6 - 3\,y^3\,x^4 + 3\,y^2\,x^5 + 8\,y^2\,x^4 + 3\,y^3\,x^2 - 6\,y^2\,x^3$$

$$+ \, 3\,y\,x^4 - 16\,y^2\,x^2 + 16\,y\,x^3 - y^3 + 3\,y^2\,x$$

$$+ \, 23\,y\,x^2 + x^3 + 8\,y^2 - 16\,y\,x + 8\,x^2 - 26\,y$$

$$+ \, 26\,x + 40$$

```
> simplify( f, { u = x^2*y - y + x + 4 }, {x,y} );
```

$$u^3 - 4\,u^2 + 10\,u$$

By pencil and paper such decompositions of polynomials are difficult to find and to check.

In many cases the procedure **match** may be a good alternative because it uses a polynomial time algorithm of algebraic pattern matching, whereas the time and memory requirements for Gröbner basis calculations can be immense.

```
> guess := a*u^3 + b*u^2 + c*u + d:
> u := x^2*y - y + x + 4:
> match( f=guess, x, ´parms´ );
```

$$true$$

```
> subs( parms, eval(guess,1) );
```

$$u^3 - 4\,u^2 + 10\,u$$

By the way, Maple provides the procedure **compoly** for finding a composition of univariate polynomials.

```
> f := x^6 + 6*x^4 + x^3 + 9*x^2 + 3*x - 5;
```

$$f := x^6 + 6\ x^4 + x^3 + 9\ x^2 + 3\ x - 5$$

```
> compoly(f,x);
```

$$x^2 - \frac{21}{4}, \quad x = \frac{1}{2} + 3\ x + x^3$$

So, f composes as $g \circ h$, where $g = x^2 - \frac{21}{4}$ and $h = x^3 + 3x + \frac{1}{2}$. Let Maple check its answer.

```
> subs( "[2], "[1] );
```

$$\left(\frac{1}{2} + 3\ x + x^3 \right)^2 - \frac{21}{4}$$

```
> expand( " - f );
```

$$0$$

The algorithm used is described in [64]. The more general case of composing a rational function in one variable into a composition of rational functions is treated in [125].

13.8 Exercises

1. Check how the following pairs of symbolic expressions can be transformed into each other by Maple.

   (a) $x + y + \dfrac{1}{x+y}$ and $\dfrac{(x+y)^2 + 1}{x+y}$

   (b) $\exp(x+y)$ and $\exp(x)\exp(y)$

   (c) $\ln(x/y)$ and $\ln(x) - \ln(y)$

   (d) $x^{(y+z)}$ and $x^y x^z$

   (e) $\sqrt{x^2 - 1}$ and $\sqrt{x-1}\sqrt{x+1}$

2. Simplify the following symbolic expressions.

   (a) $\dfrac{e^x + x}{e^{2x} + 2xe^x + x^2}$

(b) $\sqrt[3]{x^5 + 40x^4 + 595x^3 + 3905x^2 + 9680x + 1331}$

(c) $\dfrac{(x-2)^{3/2}}{(x^2 - 4x + 4)^{1/4}}$

(d) $\dfrac{\sqrt{x} - y}{x - y^2}$

(e) $\dfrac{1}{2 + 5^{1/3}}$

(f) $\cos(x+y) + \sin x \sin y + 2^{x+y}$

(g) $2\cos^2 x - \cos 2x$

3. Solve the following zero-equivalence problem with Maple.

(a) $(2^{1/3} + 4^{1/3})^3 - 6(2^{1/3} + 4^{1/3}) - 6 = 0$

(b) $\ln \tan(\frac{1}{2}x + \frac{1}{4}\pi) - \operatorname{arcsinh} \tan x = 0$

4. Use Maple to check the following trigonometric identities.

(a) $\sin x + \sin y = 2 \sin \frac{1}{2}(x+y) \cos \frac{1}{2}(x-y)$

(b) $\sin 5x = 5 \sin x - 20\sin^3 x + 16\sin^5 x$

(c) $\cot^2 x + 1 = \csc^2 x$

(d) $\tan x + \tan y = \dfrac{\sin(x+y)}{\cos x \cos y}$

(e) $\cos^6 x + \sin^6 x = 1 - 3\sin^2 x \cos^2 x$

(f) $\sinh 2x = 2\dfrac{\tanh x}{1 - \tan h^2 x}$

(g) $\dfrac{\sin 2x + \sin 2y}{\cos 2x + \cos 2y} = \tan(x+y)$

5. Verify with Maple the equality $\pi/4 = 4\arctan(1/5) - \arctan(1/239)$.

6. Compute the following indefinite integrals and check the answers through differentiation and simplification.

(a) $\displaystyle\int \dfrac{2}{\sqrt{4 + x^2}}\, dx$

(b) $\displaystyle\int \sqrt{(1 - cx^2)^3}\, dx$

(c) $\displaystyle\int \dfrac{1}{x^4 - 1}\, dx$

(d) $\displaystyle\int \dfrac{1}{x^4 - 4}\, dx$

(e) $\displaystyle\int \sin 3x \cos 2x\, dx$

7. Integrate the real function

$$x \mapsto \frac{1}{(a\,x + b)^2 (c\,x + d)^2}$$

and bring the result into the following form.

$$\frac{2a\,c \ln\left(\dfrac{c\,x + d}{a\,x + b}\right)}{(a\,d - b\,c)^3} - \frac{2a\,c\,x + a\,d + b\,c}{(a\,d - b\,c)^2(a\,x + b)(c\,x + d)}$$

Simplification Chart

procedure	trigonometric functions	exp and log	powers	special functions
expand	$\cos(x+y) \to \cos x \cos y - \sin x \sin y$ $\cos 2x \to 2\cos^2 x - 1$ $\cosh 3x \to 4\cosh^3 x - 3\cosh x$	$\exp(x+y) \to \exp x \exp y$ $\ln(xy) \to \ln x + \ln y$ $\ln(x/y) \to \ln x - \ln y$	$x^{(y+z)} \to x^y x^z$ $(xy)^z \to x^z y^z$ $(x/y)^z \to x^z/y^z$	$(n+1)! \to (n+1)n!$ $\Gamma(n+\frac{3}{2}) \to (n+\frac{1}{2})\Gamma(n+\frac{1}{2})$ $-\mathrm{dilog}(\frac{1}{x}) \to \mathrm{dilog}(x) + \frac{1}{2}\ln^2 x$
combine	$\cos x \cos y - \sin x \sin y \to \cos(x+y)$ $2\sinh x \cosh x \to \sinh 2x$ $4\cos^3 x \to \cos 3x + 3\cos x$	$\exp x \exp y \to \exp(x+y)$ $\ln x + \ln y \to \ln(xy)$ $\exp(x + a\ln y) \to y^a \exp x$	$x^y x^z \to x^{(y+z)}$ $(x^y)^z \to x^{yz}$ $\sqrt{x+1}\sqrt{x} \to \sqrt{x^2+x}$	$\sum_k a_k + \sum_k b_k \to \sum_k (a_k + b_k)$ $\int f + \int g \to \int f + g$
simplify	$\cos^2 x + \sin^2 x \to 1$ $\cosh^2 x - \sinh^x \to 1$ $\tan x \to \sin x / \cos x$	$\exp x \exp y \to \exp(x+y)$ $\ln x + \ln y \to \ln(xy)$ $\ln(x^y) \to y\ln x$	$x^y x^z \to x^{(y+z)}$ $(x/y)^z \to x^z y^{-z}$ $\sqrt{x^2+2x+1} \to x+1$	$\Gamma(n+\frac{1}{2})/\Gamma(n-\frac{1}{2}) \to n - \frac{1}{2}$ ${}_2F_1\left(\frac{1-n}{2}, \frac{-n}{2}; \frac{1}{2}; \frac{z^2}{t^2}\right) \to$ $\left((t+z)^n + (t-z)^n)\right)/2t^n$
convert	$\cos x \to (e^{ix} + e^{-ix})/2$ $\mathrm{arcsinh}\, x \to \ln(x + \sqrt{x^2+1})$ $\sin 2x \to 2\tan x/(1+\tan^2 x)$	$e^{ix} \leftrightarrow \cos x + i\sin x$	$\sqrt{a} \leftrightarrow \mathrm{RootOf}(\_Z^2 - a)$	$\binom{n}{k} \to \dfrac{n!}{k!(n-k)!}$ and other type conversions

14

Graphics

Two-dimensional graphics supported by Maple V Release 2 includes

- curves defined by functions of a single real variable,
- curves defined by parametric equations,
- implicit curves defined by an equation,
- data plots, and
- animation of two-dimensional graphics objects.

Maple provides three-dimensional graphics facilities to

- generate surfaces defined by functions of two real variables,
- generate space curves, tubes, and surfaces defined by parametric equations,
- generate implicit surfaces defined by an equation,
- generate surfaces from lists of three-dimensional data points, and
- show an animation of three-dimensional graphics objects.

When producing a two- or three-dimensional plot, Maple makes decisions about the number of sample points, positions of axes and tick marks, ranges of values to display, shading or coloring of the graph, and so on. You can modify graphs by using various options, such as choosing another coordinate system (polar, spherical, or cylindrical), or changing the grid size of a surface.

In this chapter, we shall describe the graphics facilities of Maple V Release 2 under the X Window System. However, most of the graphics examples are also possible when using a different user interface. We shall not treat every possible graphical routine and display option, but put stress on understanding the graphical structure underneath the plotting routines.

14.1 Some Basic Two-Dimensional Plots

Maple provides the procedure **plot** for graphing a function in one variable. Maple must of course know what kind of plotting or output device you are using. If you run Maple on a Macintosh, an MS-DOS computer, or on a Unix type computer with the worksheet user interface, then the system selects the display device and display driver automatically. Otherwise, you must inform Maple and, if necessary, allow it to send special character sequences for switching from text mode to graphics mode.

For example, if you want to use **plot** in a Tektronix emulation under MS-KERMIT on an MS-DOS machine you must first enter

```
> interface( plotdevice=tek, preplot=[27,12],
>    postplot=[24] ):
```

This command can be understood as follows:

▷ you inform Maple that you use a Tektronix 4014 terminal or some Tektronix emulation,

▷ the interface variable `preplot` is a list of integers which represent the ASCII codes of the characters `escape` and `formfeed`, which are sent before a plot to enter graphics mode, and

▷ the interface variable `postplot` represents the ASCII code of the character `cancel`, which is sent after completion of the plot and after pressing the Return key to re-enter text mode.

In some cases you can make the necessary arrangements swiftly with the procedure **plotsetup**. Details about available user interfaces can be found in the Maple Language Reference Manual [25].

Henceforth, we shall assume that Maple runs under the X Window System because this display driver will also meet the demands for producing three-dimensional plots.

Consider the function $f\colon x \longmapsto e^{-x^2}\sin(\pi x^3)$ on the interval $(-2,2)$.

```
> f := x -> exp(-x^2) * sin(Pi*x^3);
```
$$f := x \to e^{-x^2}\sin(\pi\, x^3)$$

The plot of this function is invoked by the command

```
> plot( f, -2..2 );
```

A 2D-plot window appears containing the graph of the function; the menu allows you to display and manipulate the Maple plot data structure. As shown in the screen dump below, you also copy the picture into the worksheet.

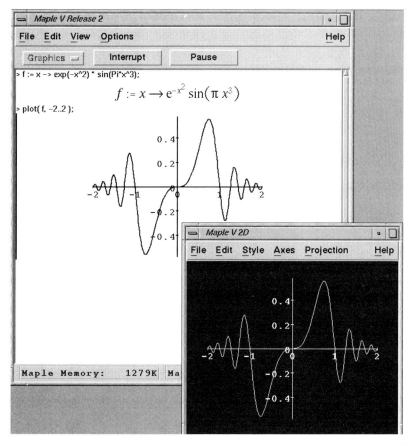

The above command is an example of the following general format for drawing a *function f* over the interval (a, b)

$$\textbf{plot}(\ f,\ a \mathbin{..} b, options\ );$$

where *options* describes zero or more options, as will be discussed in the next section.

An alternative way to obtain the graph of a function f defined by the *formula f(x)* is

$$\textbf{plot}(\ f(x),\ x = a \mathbin{..} b, options\ );$$

where $a \mathbin{..} b$ is the horizontal range (of x), and where *options* describes zero or more options. Note the difference in specifying the horizontal range when plotting a *function* and a *formula* — a function only needs a *range*, whereas a formula needs an equation of the form *variable = range*.

So, to plot the formula $e^{-x^2} \sin(\pi x^3)$ for x ranging from -2 to 2, you enter

```
> plot( f(x), x = -2..2 );
```

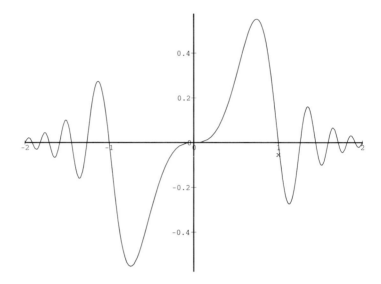

You can also look at the graph of the function over the entire real line or over a half-line.

```
> plot( f, -infinity .. infinity );
```

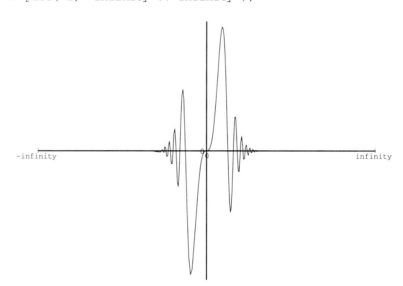

In this case, Maple transforms the entire real line into the interval $(-1, 1)$ by a function that approximates $x \longmapsto \frac{2}{\pi} \arctan(\frac{x}{2\pi})$.

You may plot more than one function at the same time, and on a color display Maple will choose different colors for the graphics objects.

```
> plot( {f(x), exp(-x^2), -exp(-x^2)}, x=-2..2 );
```

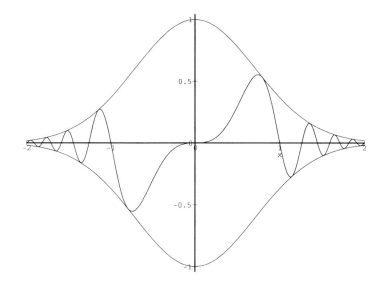

If you want to print a plot or place a plot in PostScript format into some file, you can tell Maple so.

```
> interface( plotdevice = postscript,
>    plotoutput = plotfile ):
```

Henceforth Maple directs the PostScript code which describes the picture to the file `plotfile`. You can simply print this file on a PostScript compatible printer — the picture is rotated ninety degrees and scaled so that it fits on a page of A4 format. You can also edit the file if necessary. You will have to do this when you want to embed the picture in some text: remove the lines

```
540 82 translate
90 rotate
```

which are close to the beginning of the PostScript file, and delete the line

```
showpage
```

at the end of the file. You may also need to adjust the scaling of the picture (by a command of type x y `scale`). After this editing you are ready to embed the PostScript code into other programs, such as FrameMaker or TEX. Less editting of the PostScript code generated by Maple is needed when it is used in combination with the psfig macro of TeX. This is how the pictures in this book are embedded in the text. In addition, we have removed the PostScript code that generates the frame around the plot.

You can reset the plotting to the X Windows display with

```
> interface( plotdevice = x11 ):
```

By the way, both this command and **plotsetup**(x11) suffice to inform Maple about how to display graphics when using the tty user interface of Maple under the X Window System.

14.2 Options of plot

When Maple plots a graph, it makes many choices. For example, it chooses the depicted range of the graph, sample points to make a smooth curve, which tickmarks to show, and so on. Maple takes care of choosing values for these options that are most convenient in daily use. However, you can customize it to your needs.

For example, to restrict the vertical range of a graph, you can add the range information to the plot command as a third argument. With the following command you plot the graph of the function defined by the formula $\frac{\sin^2 x}{x^2}$ over the interval $(-6,6)$, where parts of the graph outside the vertical range $[0,1]$ are not shown.

```
> plot( sin(x^2)/x^2, x=-6..6, 0..1 );
```

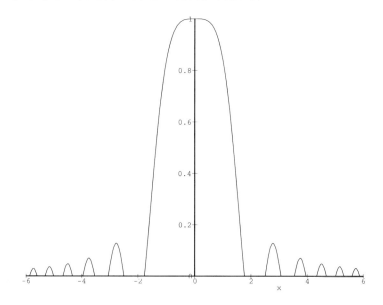

Note that Maple chooses the vertical scale which allows the largest display of the plot. When you want the same horizontal as vertical scale you can change this interactively or add the option `scaling=constrained` to the **plot** command.

```
plot( sin(x^2)/x^2, x=-6..6, scaling=constrained );
```

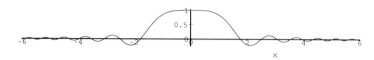

Sometimes, you must restrict the vertical range to get a good picture. In the graph below, you see that a few function values dominate over all the others so that the behavior of the tangent function over the given domain is not displayed very well. Often the only way to avoid (spurious) spikes in a graph is to specify a "reasonable" vertical range or to increase the number of sample points.

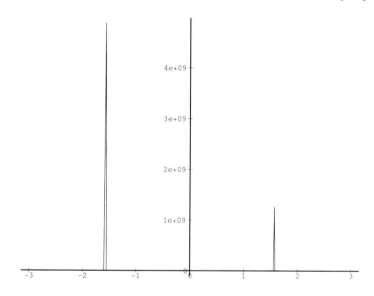

With the following command you plot the graph of the tangent over the interval $(-\pi, \pi)$, where parts of the graph outside the vertical range $[-10, 10]$ are not shown.

```
> plot( tan, -Pi..Pi, -10..10 );
```

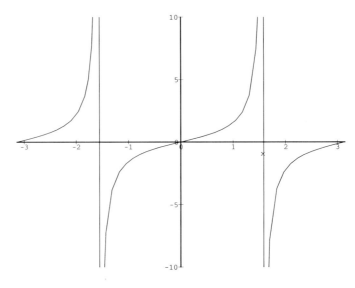

You may label a graph and the axes, and set the number of tickmarks along the axes.

```
> j := (n,x) -> sqrt(Pi/(2*x)) * BesselJ(n+1/2,x):
> plot( j(0,x), x=0..20, `j(0,x)`=-0.5..1,
> xtickmarks=8, ytickmarks=4, title=
> `Spherical Bessel function j(0,x) of the first kind` );
```

Spherical Bessel function j(0,x) of the first kind

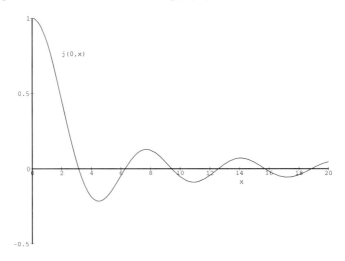

When labeling is done in the above way, you cannot do much about the size and placement of the labels but make specific changes in the PostScript code of the plot itself. Alternatively, you can use the command **textplot** and **display** from the *plots* package to draw text on a specific position and to display more than one plot in one picture, respectively.

```
> plot1 := plot( x->j(0,x), 0..20, -0.5..1, title=
>     `Spherical Bessel function j(0,x) of the first kind`,
>     xtickmarks=8, ytickmarks=4 ):
> plot2 := plots[textplot]( { [2,0.75,`j(0,x)`],
>     [14,-0.1,`x`] }, align={ABOVE,RIGHT} ):
> plots[display]( { plot1, plot2 } );
```

Spherical Bessel function j(0,x) of the first kind

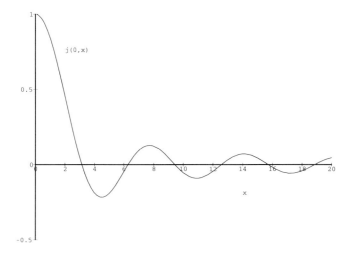

When graphing a function, Maple first computes a number of points of the graph — the number of sample points can be set via the option numpoints — and, by default, connects these points by straight lines.

Instead of using the plot style line, you may select other ones like point or patch (only affecting drawings of polygons). If you select the point style, Maple will draw crosses centered around the computed plot points.

```
> plot( sin, 0..2*Pi, scaling=constrained, style=point );
```

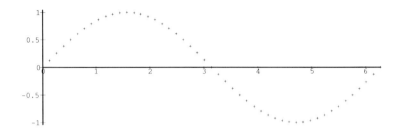

Data plots can easily be produced with point plot style; you put the data points in a list and plot the points with the point style. For example, to plot the first 9 prime numbers you can do

```
> plotpoints := [ seq( [i,ithprime(i)], i=1..9 ) ];

    plotpoints := [ [ 1, 2 ], [ 2, 3 ], [ 3, 5 ], [ 4, 7 ],

            [ 5, 11 ], [ 6, 13 ], [ 7, 17 ], [ 8, 19 ], [ 9, 23 ]

            ]

> plot( plotpoints, style=point );
```

As an example of the default `line` style we consider a graphical trace of twenty iterations of the cosine function with starting value 1.2. First we have to generate the list of points.

$$[1.2, \cos(1.2), \cos(1.2), \cos(1.2), \cos(1.2), \cos\big(\cos(1.2)\big),$$

$$\cos\big(\cos(1.2)\big), \cos\big(\cos(1.2)\big), \cos\big(\cos(1.2)\big), \cos\Big(\cos\big(\cos(1.2)\big)\Big), \ldots]$$

The most efficient way of producing the plot points is

```
> plotpoints := [seq( (cos@@(trunc((i+2)/4)))(1.2),
>    i=1..80 )]:
```

Next, we generate plots of this list of points connected by straight lines, of the identity function, and of the cosine function on the interval $(0, \pi/2)$ and with vertical range $[0, 1]$.

```
> plot1 := plot( plotpoints, x=0..Pi/2, y=0..1,
>    style=line ):
> plot2 := plot( x, x=0..Pi/2, y=0..1 ):
> plot3 := plot( cos(x), x=0..Pi/2, y=0..1 ):
```

We show the plots in one picture with the command **display** from the *plots* package.

```
> plots[display]( { plot1, plot2, plot3 }, title=
>    `cobweb-model of iterated cosine starting at 1.2` );
```

cobweb-model of iterated cosine starting at 1.2

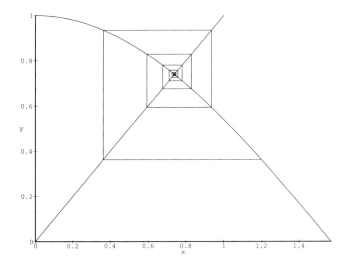

14.3 The Structure of Two-Dimensional Graphics

To know how reliable the plotting facilities of Maple are, it is important to have a good idea of how plotting is done. The making of a plot proceeds in two phases. In the first phase, the plot points are computed and put in a **PLOT** object. In the second phase, this object is rendered on the screen. In this section, we shall concentrate on the first phase of plotting.

A two-dimensional graphics object in Maple is a **PLOT** function call with arguments describing the axes, function, computed plot points, plot style, and so on. The following object describes a triangle with vertices (1,1), (2,2), and (3,1).

```
> PLOT( CURVES( [ [1,1], [2,2], [3,1], [1,1] ] ),
>    AXESSTYLE(NONE) );
```

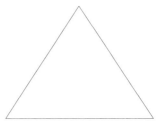

The arguments CURVES(...) and AXESSTYLE are parts of the arguments of the graphics object obtained by

```
> P := plot( [ [1,1], [2,2], [3,1], [1,1] ], axes=none );

    P := PLOT( CURVES(

            [ [ 1., 1. ], [ 2., 2. ], [ 3., 1. ], [ 1., 1. ] ],

            COLOUR( RGB, 0, 0, 0 ) ),

            VIEW( DEFAULT, DEFAULT ),

            AXESTICKS( DEFAULT, DEFAULT ), AXESSTYLE( NONE ) )

> P;    # plot the graphics object
```

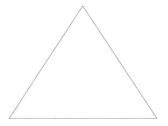

A more general example of a graphics object behind a plot is the plot structure for the graph of the function

$$x \longmapsto \sqrt{2} - \sqrt{2\sqrt{x}}\,.$$

```
> f := x -> sqrt(2) - sqrt(2*sqrt(x)):
> P := plot( f(x), x=0..1, y=0..sqrt(2),
>    title=`graph of sqrt(2) - sqrt(2*sqrt(x))` );
```

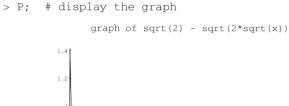

P := PLOT(CURVES([[0, 1.414213562373095],

. . . . . .

[.9798891848, .007164507115447138], [1., 0]]

, COLOUR(*RGB*, 0, 0, 0)),

TITLE(*graph of sqrt(2) - sqrt(2*sqrt(x))*),

AXESLABELS(*x*, *y*),

VIEW(0 .. 1., 0 .. 1.414213562),

AXESTICKS(*DEFAULT*, *DEFAULT*))

Maple associates a graphics object with a function in one variable on an interval. This object, which is a regular Maple object, will be used for straight line interpolation between computed plot points.

```
> P;   # display the graph
```

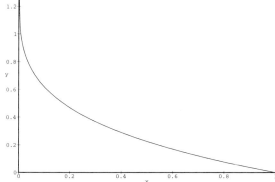

First, the argument in the **plot** call which describes the function is
evaluated. Hereafter, the function values at the sample points are computed
numerically. In order to increase the speed of plotting, this computing of
function values is usually done in hardware floating-point arithmetic.

To obtain nice smooth plots Maple has an algorithm for refining the
number of sample points where necessary. First, the function values of
49 almost equidistant points which span the interval are computed. Next,
Maple looks at these points as being connected by line segments. If the
kink angle between two adjacent line segments is too large, then Maple will
sample more points around this kink. Maple will not go on forever with
subdividing the plot interval: the maximum resolution is controlled by the
option `resolution`. The default value of the display resolution is 200. So,
by default, the number of sample points is between 49 and 200.

You can zoom in or out by the **replot** command in the *plots* package.

```
> plots[replot]( P, x=0..0.01, y=1..sqrt(2), title=
>     `zoomed-in graph of sqrt(2) - sqrt(2*sqrt(x))` );
```

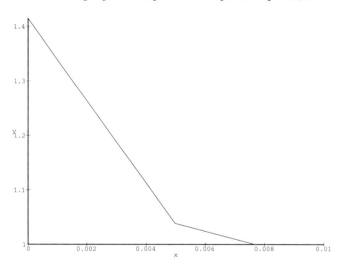

zoomed-in graph of sqrt(2) - sqrt(2*sqrt(x))

In the above example, Maple already uses the adaptive sampling scheme
for small values of x. You are informed about this when you set a higher
value to `infolevel[plot]`.

```
> infolevel[plot] := 2:
> plot( f(x), x=0..1, y=0..sqrt(2) ):
```

```
plot/usual:   subdividing interval   [0, 1.414213562373095]   [
1992940812.0E-11, .8828538807382116]   [4125819458.0E-11, .
7768421906038662]
plot/usual:   subdividing interval   [0, 1.414213562373095]   [
1992940812.0E-11, .8828538807382116]   [3059380135.0E-11, .
8227563140681077]
plot/usual:   subdividing interval   [0, 1.414213562373095]   [
9964704060.0E-12, .9673951108759665]   [1992940812.0E-11, .
8828538807382116]
plot/usual:   subdividing interval   [4982352030.0E-12, 1.
038485528239944]   [9964704060.0E-12, .9673951108759665]   [
1992940812.0E-11, .8828538807382116]
plot/usual:   subdividing interval   [1992940812.0E-11, .
8828538807382116]   [3059380135.0E-11, .8227563140681077]   [
4125819458.0E-11, .7768421906038662]
plot/usual:   subdividing interval   [3059380135.0E-11, .
8227563140681077]   [4125819458.0E-11, .7768421906038662]   [
6272836207.0E-11, .7064617588338121]
```

Whenever you notice some irregularities in a graph, such as in the graph of the function defined by $\dfrac{x}{1-\cos 5x}$ over the interval $(-5, 5)$,

```
> plot( x/(1-cos(5*x)), x=-5..5, -5..5 );
```

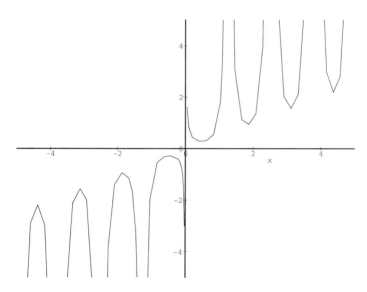

you can try to improve the picture and get a nicer, smoother plot by increasing the number of sample points. Just set a higher values to the option numpoints.

```
> plot( x/(1-cos(5*x)), x=-5..5, -5..5, numpoints=200 );
```

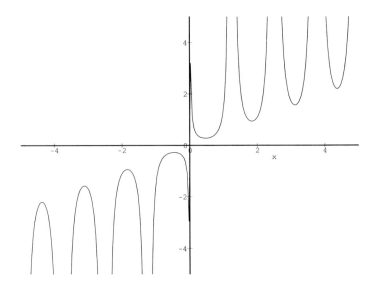

Until now we reset options of individual plot commands. If you want to change a default option for all subsequent plots in a session, then you should use the procedure **setoptions**.

14.4 Special Two-Dimensional Plots

There is more to graphics than plotting a function in one unknown. In this section, we shall list a few more two-dimensional graphics capabilities

Parametric Plots

The general format for drawing a two-dimensional plane curve defined in the Cartesian coordinate system by parametric *formulas* $x = f(t)$, $y = g(t)$ is

$$\textbf{plot}(\ [\ f(t),\ g(t),\ t = a \mathbin{..} b],\ options\ );$$

where $a \mathbin{..} b$ is the range of the independent variable t, and where *options* describes zero or more options.

As an example, we draw a spiral in the plane.

```
> plot( [ t*cos(2*Pi*t), t*sin(2*Pi*t), t=0..10 ],
>    numpoints=500, scaling=constrained, axes=none );
```

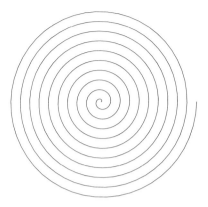

When the parametric curve is defined by *functions*, the independent variable must be omitted in the **plot** command. An example:

```
> plot( [ cos, sin, 0..2*Pi ], scaling=constrained );
```

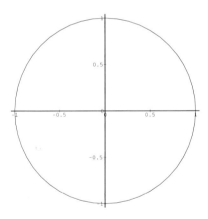

Polar Plots

Polar plots can be produced in the same way as parametric two-dimensional plots except that the option `coords = polar` should be added. The general command is

$$\textbf{plot}(\,[\,r(t)\,,\;\phi(t)\,,\;t = t_0 \mathinner{..} t_1],\,\texttt{coords} = \texttt{polar}\,,\;\textit{options}\,);$$

where $r(t)$ and $\phi(t)$ are the radial and angular function, respectively. An example:

```
> plot ( [ sin(t)/t, t, t=-6*Pi..6*Pi ], coords=polar,
>    numpoints=250, title=`Cochleoid` );
```

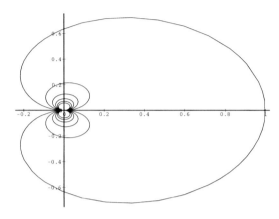

Cochleoid

Let us include, just for fun, a look-alike of the Maple logo. It is produced as a polar plot by the command **polarplot** from the *plots* package; we use the functional variant of the procedure call.

```
> S := t -> 100/(100+(t-Pi/2)^8): # for scaling
> R := t -> S(t)*(2-sin(7*t)-cos(30*t)/2):
> plots[polarplot]( [ R, t->t, t=-Pi/2..3/2*Pi ],
>    axes=none, numpoints=1000 ):
```

Plots of Plane Algebraic Curves

In the *plots* package resides the procedure **implicitplot** to draw a two-dimensional plane curve defined by an equation. An example:

```
> with( plots, implicitplot ): # load the library function
> implicitplot( x^3 + y^3 - 5*x*y +1/5 = 0,
>    x=-3..3, y=-3..3, grid=[50,50] );
```

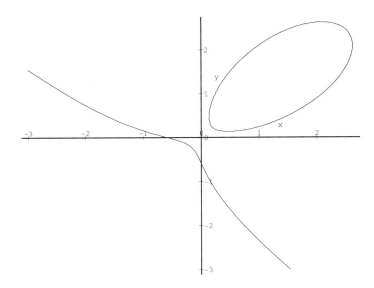

In essence, the method used is to consider the equation as a function in three-dimensional space and generate a contour of the equation cutting through the *z*-plane. Drawbacks of this method are that it generates rough graphs (cf. the graph obtained without the grid option used), and that it does not guarantee correct drawings near singularities and intersections of the curve. Algebraically, this means that Maple may have problems with any point (x, y) on the curve $f(x, y) = 0$ where the partial derivatives $\frac{\partial f}{\partial x}(x, y)$ and $\frac{\partial f}{\partial y}(x, y)$ are both zero. A typical example is the curve

$$2x^4 + y^4 - 3x^2y - 2y^3 + y^2 = 0,$$

which has has two singular points, (0,0) and (0,1), where the branches intersect [121]. Even when a very fine grid is used, Maple cannot draw the graph correctly with **implicitplot**. For example, the following computation took one hour and requested 22 MB main memory on a Silicon Graphics Indigo Server, and still does not provide a satisfactory plot around the origin.

```
> implicitplot( 2*x^4 + y^4 - 3*x^2*y - 2*y^3 + y^2,
>    x=-5/2..5/2, y=-5/2..5/2, grid=[300,300],
```

```
>    scaling=constrained );
```

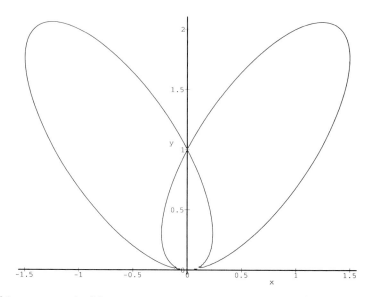

In this case, you had better compute a parametrization of the curve.

```
> subs( x=r*cos(phi), y=r*sin(phi),
>    2*x^4 + y^4 - 3*x^2*y - 2*y^3 + y^2 ):
> factor(");
```

$$r^2 \left(2 \; r^2 \; \cos(\phi)^4 + r^2 \; \sin(\phi)^4 - 3 \; r \; \cos(\phi)^2 \; \sin(\phi) \right.$$
$$\left. - \; 2 \; r \; \sin(\phi)^3 + \sin(\phi)^2 \right)$$

```
> eqn := op(2,"):
> sols := map( simplify, { solve(eqn,r) },
>   {sin(phi)^2 + cos(phi)^2 = 1}, [cos(phi),sin(phi)] ):
> sols := map( unapply, sols, phi );
```

$$sols := \left\{ \phi \rightarrow \left(-\sin(\phi)^3 + 3 \; \sin(\phi) \right. \right.$$
$$\left. - \; \sin(\phi) \; \cos(\phi) \; \sqrt{11 \; \sin(\phi)^2 + 1} \right) \bigg/ \bigg($$
$$6 \; \sin(\phi)^4 - 8 \; \sin(\phi)^2 + 4 \bigg), \; \phi \rightarrow \left(-\sin(\phi)^3 \right.$$
$$\left. + \; 3 \; \sin(\phi) + \sin(\phi) \; \cos(\phi) \; \sqrt{11 \; \sin(\phi)^2 + 1} \right.$$
$$\left. \right) \bigg/ \bigg(6 \; \sin(\phi)^4 - 8 \; \sin(\phi)^2 + 4 \bigg) \right\}$$

```
> plots[polarplot]( sols, 0..2*Pi, view=[-5/2..5/2,
>    0..9/4], scaling=constrained, color=black );
```

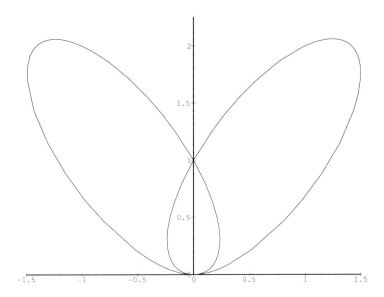

Logarithmic Plots

Logarithmic plots and double-logarithmic plots are available in Maple through the procedure **logplot** and **loglogplot** in the *plots* package, respectively.

```
> with( plots, logplot, loglogplot ):
> # use a random number generator for normal distribution
> random := stats[RandNormal](0,1):
> # generate data around the function x -> x+sin(x)
> plotpoints := [ seq( [ 0.2*i,
>    exp(0.2*i) + 0.1*random() ], i=0..20 ) ]:
> logplot( plotpoints, style=point );
```

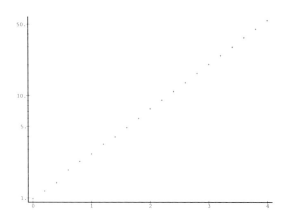

```
> loglogplot( x^3 + exp(-x), x=1/10..100,
>    scaling=constrained );
```

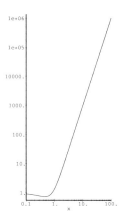

Plots of Conformal Mappings

One example of the procedure **conformal** in the *plots* package will suffice.
The logarithm maps the following rectangular grid in the complex plane.

```
> with( plots, conformal ): # load the library function
> conformal( z, z=-2..2+3*I, -2..2+3*I,
>    grid=[15,15], axes=frame );
```

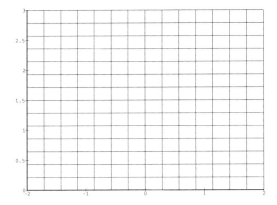

to the grid

```
> conformal( ln(z), z=-2..2+3*I, -2..2+3*I,
>    grid=[15,15], numxy=[100,100], axes=frame );
```

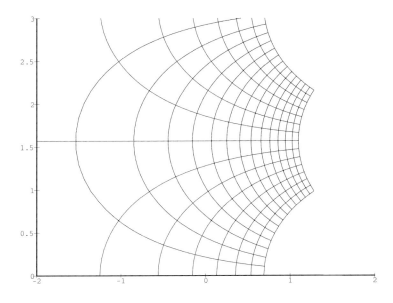

Curve Fitting

In the statistics package *stats* resides a facility to apply the linear regression method to numerical data and plot the least-squares fit. An example will suffice.

First, we load the statistics package, decrease precision, and use a random number generator for normal distribution to generate data around the function $x \longmapsto x + \sin x$.

```
> with(stats):  Digits := 5:  N :=  RandNormal(0,1):
> data := array( [ seq( [ 0.3*i,
>    0.3*i + sin(0.3*i+0.5*N()) ], i=0..10 ) ] ):
> statmat := putkey( data, [x,y] ); # statistical matrix
```

$$
statmat := \begin{bmatrix} x & y \\ 0 & .82273 \\ .3 & .22935 \\ .6 & 1.3070 \\ .9 & 1.8091 \\ 1.2 & 1.9199 \\ 1.5 & 2.4785 \\ 1.8 & 2.5467 \\ 2.1 & 2.8634 \\ 2.4 & 2.8543 \\ 2.7 & 3.1021 \\ 3.0 & 3.6508 \end{bmatrix}
$$

Next, we fit these data to the function $x \longmapsto a + bx + c\sin x$, and plot the
original data together with the fitted curve.

```
> parms := regression( statmat, y = a + b*x + c*sin(x) );
```

$$parms := \{\, c = .34586, \ a = .46216, \ b = .98174 \,\}$$

```
> assign( parms ): # assign values to a, b, and c
> statplot( statmat, y=a+b*x+c*sin(x) );
```

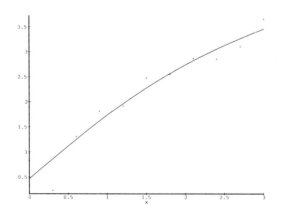

14.5 Plot Aliasing

Adaptive two-dimensional plotting produces, in most cases, reasonable
graphs with a minimum of sample points. But you should keep alert for
insufficient sampling. As rather extreme case of plot aliasing, we plot the
function $x \longmapsto x + \sin(2\pi x)$ on the interval $(0, 49)$.

```
> plot(x+sin(2*Pi*x),x=0..49);
```

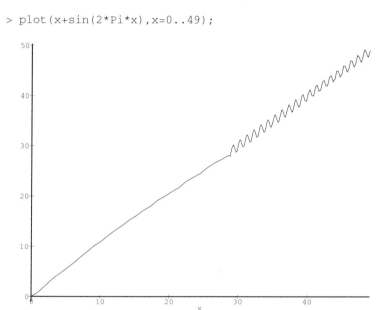

For x-values smaller than thirty, the plot is close to the line $y = x$. This
is wrong! The reason is that because of the default choice of forty-nine,
almost equidistant sample points, the computed function values first tend
to be close to the identity function. Maple has no reason to believe that
there is something wrong and no reason to sample more points or to sample
other points. You yourself will have to decide to sample more point (by
the option `numpoints`) or choose another plot range.

14.6 A Common Mistake

When you ask Maple to plot a function, say f, as a function of x by entering
a command of the form **plot**($f(x)$, $x = x_{\min}..x_{\max}$), Maple first evaluates
the $f(x)$, presumably getting a symbolic expression in terms of x, and
subsequently evaluates this expression numerically for the sample points.
This may cause you some problems when you try to plot a piecewise defined
function or a numerical function. Below we present one example and two
ways to overcome these problems.

Suppose that you have defined the function f by

```
> f := t -> if t>0 then exp(-1/t^2) else 0 fi:
```

and want to plot it.

```
> plot( f(t), t=-1..4 );
Error, (in f) cannot evaluate boolean
```

As you see, you get an error message back instead of a graph. The reason
is that Maple evaluates f(t) and the system gets into trouble because it
cannot pass the test t>0. The trick of the trade is to avoid premature
evaluation by using apostrophes around the first argument.

```
> plot( 'f(t)', t=-1..4 );
```

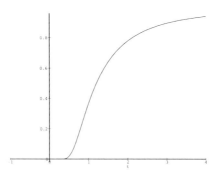

Another option is to use the functional notation. For example, the function
f and its derivative f' can be plotted in one picture with

```
> plot( {f,D(f)}, -1..4 );
```

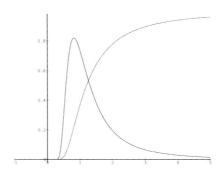

14.7 Some Basic Three-Dimensional Plots

Plotting a function of two variables is as easy as plotting a function in one variable. Simply use the Maple procedure **plot3d** and specify the ranges of both variables. As an example, let us plot the surface defined by $z = \cos(x\,y)$, where x and y range from -3 to 3.

```
> plot3d( cos(x*y), x=-3..3, y=-3..3 );
```

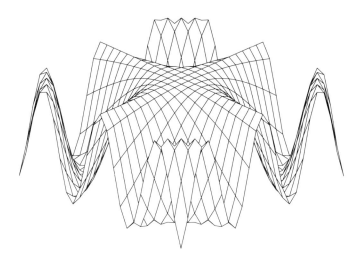

The above command is an example of the following general format for drawing a surface defined by the formula $f(x, y)$ of two variables x and y:

$$\textbf{plot3d}(\ f(x,y),\ x = a\mathrel{..}b,\ y = c\mathrel{..}d,\ \textit{options}\ );$$

where $a \mathrel{..} b$ and $c \mathrel{..} d$ define the range of x and y, and where *options* describes zero or more options, as will be discussed in the next section.

An alternative way of obtaining the graph of a function f in two variables is

$$\textbf{plot3d}(\ f,\ a\mathrel{..}b,\ c\mathrel{..}d,\ \textit{options}\ );$$

where $a \mathrel{..} b$ and $c \mathrel{..} d$ define the two horizontal ranges, and where *options* describes zero or more options.

Below we draw again the surface of the function $(x, y) \longmapsto \cos(x\,y)$, but now we choose the functional notation and change some of the options. This can be done interactively by selecting proper menu items from the 3D-plot window. But to ensure that you can reproduce the graph, we have added all options in the **plot3d** command.

```
> f := (x,y) -> cos(x*y):
> plot3d( f, -3..3, -3..3, grid=[49,49], axes=boxed,
>     scaling=constrained, style=patchcontour,
>     shading=zhue );
```

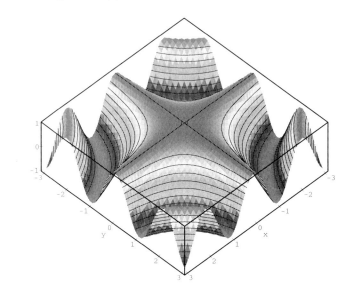

14.8 Options of plot3d

Just as in the two-dimensional case, there are many options to customize
a plot. Under the X Window System you can change many options by
selecting menu items and/or by mouse actions. We will discuss some of the
options and refer to the on-line system for others (enter **?plot3d,options**).

Style

A surface can be rendered in several ways with the optional argument
style = *displaystyle*. The simplest style is point, which only draws the
computed plot points. Plot points are connected with line segments when
the style option line is chosen. By the way, the sample points of a surface
are in general the grid points of a rectangular uniformly spaced grid. When
adjacent plot points are connected by line segments, the result is a picture
of style wireframe which approximates the shape of the surface. In the
first plot of the previous section, the line segments that would be hidden
if the surface were opaque are not displayed: this is Maple's default style
hidden. You can choose the style patch if you want to display the surface
in full color or gray shading. If you do not want the grid displayed, choose

the option `patchnogrid`. With the style option `contour` only the contour lines of the surface are drawn. A combination of two options is the style option `patchcontour`, illustrated in the last picture.

Shading

In Maple a surface can be colored (or gray shaded) in three ways: `xyz`, `xy`, and `z` shading. When you choose the option `shading` = `z`, the color/gray shading is according to the z value of the points on the surface. In the `xy` or `xyz` shading schemes, each of the axes has its own range of colors and these colors are added together for a point on the surface. The options `zhue` and `zgrayscale` produce graphs with color hues and gray levels depending on the z-values.

Axes

With the option `axes` you specify how the axes are to be drawn. There are four choices: `none`, `normal`, `boxed`, and `framed`. The names speak for themselves; we only remark that framed axes are drawn along the edges of the surface and in this way interfere the least with the surface.

Orientation and Projection

Rendering of a three-dimensional graphics object in two dimensions on a screen or on paper is commonly done by projection. The center of projection (or view point) is described in spherical coordinates with respect to the local Cartesian coordinate system at the center of the bounding box.

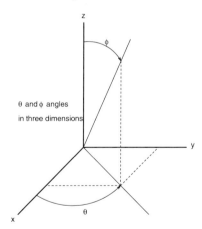

The angles θ and ϕ can be set with the option `orientation` = $[\theta, \phi]$. Increasing the value of rotation angle θ rotates the plot counter-clockwise. When the rotation angle is set to zero, you look down on the front side of the surface.

The angle ϕ controls how high above the surface you are: the value zero means that you look straight down on the surface, ninety degrees means

that you look edge on at the xy plane, and more than ninety degrees means
that look up from beneath the surface.

The option `projection` = r, where r is a real constant in the range
$[0, 1]$, specifies the distance from the view point to the surface. Value
0 (`fisheye`) means touching, 1 (`orthogonal`) means infinitely far away;
`normal` value is $\frac{1}{2}$.

Pictures tell you more than words. Below, plots generated initially by

```
> plot( x^3-3*x*y^2, x=-1..1, y=-1..1,
>     style=patch, axes=boxed );
```

are shown from different points of view.

theta=45, phi=45

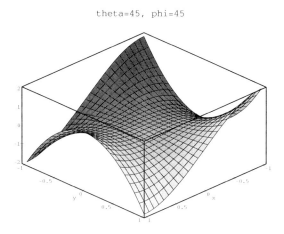

theta=5, phi=45

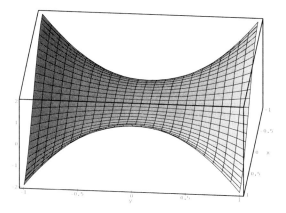

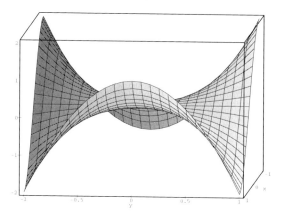

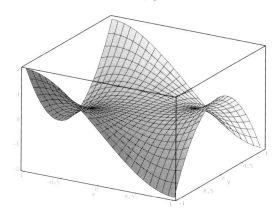

Note that changing the coloring scheme or changing the view point does not imply recomputing the graphics object. It is only a matter of rendering the picture on the screen. This does not hold for the next option.

Grid Size

In the three-dimensional case, Maple has no algorithm to refine the grid of sample points. In other words, unlike two-dimensional plotting, **plot3d** uses no adaptive sampling scheme. A default grid with twenty-five equidistant points in both directions is used. This can be changed by the option grid = $[m,n]$, if you want m points in the x direction and n points in the y direction.

View Frame

Like in two-dimensional plotting, you may want to restrict the vertical range, or even all three ranges of the surface. This is possible with the option `view`. There are two formats:

$$view = z_{min}..z_{max}$$

and

$$view = [x_{min}..x_{max}, y_{min}..y_{max}, z_{min}..z_{max}].$$

You can reset default options for all subsequent calls of **plot3d** by the procedure **setoptions3d**.

14.9 The Structure of Three-Dimensional Graphics

The making of a three-dimensional plot proceeds in two phases, similar to the way two-dimensional plots are generated. In the first phase, the plot points are computed and put in a **PLOT3D** object. In the second phase, this object is rendered on the screen. In this section, we shall present two examples of three-dimensional graphics objects, which can serve as prototypes for others.

A three-dimensional graphics object in Maple is a **PLOT3D** function call with arguments describing the axes, function, computed plot points, plot style, grid size, coloring, and so on.

The following object describes the edges of the tetrahedron with vertices $(1, 1, 1), (-1, -1, 1), (-1, 1, -1)$, and $(1, -1, -1)$.

```
> PLOT3D( POLYGONS( [ [1,1,1], [-1,-1,1], [-1,1,-1] ],
>    [ [1,1,1], [-1,-1,1], [1,-1,-1] ],
>    [ [-1,1,-1], [1,-1,-1], [-1,-1,1] ],
>    [ [-1,1,-1], [1,-1,-1], [1,1,1] ] ),
>    STYLE(LINE), AXESSTYLE(BOX),
>    ORIENTATION(30,60) );
```

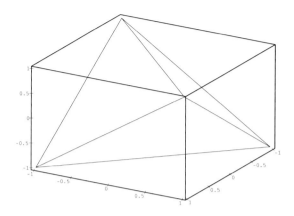

The arguments POLYGONS(...), STYLE(...), and AXESSTYLE(...) are
parts of the arguments of the graphics object obtained by

```
> P := plots[polygonplot3d]( [
>    [ [1,1,1], [-1,-1,1], [-1,1,-1] ],
>    [ [1,1,1], [-1,-1,1], [1,-1,-1] ],
>    [ [-1,1,-1], [1,-1,-1], [-1,-1,1] ],
>    [ [-1,1,-1], [1,-1,-1], [1,1,1] ] ],
>    style=line, axes=boxed, orientation=[30,60],
>    color=red );

     P := PLOT3D( POLYGONS( [

              [ 1., 1., 1. ], [ -1., -1., 1. ], [ -1., 1., -1. ]

              ], [

              [ 1., 1., 1. ], [ -1., -1., 1. ], [ 1., -1., -1. ]

              ], [ [ -1., 1., -1. ], [ 1., -1., -1. ],

              [ -1., -1., 1. ] ], [

              [ -1., 1., -1. ], [ 1., -1., -1. ], [ 1., 1., 1. ]

              ] ), STYLE( LINE ), AXESSTYLE( BOX ),

              COLOUR( RGB, 1.00000000, 0, 0 ),

              PROJECTION( 30., 60., 1 ) )
```

```
> P;   # plot the graphics object
```

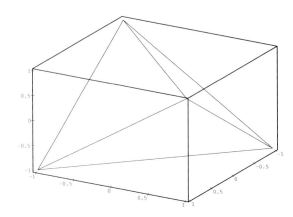

A more general example of a graphics object behind a plot is the plot structure for the graph of the function $(x, y) \longmapsto x\,y^2$.

```
> P := plot3d( x*y^2 , x=-1..1, y=-1..1, grid=[5,5],
>    axes=boxed, orientation=[30,30], style=line,
>    title=`graph of z=xy^2` );
```

P := PLOT3D(GRID(-1. .. 1., -1. .. 1., [[-1.,

    -.2500000000000000, 0, -.2500000000000000, -1.]

    , [-.5000000000000000, -.1250000000000000, 0,

    -.1250000000000000, -.5000000000000000],

    [0, 0, 0, 0, 0], [.5000000000000000,

    .1250000000000000, 0, .1250000000000000,

    .5000000000000000], [

    1., .2500000000000000, 0, .2500000000000000, 1.

    ]]), STYLE(*LINE*), AXESSTYLE(*BOX*),

    TITLE(*graph of z=xy^2*), AXESLABELS(*x, y,*),

    PROJECTION(30., 30., 1))

Maple associates a graphics object with a function in two variables on a rectangular grid. This object, which is a regular Maple object, will be used for straight line interpolation between adjacent plot points.

```
> P;   # display the graph
```

graph of z=xy^2

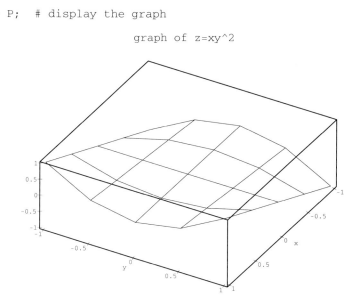

First, the argument in the **plot3d** call which describes the function is evaluated. Hereafter, the function values at the grid points are computed numerically, row by row. In order to increase the speed of plotting, this computation of function values is usually done in hardware floating-point arithmetic. Unlike two-dimensional plotting, no automatic refinement of the grid takes place when kink angles become large.

14.10 Special Three-Dimensional Plots

The Maple *plots* package, which provides provides utility routines for two- and three-dimensional plotting, has been mentioned several times before in this chapter. Most special three-dimensional plots can be generated with procedures from this package. Therefore, let us load the package and see what are its contents.

```
> with(plots);
```

[*animate*, *animate3d*, *conformal*, *contourplot*,

cylinderplot, *densityplot*, *display*, *display3d*,

> *fieldplot*, *fieldplot3d*, *gradplot*, *gradplot3d*,
>
> *implicitplot*, *implicitplot3d*, *loglogplot*,
>
> *logplot*, *matrixplot*, *odeplot*, *pointplot*,
>
> *polarplot*, *polygonplot*, *polygonplot3d*,
>
> *polyhedraplot*, *replot*, *setoptions*,
>
> *setoptions3d*, *spacecurve*, *sparsematrixplot*,
>
> *sphereplot*, *surfdata*, *textplot*, *textplot3d*,
>
> *tubeplot*]

We give a few examples, which also show you uses of some of the options described in §14.8.

Parametric Plots

A three-dimensional space curve can be drawn with **spacecurve**.

```
> spacecurve( {
>    [t*cos(2*Pi*t),t*sin(2*Pi*t),2+t],
>    [2+t,t*cos(2*Pi*t),t*sin(2*Pi*t)],
>    [t*cos(2*Pi*t),2+t,t*sin(2*Pi*t)] }, t=0..10,
>    numpoints=400, orientation=[40,70],
>    style=line, axes=boxed );
```

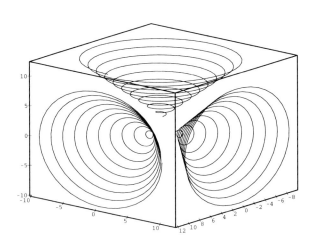

The general format for drawing a three-dimensional surface defined in the Cartesian coordinate system by parametric *formulas*

$$x = f(s,t),\ y = g(s,t),\ z = h(s,t)$$

is

> **plot3d(** $[\ f(s,t),\ g(s,t),\ h(s,t),\ s = a \mathbin{..} b,\ t = c \mathbin{..} d\ ]$ *options* **);**

where $a \mathbin{..} b$ and $c \mathbin{..} d$ are the ranges of the independent variables s and t, and where *options* describes zero or more options.

As an example, we draw the Helicoid defined by the parametrization

$$(\phi, z) \longmapsto (r \cos \phi,\ r \sin \phi,\ \phi),$$

where $0 \le r \le 1$ and $0 \le \phi \le 6\pi$.

```
> plot3d( [ r*cos(phi), r*sin(phi), phi ],
>    r=0..1, phi=0..6*Pi, grid=[15,45], style=patch,
>    orientation=[55,70], shading=zhue, axes=boxed );
```

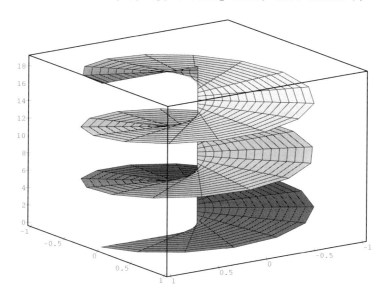

Spherical and cylindrical coordinate systems are also supported by Maple. A few examples:

```
> S := sphereplot( 1, theta=0..2*Pi, phi=0..Pi,
>    style=patch, scaling=constrained ):  S;
```

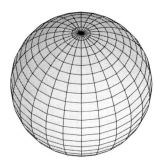

```
> C := cylinderplot( 1/2, theta=0..2*Pi, z=-2..2,

>    style=patch, scaling=constrained ):  C;
```

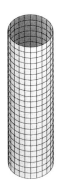

```
> display3d( {S,C}, style=patchcontour, axes=boxed,

>    orientation=[20,70], scaling=constrained );
```

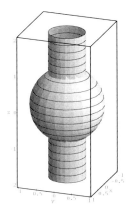

Tube Plot

The **tubeplot** procedure defines a tube about one or more three-dimensional space curves. Let us draw in this way the torus of type (4,7).

```
> r := a + b*cos(n*t):   z := c*sin(n*t):
> curve:=[ r*cos(m*t), r*sin(m*t), z ]:
> a:=2:   b:=4/5:   c:=1:   m:=4:   n:=7:
> tubeplot( curve, t=0..2*Pi, radius=1/4, numpoints=200,
>    tubepoints=20, orientation=[45,10], style=patch,
>    shading=xyz, title=`torusknot of type 4,7` );
```

torusknot of type 4,7

Contour Plot

contourplot does what its name suggests. The number of contours can be set by the option `contours` (default value: twenty). As an application of contour plotting, we draw potential lines of a configuration of four unit point charges located in a plane at positions $(-1,0)$, $(1,0)$, $(0,-1)$, and $(0,1)$. In general, the strength of the potential field at position P when point charges q_i are located at positions P_i is given by

$$U = \sum_i q_i \, \log\big(distance(P, P_i)\big).$$

```
> U := log(sqrt((x+1)^2+y^2)) + log(sqrt((x-1)^2+y^2))
>   + log(sqrt((y+1)^2+x^2)) + log(sqrt((y-1)^2+x^2)):
> contourplot( U, x=-3/2..3/2, y=-3/2..3/2, contours=30,
>   numpoints=2500, color=black ) ;
```

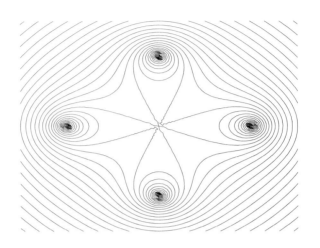

A density plot of U can be generated with **densityplot**.

```
> densityplot( U, x=-3/2..3/2, y=-3/2..3/2,
>   numpoints=1225, axes=boxed);
```

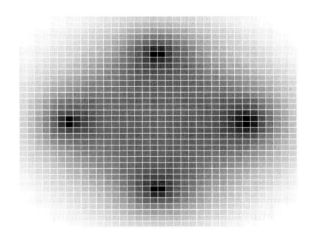

Implicit Plot

Non-singular surfaces defined by an equation in the Cartesian coordinate system can be plotted with **implicitplot3d**. The Catenoid is defined by $\cosh z = \sqrt{x^2 + y^2}$, and can be drawn as follows.

```
> implicitplot3d( cosh(z)=sqrt(x^2+y^2),
>    x=-3..3, y=-3..3, z=-5..5, grid=[15,15,20],
>    style=patchcontour, axes=boxed, orientation=[30,70] );
```

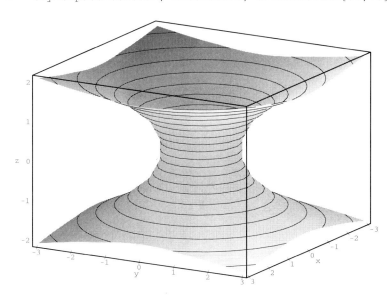

Polyhedra

Some popular polyhedra such as the tetrahedron, octahedron, and dodecahedron can easily be drawn with **polyhedraplot**. From the help file:

```
> polyhedraplot( [0,0,0], polytype=dodecahedron,
> style=patch, scaling=constrained, orientation=[71,66] );
```

14.11 Animation

We end this chapter with some animations. Maple animations are a
sequence of pictures ("frames") which are displayed in rapid succession
in an animation window. In the screen dump below, you see the animation window of a moving sine wave. You see that it is generated with the
procedure **animate**

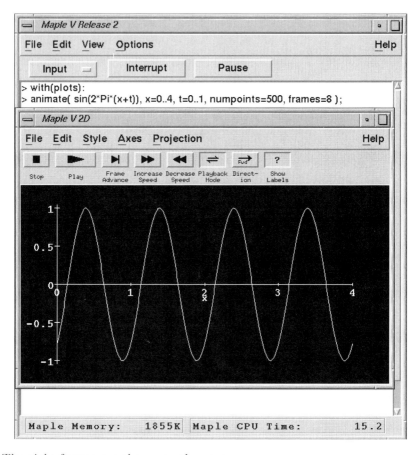

The eight frames are shown on the next page.

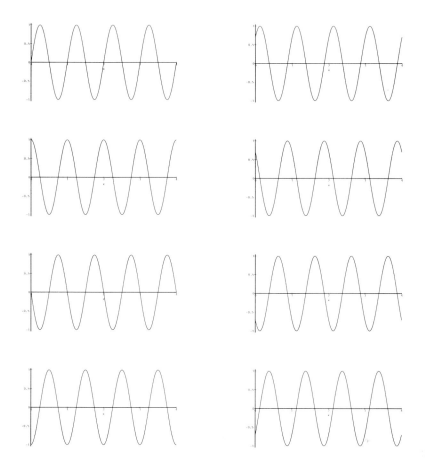

Animations of three-dimensional surfaces generated by a formula or function and surfaces in parametric representation can be made with **animate3d**. Experiment with deformations of your favorite surface.

We want to stress that animations, like other plot structures, are regular Maple data structures. To illustrate this, we produce below an animation of implicit plots, by building up the necessary animation structure. First, we generate a table of implicit plots.

```
> for i from 0 to 8 do
>    P[i] := implicitplot( x^3 +y^3 - 5*x*y = 1-i/4,
>    x=-3..3, y=-3..3 )
> od:
```

From each plot data structure P[i] we select the CURVES part.

```
> for i from 0 to 8 do
>   C[i] := [ op(1,P[i]) ]
> od:
```

From these curves we build the animation structure, which is of type

$$\text{PLOT}(\textbf{ANIMATE}([\textit{graphics object}_1], \ldots, [\textit{graphics object}_n])).$$

```
> PLOT( ANIMATE( seq( C[i], i=0..8 ) ) );
```

The subsequent frames are the following.

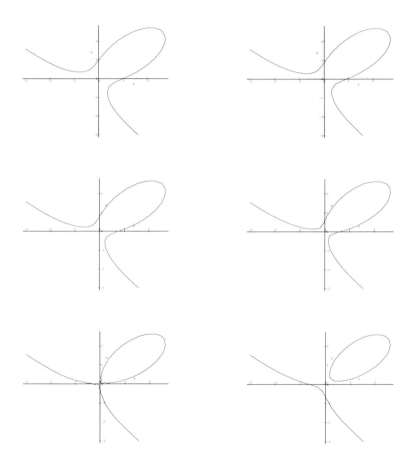

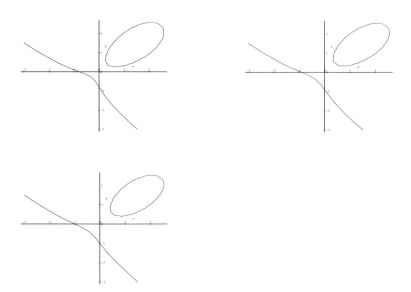

Of course, this is the hard way to generate the animation of the implicit plots. It is much easier to use the **display** routine from the *plots* package to display the implicit plots in sequence, i.e., to produce the animation.

```
> plots[display]( [ seq( P[i], i=0..8 ) ],
>    insequence=true );
```

We omit the animation, which is the same as before.

14.12 Exercises

1. Plot the function $x \longmapsto \dfrac{\sin 2x}{\sin x}$ on the interval $(0, 4\pi)$.

2. Plot the sine integral Si over the interval $(0,100)$, compute $\lim\limits_{x \to \infty} Si(x)$, and compare this with the result that you read off the picture.

3. Plot the factorial function $x \longmapsto x!$ and its derivative over the interval $(-4, 4)$.

4. Enter the command

```
plot( cosh(x)^2 - sinh(x)^2 - 1,   0..10 );
```

and explain what you see. Can you improve the result?

5. Plot the function $x \longmapsto x \sin(1/x)$ over an "interesting" domain around zero.

6. Plot the function

$$t \longmapsto \int_{-\infty}^{t} e^{-\theta^4} \, d\theta$$

on the interval $(-2, 2)$.

7. Plot the function $x \longmapsto \int_{0}^{x} \sin(\sin \xi) \, d\xi$ on the interval $(0, 2\pi)$.

8. Plot some Lissajous figures, which are defined in parametric form by

$$t \longmapsto \big(\sin(m\,t), \sin(n\,t)\big),$$

for integers m and n. Pay special attention to the case where m and n are consecutive Fibonacci numbers.

9. Draw the lemniscate of Bernoulli defined by
   (a) the equation $(x^2 + y^2)^2 = (x^2 - y^2)$,
   (b) the polar equation $r^2 = \cos 2\phi$, and
   (c) the parametrization $x = \dfrac{\cos t}{1 + \sin^2 t}, \ y = \dfrac{\cos t \sin t}{1 + \sin^2 t}$, for $-\pi \le t \le \pi$.

10. Draw the following parametric plots.
   (a) $t \longmapsto \left(\dfrac{t^2 - 1}{t^2 + 1}, \dfrac{2t}{t^2 + 1} \right)$, for $t \in (-\infty, \infty)$.
   (b) $t \longmapsto (\frac{4}{9}t^3 - \frac{14}{9}t^2 + \frac{1}{9}t + 1, -\frac{4}{9}t^3 - \frac{1}{9}t^2 + \frac{14}{9}t)$, for $t \in (0, 1)$.
   (c) Draw the previous parametric plot together with the plot of
       $t \longmapsto \big(\cos(\frac{\pi}{2}t), \sin(\frac{\pi}{2}t)\big)$ for $t \in (0, 1)$.

11. Plot the Heaviside step function H and next draw the graphs of the functions below.
   (a) $H(x - 1) - H(x - 2)$
   (b) $\displaystyle\sum_{i=0}^{10} (-1/2)^i H(x - i/2)$
   (c) $(1 - |x|)\big(H(x + 1) - H(x - 1)\big)$

12. Draw the parametric plot $t \longmapsto \big(FresnelC(t), FresnelS(t)\big)$ for t in $(0, 6)$ and describe the asymptotic behavior of this parametric curve.

13. Plot the Folium, which is defined as a polar plot with radial function $\cos\theta(4\sin^2\theta - 1)$.

14. (a) Plot the function $x \longmapsto x + \cos(\pi x)$ on the interval (-49,49) without changing the defaults of **plot**.
    (b) Plot the same function with different options.

15. Plot the function $x \longmapsto e^x + \ln|4 - x|$ on the interval (0,5). What do you think of it?

16. Plot the graph of the function $(x, y) \longmapsto \dfrac{x}{x^2 + y^2}$, for x and y ranging from -1 to 1.

17. Plot the "monkey saddle" defined by the function $(x, y) \longmapsto x(x^2 - 3y^2)$ under various options.

18. Plot the function $(x, y) \longmapsto \sin(2\pi x) \sin(2\pi y)$, for x and y ranging from 0 to 25, without changing the default options. What do you think of it?

19. Plot the surface parametrized by

$$(\phi, \theta) \longmapsto \big(\cos\phi\sin(2\theta), \; \sin\phi\sin(2\theta), \; \sin\theta\big),$$

where ϕ and θ range from 0 to 2π.

20. Draw a contour plot and a density plot of the strength of the potential field of a configuration of unit charges at positions $(-1,0)$ and $(1,0)$.

21. Draw Klein's bottle in Dieudonné's parametrization [40]

$$x = \big(a + \cos(u/2)\sin t - \sin(u/2)\sin(2t)\big)\cos u,$$
$$y = \big(a + \cos(u/2)\sin t - \sin(u/2)\sin(2t)\big)\sin u,$$
$$z = \sin(u/2)\sin t + \sin(u/2)\sin(2t),$$

where $0 \le u \le 2\pi$, $0 \le t \le 2\pi$, and $a = 2$. Compare the result with the first example in the "graphics gallery" in [89].

22. Draw Klein's bottle in Banchoff's parametrization [3]

$$x = \Big(\cos(\theta/2)\big(\sqrt{2} + \cos\phi\big) + \sin(\theta/2)\big(\cos\phi\sin\phi\big)\Big)\cos\theta,$$
$$y = \Big(\cos(\theta/2)\big(\sqrt{2} + \cos\phi\big) + \sin(\theta/2)\big(\cos\phi\sin\phi\big)\Big)\sin\theta,$$
$$z = -\sin(\theta/2)\big(\sqrt{2} + \cos\phi\big) + \cos(\theta/2)\big(\cos\phi\sin\phi\big),$$

where $0 \le \theta \le 4\pi$, $0 \le \phi \le 2\pi$, and $a = 2$. Compare the result with the color graph in [74].

23. Draw the Möbius strip. (Hint: make a parametrization by rotating a line segment along a circle with varying elevation angle.)

24. Draw the Catenoid defined by the parametrization

$$(\theta, z) \longmapsto (\cos \theta \cosh z, \; \sin \theta \cosh z, \; z),$$

where $0 \le \phi \le 2\pi$ and $-1 \le z \le 1$, directly with this parametrization, and as a cylindrical plot.

25. Draw Enneper's minimal surface defined by the parametrization

$$(u, v) \longmapsto \left(\frac{u}{2} - \frac{u^3}{6} + \frac{uv^2}{2}, \; -\frac{v}{2} + \frac{v^3}{6} - \frac{vu^2}{2}, \; \frac{u^2}{2} - \frac{v^2}{2} \right).$$

26. Draw Scherk's minimal surface defined by the equation
$\exp(z) \cos x = \cos y$.

27. Generate a contour plot and a density plot of the function
$(x, y) \longmapsto \sin(xy)$.

28. Plot the two-dimensional gradient vector field of the function
$(x, y) \longmapsto \sin x \cos y$.

29. Make an animation of a rotating spiral.

Solving Equations

In this chapter, we shall look at several methods implemented in Maple to solve (systems of) equations of various types. Special attention will be paid to systems of polynomial equations: the use of the Gröbner basis package will pass in review. Recurrence relations will be another type of equation, which will be treated in detail. We shall consider exact methods (over various domains) as well as approximate, numerical methods. Examples in this chapter come from application areas such as electronic circuit design, chemical kinetics, neural networks, geodesy, and dimensional analysis.

15.1 Equations in One Unknown

In its simplest form, the Maple procedure **solve** takes an equation in one unknown and tries to solve it analytically.

```
> eqn := (x-1)*(x^2+x+1);
```

$$eqn := (x - 1) (x^2 + x + 1)$$

```
> solve( eqn, x );
```

$$1, \; -\frac{1}{2} + \frac{1}{2} I \sqrt{3}, \; -\frac{1}{2} - \frac{1}{2} I \sqrt{3}$$

The equations may contain several unknowns and still you can ask Maple to solve it for one of the unknowns, in terms of the others.

```
> eqn := x^3 - 5*a*x^2 + x = 1;
```

$$eqn := x^3 - 5 \, a \, x^2 + x = 1$$

```
> solve( eqn, x );
```

$$\%1^{1/3} - \%2 + \frac{5}{3} \, a,$$

$$-\frac{1}{2} \, \%1^{1/3} + \frac{1}{2} \, \%2 + \frac{5}{3} \, a + \frac{1}{2} I \sqrt{3} \, (\, \%1^{1/3} + \%2 \,),$$

$$- \frac{1}{2} \, \%1^{1/3} + \frac{1}{2} \, \%2 + \frac{5}{3} \, a - \frac{1}{2} \, I \, \sqrt{3} \; (\%1^{1/3} + \%2)$$

$$\%1 := - \frac{5}{6} \, a + \frac{1}{2} + \frac{125}{27} \, a^3$$

$$+ \frac{1}{18} \, \sqrt{31 - 25 \, a^2 - 90 \, a + 500 \, a^3} \, \sqrt{3}$$

$$\%2 := \frac{\frac{1}{3} - \frac{25}{9} \, a^2}{\%1^{1/3}}$$

Maple finds the three (complex) solutions, which are represented as a sequence of formulae. From the example, it is clear again how Maple represents complicated expressions; the system looks for common subexpressions and gives them names like %1, %2, and so on. You can refer to these labels as long as they are not replaced by other values. In practice this means that only immediate reference is safe; the system itself may reuse the labels and destroy former information. So don't be surprised when you are confronted with sessions like the following.

```
(%2)^2+1;   # label %2 can still be used
```

$$\left(\frac{1}{3} - \frac{25}{9} \, a^2 \right)^2 \Bigg/ \left(- \frac{5}{6} \, a + \frac{1}{2} + \frac{125}{27} \, a^3 \right.$$

$$\left. + \frac{1}{18} \, \sqrt{31 - 25 \, a^2 - 90 \, a + 500 \, a^3} \, \sqrt{3} \right)^{2/3} + 1$$

```
> solve( x^3 + x = 1, x );   # new label %1
```

$$\%1^{1/3} - \frac{1}{3} \, \frac{1}{\%1^{1/3}},$$

$$- \frac{1}{2} \, \%1^{1/3} + \frac{1}{6} \, \frac{1}{\%1^{1/3}} + \frac{1}{2} \, I \, \sqrt{3} \left(\%1^{1/3} + \frac{1}{3} \, \frac{1}{\%1^{1/3}} \right),$$

$$- \frac{1}{2} \, \%1^{1/3} + \frac{1}{6} \, \frac{1}{\%1^{1/3}} - \frac{1}{2} \, I \, \sqrt{3} \left(\%1^{1/3} + \frac{1}{3} \, \frac{1}{\%1^{1/3}} \right)$$

$$\%1 := \frac{1}{2} + \frac{1}{18} \, \sqrt{31} \, \sqrt{3}$$

```
> %2;   # label %2 cannot be referred to anymore
Undefined label:
%2;
    ^
```

15.2 Abbreviations in solve

Maple expects an equation or a set of equations as the first argument in a call to **solve**, but the system kindly supplements expressions with `"= 0"`.

```
> solve( a + ln(x-3) - ln(x), x );
```

$$3 \, \frac{1}{1 - e^{-a}}$$

As the second argument, Maple expects a variable or a set of variables. When this argument is absent, Maple finds all indeterminates in the first argument with the command

indets(eqns, 'name') minus { constants }

and uses the result as the second argument of **solve**. This is convenient, but sometimes it has a strange effect.

```
> solve( a + ln(x-3) - ln(x) );
```

$$\{ a = -\ln(x - 3) + \ln(x), \; x = x \}$$

Maple solved the equation for x and a. The solution $x = x$ means that x can have any value.

You have seen that Maple uses labels to abbreviate large common subexpressions. The system sometimes uses another kind of abbreviation.

```
> x^7 - 2*x^6 - 4*x^5 - x^3 + x^2 + 6*x + 4;
```

$$x^7 - 2 \, x^6 - 4 \, x^5 - x^3 + x^2 + 6 \, x + 4$$

```
> solve(");
```

$$1 + \sqrt{5} , \; 1 - \sqrt{5} , \; \text{RootOf}(\_Z^5 - \_Z - 1)$$

In this way, Maple informs you that it has found two real solutions, viz., $1 + \sqrt{5}$ and $1 - \sqrt{5}$, in analytical form, and that the other solutions are roots of the polynomial equation $\_Z^5 - \_Z - 1 = 0$ in $\_Z$.

15.3 Some Difficulties

Often it is known that there exist solutions for an equation or system of equations, but no general method for finding the solutions is available. There are cases where, from mathematical point of view, it is hopeless to find a general solution in analytical form. It is well-known from Galois theory that a general formula using radicals only for roots of polynomials of degree five or higher does not exist. From Maple you cannot expect more; it only provides you with a set of reasonably good algorithms for solving equations. Nevertheless, in quite a few mathematical problems general methods fail whereas the user recognizes a way to find a solution. Quite often this is based on recognizing some pattern within a formula, which the computer algebra system does not see.

When Maple does not find any solution, the system keeps silent.

```
> solve( cos(x)=x, x );

>
```

Maple is more communicative when you increase the value of the variable `infolevel[solve]`.

```
> infolevel[solve] := 2:  # make Maple more communicative
> solve( cos(x)=x, x );
solve:    Warning: no solutions found
```

It is known that no closed-form solution of this equation exists. So, in this case, you can praise Maple for not having found a solution. However, sometimes results of **solve** are a bit disappointing. For example, computations in which trigonometric functions are involved usually do not come easily to computer algebra systems, and Maple is no exception in this respect.

```
> infolevel[solve] := 1:  # reset userinfo
> solve( sin(x) = 3*x/Pi, x );
```
$$0$$

Maple is satisfied with one solution. From a plot of the sine function and the function $x \longmapsto 3x/\pi$ it is clear that there exist three solutions, and you know them: $\pi/6$, $-\pi/6$, and 0.

Before trying to find solutions, Maple first tries to simplify the equations. This is done without any scruples.

```
> (x-1)^2/(x^2-1);
```
$$\frac{(x - 1)^2}{x^2 - 1}$$

```
> solve(");
```
$$1$$

Maple can check itself that its solution is not valid when $\dfrac{(x-1)^2}{x^2-1}$ is considered as a real function.

```
> subs ( x=1, "" );
```

```
Error, division by zero
```

But of course, considered as elements from the quotient field $\mathbb{R}(x)$, the expressions $\dfrac{(x-1)^2}{x^2-1}$ and $\dfrac{x-1}{x+1}$ are equivalent. For the analytical continuation it is true that $x = 1$ is a solution.

```
> limit ( "", x=1 );
```

$$0$$

The situation gets worse in the case of powers with fractional exponents.

```
> sqrt (x-8) + sqrt (x) = 2;
```

$$\sqrt{x-8} + \sqrt{x} = 2$$

```
> solve (");
```

$$9$$

While the procedure **solve** is a convenient tool, blind trust in its results for nonlinear equations is unwise; you better check the results.

Occasionally, one is confronted with the environment variable _MaxSols which limits the number of solutions sought for. Its default value is one hundred, but if necessary it can be reset.

```
> eqns := { seq( x[i]^2 = x[i], i=1..7 ) };
```

$$eqns := \left\{ x_{[1]}^{2} = x_{[1]}, \; x_{[2]}^{2} = x_{[2]}, \; x_{[3]}^{2} = x_{[3]}, \right.$$

$$x_{[4]}^{2} = x_{[4]}, \; x_{[5]}^{2} = x_{[5]}, \; x_{[6]}^{2} = x_{[6]}, \; x_{[7]}^{2} = x_{[7]}$$

$$\left. \right\}$$

```
> nops ( { solve (eqns) } );
```

$$100$$

```
> _MaxSols := 500:
```

```
> nops ( { solve (eqns) } ); # true number of solutions
```

$$128$$

We end with an example of the problem of not being able to specify criteria for parametrization of solutions of equations.

```
> eqns := { w +x +y + z = 1, w + y = 0,
>    2*w + z = 2, v + z = 0 }:
> solve( eqns );
    { z = -2 w + 2, x = 2 w - 1, v = 2 w - 2, w = w, y = -w }
```

When you solve a system of equations with respect to all unknowns, Maple chooses the parametrization of the solutions on the basis of criteria like "select the equation with the least number of terms" or "select the equation with the simplest coefficients", and so on. But what is there to do if you have different criteria? You can use simplification with respect to side relations to express a variable in terms of the others.

```
> simplify( {v,w}, eqns, [v,w,x,y,z] );
```
$$\left\{ -z, \ -\frac{1}{2} z + 1 \right\}$$

```
> simplify( {v,w}, eqns, [v,w,z,y,x] );
```
$$\left\{ x - 1, \ \frac{1}{2} x + \frac{1}{2} \right\}$$

But this does not mean that you have solved the original system of equations. This method only works when you know beforehand which variables can be used as parameters. Then you can also leave the parameters out of the set of unknowns.

```
> solve( eqns, {v,w,y,z} );
```
$$\left\{ w = \frac{1}{2} x + \frac{1}{2}, \ z = -x + 1, \ y = -\frac{1}{2} - \frac{1}{2} x, \ v = x - 1 \right\}$$

15.4 Systems of Equations

The last examples of the previous section shows that **solve** can be used to solve systems of equations. For **solve**, the equations and unknowns should be presented as sets. Even with a system of equations in one unknown this variable must be presented as a set. In this section, we shall look at some practical examples of how to solve systems of equations.

First we shall look at a system of equations which describes the relations between voltages, currents, and resistors in the following electronic circuit of resistors (taken from [43]).

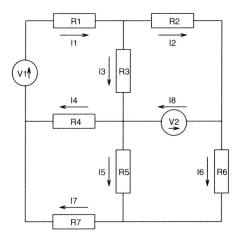

Applying Kirchhoff's laws you get the following system of equations.

```
> eqns := { R1*I1+R3*I3+R4*I4-V1=0, R2*I2-V2-R3*I3=0,
>    R5*I5-R6*I6-V2=0, R5*I5+R7*I7-R4*I4=0, I1-I2-I3=0,
>    I2-I6-I8=0, I5+I6-I7=0, I4+I7-I1=0, I3+I8-I4-I5=0 };
```

$$eqns := \{\ I1\ -\ I2\ -\ I3 = 0,\ I2\ -\ I6\ -\ I8 = 0,$$
$$I5\ +\ I6\ -\ I7 = 0,\ I4\ +\ I7\ -\ I1 = 0,$$
$$I3\ +\ I8\ -\ I4\ -\ I5 = 0,\ R2\ I2\ -\ V2\ -\ R3\ I3 = 0,$$
$$R5\ I5\ -\ R6\ I6\ -\ V2 = 0,$$
$$R5\ I5\ +\ R7\ I7\ -\ R4\ I4 = 0,$$
$$R1\ I1\ +\ R3\ I3\ +\ R4\ I4\ -\ V1 = 0\ \}$$

Consider it as a linear system of equations in which the resistors and voltages are parameters and the currents actually are the unknowns.

```
> currents := { seq( I[i], i=1..8 ) }:
Error, Illegal use of an object as a name
```

The problem here is that Maple uses I as an alias for the complex number i. If you insist on its use as a variable, then you must first unalias it.

```
> alias( I=I ):   # alias I character to itself
> currents := { seq(I.i,i=1..8) }:
> resistors := { seq( R[i], i=1..7 ) }:
> voltages := { V1, V2 }:
```

```
> sol := solve( eqns, currents ):
```

The solution is not shown. Instead we shall look for a simple formula of current I5. But first we assign the values of currents in the solution, because this is not done automatically by **solve**, and print the formula for I5 obtained with **solve**.

```
> assign( sol ):
> I5;
```

$$(R3\ R4\ R6\ V2\ +\ R1\ R2\ R7\ V2\ +\ R3\ R4\ R7\ V2$$

$$+\ R3\ R1\ R7\ V2\ +\ R4\ R2\ R7\ V2\ +\ R3\ R2\ R7\ V2$$

$$+\ R3\ R4\ R6\ V1\ +\ R4\ R6\ R2\ V1\ +\ R1\ R2\ R4\ V2$$

$$+\ R3\ R2\ R4\ V2\ +\ R3\ R1\ R4\ V2\ )\big/(\ R3\ R1\ R5\ R6$$

$$+\ R3\ R2\ R5\ R7\ +\ R3\ R4\ R7\ R6\ +\ R3\ R4\ R5\ R6$$

$$+\ R1\ R2\ R5\ R7\ +\ R3\ R2\ R5\ R6\ +\ R3\ R1\ R7\ R6$$

$$+\ R3\ R1\ R4\ R6\ +\ R3\ R1\ R5\ R4\ +\ R1\ R2\ R5\ R4$$

$$+\ R3\ R4\ R5\ R7\ +\ R3\ R2\ R5\ R4\ +\ R3\ R1\ R5\ R7$$

$$+\ R4\ R2\ R5\ R6\ +\ R1\ R2\ R4\ R6\ +\ R1\ R2\ R5\ R6$$

$$+\ R4\ R2\ R5\ R7\ +\ R3\ R2\ R7\ R6\ +\ R3\ R2\ R4\ R6$$

$$+\ R4\ R2\ R7\ R6\ +\ R1\ R2\ R7\ R6\ )$$

To simplify this formula we introduce short names for subexpressions and simplify I5 in terms of the new variables.

```
> relations := {
>    A = R1*R2*R4 + R1*R3*R4 + R2*R3*R4,
>    B = R5*R6 + R5*R7 + R6*R7,
>    C = R1*R2 + R1*R3 + R2*R3 + R2*R4 + R3*R4,
>    D = R4*R6 }:
> I5 := map( simplify, I5, relations );
```

$$I5\ :=\ (V1\ R2\ D\ +\ V2\ A\ +\ V2\ C\ R7\ +\ (V2\ +\ V1\ )\ R3\ D\ )\big/($$

$$R6\ A\ +\ R5\ A\ +\ B\ C\ )$$

```
> I5 := map( collect, I5, [V1,V2,D] );
```

$$I5 := \frac{(\ R2\ +\ R3\ )\ D\ V1\ +\ (\ A\ +\ C\ R7\ +\ R3\ D\ )\ V2}{R6\ A\ +\ R5\ A\ +\ B\ C}$$

As a second example we consider a system of equations describing the *pseudo steady state* of an enzyme-catalyzed reaction. We shall apply the Michaelis-Menten theory to the following dimeric enzymatic reaction.

$$E \underset{k_{11}}{\overset{k_1}{\rightleftharpoons}} C_1 \underset{k_{55}}{\overset{k_5}{\rightleftharpoons}} E + P$$

$$E + S \underset{k_{22}}{\overset{k_2}{\rightleftharpoons}} C_2$$

$$C_2 + S \underset{k_{33}}{\overset{k_3}{\rightleftharpoons}} C_3 \underset{k_{44}}{\overset{k_4}{\rightleftharpoons}} C_1 + S$$

$$C_3 \underset{k_{66}}{\overset{k_6}{\rightleftharpoons}} C_2 + P$$

Here, S, P, E, C_1, C_2, and C_3 are the concentrations of the substrate, product, free enzyme, and the three enzyme–substrate complexes, respectively. The deterministic mathematical model which describes the kinetics of this reaction is the following system of differential equations.

$$S' = -(k_1 + k_2)ES + k_4 C_1 S - k_3 C_2 S + k_{11} C1 + k_{22} C_2 + (k_{33} + k_{44})C_3$$
$$P' = k_5 C_1 + k_6 C_3 - P(k_{55} E + k_{66} C_2)$$
$$E' = -E((k_1 + k_2)S + k_{55} P) + (k_{11} + k_5)E_1 + k_{22} E_2$$
$$C_1' = (k_1 S + k_{55} P)E + k_{44} C_3 - C_1(k_{11} + k_5 + k_4 S)$$
$$C_2' = k_2 ES + (k6 + k_{33})C_3 - C_2(k_{22} + k_3 S + k_{66} P)$$
$$C_3' = C_2(k_{66} P + k_3 S) + k_4 S C_1 - C_3(k_{33} + k_{44} + k_6)$$

Let us concentrate on the first of these equations.

```
> alias( s=s(t), p=p(t) ); # s, p as functions of time t
> rs := -(k1+k2)*s*e - k4*s*c1 - k3*s*c2 + k11*c1 + k22*c2
>    + (k33+k44)*c3;

     rs := -( k1 + k2 ) s e - k4 s c1 - k3 s c2 + k11 c1

         + k22 c2 + ( k33 + k44 ) c3
```

In the pseudo steady state, it is assumed that the concentrations of the free enzyme and the complexes change very slowly, so that we may even assume them to be constant in time. Thus we get the following system of equations (linear in c1, c2, c3, and e).

```
> siderels :=
> { 0 = -e*((k1+k2)*s+k55*p) + (k11+k5)*c1 + k22*c2,
>   0 = (k1*s+k55*p)*e + k44*c3 - c1*(k11+k5+k4*s),
>   0 = k2*s*e + (k6+k33)*c3 - c2*(k22+k3*s+k66*p),
>   0 = c2*(k66*p+k3*s) + k4*s*c1 - c3*(k33+k44+k6),
>   e0 = c1+c2+c3+e};
```

$$siderels := \{\, e0 = c1 + c2 + c3 + e,\ 0 =$$
$$-e\,(\,(k1 + k2)\ s + k55\ p\,) + (\,k11 + k5\,)\ c1$$
$$+\ k22\ c2,\ 0 = k2\ s\ e + (\,k6 + k33\,)\ c3$$
$$-\ c2\,(\,k22 + k3\ s + k66\ p\,),\ 0 =$$
$$c2\,(\,k66\ p + k3\ s\,) + k4\ s\ c1$$
$$-\ c3\,(\,k33 + k44 + k6\,),\ 0 = (\,k1\ s + k55\ p\,)\ e$$
$$+\ k44\ c3 - c1\,(\,k11 + k5 + k4\ s\,)\,\}$$

Maple can solve this system of equations so that the reaction rate S' can be expressed in terms of S, P, E_0, and the rate constants. We do not show the large solution. Instead we shall show the expression when $k_{55} = 0$, $k_{66} = 0$.

```
> solve( siderels, {c1,c2,c3,e} ):
> assign("):
> k55 := 0: k66 := 0:
> # the differential equation for substrate concentration
> diff(s,t) = collect( normal(rs), s );
```

$$\frac{\partial}{\partial t}\, s = -\ s\ e0\ (\,(\,k3\ k2\ k4\ k6 + k3\ k1\ k4\ k6\,)\ s^2 + ($$
$$k3\ k11\ k2\ k6 + k4\ k1\ k22\ k6 + k44\ k5\ k2\ k3$$
$$+\ k3\ k5\ k2\ k6 + k1\ k5\ k3\ k44\,)\ s$$
$$+\ k1\ k33\ k5\ k22 + k1\ k5\ k22\ k44 + k1\ k5\ k22\ k6$$
$$)\Big/(\,(\,k1\ k3\ k4 + k2\ k3\ k4\,)\ s^3 + (\,k4\ k1\ k33$$
$$+\ k4\ k1\ k22 + k44\ k2\ k3 + k1\ k3\ k44 + k33\ k4\ k2$$
$$+\ k4\ k1\ k6 + k11\ k2\ k3 + k5\ k2\ k3 + k2\ k4\ k6\,)$$
$$s^2 + (\,k5\ k3\ k44 + k1\ k22\ k44 + k1\ k22\ k6$$

$$+ \; k33 \; k22 \; k4 \; + \; k11 \; k2 \; k6 \; + \; k11 \; k2 \; k44$$

$$+ \; k11 \; k3 \; k44 \; + \; k5 \; k2 \; k6 \; + \; k5 \; k2 \; k44 \; + \; k22 \; k4 \; k6$$

$$+ \; k33 \; k5 \; k2 \; + \; k33 \; k11 \; k2 \; + \; k33 \; k1 \; k22 \;) \;\; s$$

$$+ \; k5 \; k22 \; k44 \; + \; k33 \; k5 \; k22 \; + \; k11 \; k22 \; k6$$

$$+ \; k33 \; k11 \; k22 \; + \; k11 \; k22 \; k44 \; + \; k5 \; k22 \; k6 \;)$$

Maple can also find the analytical solution of this differential equation with **dsolve**. But more on differential equations in the next chapter.

Enough about linear system of equations: time and memory are the only computational limitations. Let us now concentrate on nonlinear systems of equations. Consider

$$x^2 + y^2 = 25, \quad x^2 - 9 = y,$$

and solve this system with Maple.

```
> eqns := { x^2 + y^2 = 25, y = x^2 - 5 };
```
$$eqns := \{ x^2 + y^2 = 25, \; y = x^2 - 5 \}$$

```
> vars := {x,y}:
> solve( eqns, vars );
```
$$\{ y = -5, \; x = 0 \}, \; \{ x = 3, \; y = 4 \}, \; \{ x = -3, \; y = 4 \}$$

This was simple, but very soon solving nonlinear equations gets more more complicated. Consider

$$x^2 + y^2 = 1, \quad \sqrt{x + y} = x - y,$$

and solve this system of equations with Maple.

```
> eqns := { x^2+y^2=1, sqrt(x+y)=x-y };
```
$$eqns := \left\{ \sqrt{x + y} = x - y, \; x^2 + y^2 = 1 \right\}$$

```
> sols := solve( eqns );
```
$$sols := \{ y = 1, \; x = 0 \}, \; \{ y = 0, \; x = 1 \}, \; \{$$
$$y = RootOf(2 \; \_Z^2 + 4 \; \_Z + 3),$$
$$x = -2 - RootOf(2 \; \_Z^2 + 4 \; \_Z + 3) \}$$

Apparently Maple finds three solutions of the given system of equations and represents them as a sequence of sets. Within each set the values

of the variables in the particular solution are denoted as equations. This
makes substitution of the solution in the original system of equations easy.

```
> subs( sols[1], eqns );
```

$$\{ 1 = 1, \ 1 = -1 \}$$

```
> subs( sols[2], eqns );
```

$$\{ 1 = 1 \}$$

This example shows that the advice to check the solutions found is
appropriate (especially in case of equations in which fractional exponents
are involved). Only the second of the first two candidate solutions is valid!

The third solution found is actually a set of two or four solutions.
When both RootOf expressions correspond with the same complex number, then there are two solutions, which can be obtained by the procedure
allvalues.

```
> allvalues( sols[3], `d` );
```

$$\left\{ y = -1 + \frac{1}{2} I \sqrt{2}, \ x = -1 - \frac{1}{2} I \sqrt{2} \right\},$$

$$\left\{ y = -1 - \frac{1}{2} I \sqrt{2}, \ x = -1 + \frac{1}{2} I \sqrt{2} \right\}$$

The second argument `d` in **allvalues** stands for *diagonal* and is used to
specify that the RootOf's in the third solution represent the same value
and should not evaluated independently of one another.

You can also consider the third solution as a set of four candidate
solutions and check them separately.

```
> sols[3];
```

$$\{ y = \text{RootOf}(2 \ \_Z^2 + 4 \ \_Z + 3),$$

$$x = -2 - \text{RootOf}(2 \ \_Z^2 + 4 \ \_Z + 3) \}$$

```
> candidates := allvalues( sols[3] ):
> for i to 4 do
>    simplify( subs( candidates[i], eqns ) )
> od;
```

$$\left\{ I \sqrt{2} = -I \sqrt{2}, \ 1 = 1 \right\}$$

$$\left\{ \sqrt{-2 + I \sqrt{2}} = 0, \ \frac{1}{2} \left(-2 + I \sqrt{2} \right)^2 = 1 \right\}$$

$$\left\{ \sqrt{-2 - I \sqrt{2}} = 0, \ \frac{1}{2} \left(2 + I \sqrt{2} \right)^2 = 1 \right\}$$

$$\left\{ 1 = 1, \ I \sqrt{2} = I \sqrt{2} \right\}$$

You see that only the fourth candidate solution is valid.

```
> candidates[4];
```

$$\left\{ y = -1 - \frac{1}{2} I \sqrt{2}, \ x = -1 + \frac{1}{2} I \sqrt{2} \right\}$$

Using Maple, you have found two valid solutions of the original system of equations. What remains is to ensure that all possible solutions have been found. In this example it is rather easy — by taking squares the system can be reduced to a system consisting of a fourth degree polynomial in x and an equation of type $y = f(x)$. Maple can assist you.

First, you take squares and write the system of equations as polynomials.

```
> P[1] := ( lhs^2 - rhs^2 )( eqns[1] );
```

$$P_{[1]} := x + y - (x - y)^2$$

```
> P[2] := ( lhs - rhs )( eqns[2] );
```

$$P_{[2]} := x^2 + y^2 - 1$$

Next, you eliminate y by computing the **resultant** with respect to this variable.

```
> eqn_x := resultant( P[1], P[2], y ) = 0;
```

$$eqn\_x := 4 x^4 + 4 x^3 - 2 x^2 - 6 x = 0$$

This 4th degree polynomial equation in x can easily be solved with Maple.

```
> x_roots := solve( eqn_x );
```

$$x\_roots := 0, \ 1, \ -1 + \frac{1}{2} I \sqrt{2}, \ -1 - \frac{1}{2} I \sqrt{2}$$

```
> eqn_y := collect( P[1] + P[2], y ) = 0;
```

$$eqn\_y := (1 + 2 \ x) \ y \ - \ 1 \ + \ x = 0$$

For $x \neq -1/2$, we rewrite the equation for y.

```
> eqn_y := y = solve( eqn_y, y );
```

$$eqn\_y := y = - \ \frac{-1 \ + \ x}{1 \ + \ 2 \ x}$$

The solutions of the new system of equations `eqn_x`, `eqn_y` are the same
four solutions which you would have gotten with the option `'d'` set in
allvalues set. Two "ghost solutions" have been introduced by taking
squares. Anyway, all solutions of the original system of equations have
been found.

By taking squares, the original system of equations was changed into
a system of polynomial equations. In this case, the newly obtained system could easily be solved. In general, analytical solutions of systems of
polynomial equations are not so easily found. A sophisticated method for
solving polynomial equations will be described in the next section.

15.5 The Gröbner Basis Method

The Gröbner basis is an important mathematical notion in the computational theory of polynomials. In §13.7 the Gröbner basis method was
applied to simplification with respect to side relations. In this section, its
role in the process of finding solutions of systems of polynomial equations
will be discussed roughly. More details, e.g., how to test whether a finite
set of solutions exists, how to work over rings instead of fields, can be found
in [18, 19, 34].

Let us see how the last example of the previous section is treated in the
Gröbner basis method. First the system of equations is transformed into
a system of polynomial equations for which the solution set contains the
solutions of the original system of equations. To this end an extra variable,
say z, is introduced: it describes the square root.

```
> eqns := { x^2 + y^2 = 1,   z = x - y,   z^2 = x + y };
```

$$eqns := \{ \ x^2 + y^2 = 1, \ \ z = x \ - \ y, \ \ z^2 = x + y \ \}$$

Next consider the set of polynomials which defines the system of equations.

```
> polys := map( lhs-rhs, eqns );
```

$$polys := \left\{ \sqrt{x + y} - x + y, \; x^2 + y^2 - 1 \right\}$$

The minimal Gröbner basis with respect to the pure lexicographic ordering of the unknowns x, y, and z, induced by $z \succ y \succ x$ is

```
> with( grobner ):   # load the Groebner basis package
> G := gbasis( polys, [z,y,x], `plex` );

    G := [ 3 z - 4 x³ + 3 - 2 x²,

          -3 x + 3 y - 3 + 4 x³ + 2 x²,

          -3 x - x² + 2 x⁴ + 2 x³ ]
```

The set of common zeros of the Gröbner basis is equivalent to the set of common zeros of the original set of polynomials. However, the Gröbner basis has in this case achieved a complete separation of the variables z and y as polynomials in x and a remaining univariate polynomial in x. The first polynomial can be trivially solved for z.

$$z = 4/3x^3 + 2/3x^2 - 1$$

The second polynomial in the Gröbner basis can be trivially solved for y.

$$y = -4/3x^3 - 2/3x^2 + x + 1$$

The roots of the third polynomial

$$2x^4 + 2x^3 - x^2 - 3x$$

can be found in analytical form. Each root can be plugged in to the equations for y and z.

```
> rootlist := [ solve( G[3] ) ];
```

$$rootlist := \left[0, \; 1, \; -1 + \frac{1}{2} I \sqrt{2}, \; -1 - \frac{1}{2} I \sqrt{2} \right]$$

```
> for i to nops( rootlist ) do
>    `x` = rootlist[i], `y` = simplify(
>    subs( x=rootlist[i], solve(G[2],y) ) ),
>    `z` = simplify( subs( x=rootlist[i],
>    solve(G[1],z) ) );
>    simplify( subs( {"}, polys ) )
> od;
```

$$x = 0, \; y = 1, \; z = -1$$

$$\{\ 0\ \}$$

$$x = 1, \quad y = 0, \quad z = 1$$

$$\{\ 0\ \}$$

$$x = -1 + \frac{1}{2}\,I\,\sqrt{2}\,, \quad y = -1 - \frac{1}{2}\,I\,\sqrt{2}\,, \quad z = I\,\sqrt{2}$$

$$\{\ 0\ \}$$

$$x = -1 - \frac{1}{2}\,I\,\sqrt{2}\,, \quad y = -1 + \frac{1}{2}\,I\,\sqrt{2}\,, \quad z = -I\,\sqrt{2}$$

$$\{\ 0\ \}$$

So, in this example you could have Maple do all the work you have done yourself in the last part of the previous section.

The second example is a system of equations which describes the steady state of an ordinary differential equation from a neural network [95]: $\{cx + xy^2 + xz^2 = 1, \quad cy + yx^2 + yz^2 = 1, \quad cz + zx^2 + zy^2 = 1\}$ We consider it as a system of equations in the unknowns x, y, and z, and with parameter c. The solution obtained with **solve** in Maple V Release 2 contains algebraic functions.

```
> eqns := { c*x + x*y^2 + x*z^2 = 1,
>      c*y + y*x^2 + y*z^2 = 1, c*z + z*x^2 + z*y^2 = 1 };
```

$$eqns := \{\, c\,y + y\,x^2 + y\,z^2 = 1,\ c\,x + y^2\,x + x\,z^2 = 1,$$
$$c\,z + z\,x^2 + z\,y^2 = 1\,\}$$

```
> solve(",{x,y,z});
```

$$\left\{\, y = \text{RootOf}(\,c\,\_Z + 2\,\_Z^3 - 1\,),\right.$$

$$z = \text{RootOf}(\,c\,\_Z + 2\,\_Z^3 - 1\,),$$

$$x = \frac{1}{c + 2\,\text{RootOf}(\,c\,\_Z + 2\,\_Z^3 - 1\,)^2}\,\Bigg\},\,\Bigg\{$$

$$y = -\frac{2\,c\,\%1 + 2\,\%1^3 - 1}{c}\,, \quad z = \%1, \quad x = c^2 \Big/ (\,c^3$$

$$+ 5 \ \%1^2 \ c^2 + 8 \ c \ \%1^4 - 4 \ c \ \%1 + 4 \ \%1^6 - 4 \ \%1^3 + 1$$

$$\left. \right) \right\}, \ \left\{ z = - \frac{2 \ c \ \%1 + 2 \ \%1^3 - 1}{c}, \ y = \%1, \ x = c^2 / (\ c^3 \right.$$

$$+ 5 \ \%1^2 \ c^2 + 8 \ c \ \%1^4 - 4 \ c \ \%1 + 4 \ \%1^6 - 4 \ \%1^3 + 1$$

$$\left. \right) \right\}, \ \left\{ z = \%2, \ y = \text{RootOf} (\ \_Z^2 + \%2 \ \_Z + c + \%2^2), \right.$$

$$x = \frac{1}{c + \text{RootOf} (\ \_Z^2 + \%2 \ \_Z + c + \%2^2)^2 + \%2^2} \left. \right\},$$

$$\left\{ y = \%1, \ z = \%1, \ x = \frac{1}{c + 2 \ \%1^2} \right\}$$

$\%1 \ := \ \text{RootOf} (\ 3 \ c \ \_Z^2 + 2 \ \_Z^4 - \_Z + c^2)$

$\%2 \ := \ \text{RootOf} (\ 1 + c \ \_Z + \_Z^3)$

This answer does not give you much structural insight. For systems of polynomial equations the procedure **gsolve** in the *grobner* package is quite useful. **gsolve** requires the equations to be expressed as pure polynomials, which are understood to be equal to 0.

```
> polys := map( lhs - rhs, eqns);

    polys := { c x + x y² + x z² - 1,

        c y + y x² + y z² - 1, c z + z x² + z y² - 1 }

> with( grobner ):
> sys := gsolve( polys, {x,y,z} );

    sys := [ [ c y + 2 y³ - 1, -y + x, z - y ],

        [ c - x y + y², y x² + x y² - 1, z - y ], [

        c + x² - z y, -x y² - x z² + 1 + x³ - z y x,

        y z² + z y² - 1 ] ]
```

You get a list of new systems of polynomials whose roots are the roots of the original system. Often these new systems of equations are easier to solve.

```
> solve( {op(sys[1])}, {x,y,z} );
```

$$\{ z = \mathrm{RootOf}(\, c\ \_Z\ -\ 1\ +\ 2\ \_Z^3\,),$$

$$x = \mathrm{RootOf}(\, c\ \_Z\ -\ 1\ +\ 2\ \_Z^3\,),$$

$$y = \mathrm{RootOf}(\, c\ \_Z\ -\ 1\ +\ 2\ \_Z^3\,)\,\}$$

```
> solve( {op(sys[2])}, {x,y,z} );
```

$$\left\{ y = \%1,\quad x = \frac{c\ +\ \%1^2}{\%1},\quad z = \%1 \right\}$$

$$\%1\ :=\ \mathrm{RootOf}(\,2\ \_Z^4\ +\ c^2\ +\ 3\ c\ \_Z^2\ -\ \_Z\,)$$

```
> solve( {op(sys[3])}, {x,y,z} );
```

$$\left\{ z = \mathrm{RootOf}(\,\_Z^2\ +\ \_Z\ \%2\ +\ \%2^2\ +\ c\,), \right.$$

$$y = \frac{\%2^2\ +\ c}{\mathrm{RootOf}(\,\_Z^2\ +\ \_Z\ \%2\ +\ \%2^2\ +\ c\,)},\quad \left. x = \%2 \right\},\ \{$$

$$x = \%1,\quad z = \mathrm{RootOf}($$

$$c\ \_Z^2\ +\ (\,-1\ +\ c\ \%1\ +\ 2\ \%1^3\,)\ \_Z\ +\ c\ \%1^2\ +\ c^2\,),\ y$$

$$=(\,c\ +\ \%1^2\,)\big/(\,\mathrm{RootOf}($$

$$c\ \_Z^2\ +\ (\,-1\ +\ c\ \%1\ +\ 2\ \%1^3\,)\ \_Z\ +\ c\ \%1^2\ +\ c^2\,))\,\}$$

$$\%1\ :=\ \mathrm{RootOf}(\,2\ \_Z^4\ +\ c^2\ +\ 3\ c\ \_Z^2\ -\ \_Z\,)$$

$$\%2\ :=\ \mathrm{RootOf}(\,1\ +\ c\ \_Z\ +\ \_Z^3\,)$$

This may give you the impression that you have not gained much more insight, but let us apply the Gröbner basis method as described at the beginning of this section to the last system of polynomials.

```
> sys3 := gbasis( sys[3], [x,y,z], `plex` );
```

$$sys3\ :=\ [$$

$$c\ x\ +\ c\ y\ -\ 1\ +\ c\ z\ +\ c^2\ z^2\ +\ z^3\ +\ 3\ c\ z^4\ +\ 2\ z^6,$$

$$3\ c\ y\ z^4\ +\ y^2\ c\ -\ y\ +\ c^2\ +\ 2\ y\ z^6\ +\ c\ z^2\ +\ c^2\ y\ z^2$$

$$+\ c\ y\ z\ +\ y\ z^3,\ c^2\ +\ (\,c^3\ -\ 1\,)\ z\ +\ 2\ c\ z^2$$

$$+\ 4\ c^2\ z^3\ +\ z^4\ +\ 5\ c\ z^5\ +\ 2\ z^7\,]$$

Once solutions for z have been found, the computation of corresponding values of x and y is trivial because the first two polynomials are of degree 1 and 2, in x and y, respectively. But the computation of values for z is not difficult either. It comes down to nothing more than finding roots of univariate polynomials of degree 3 and 4.

```
> factor( sys3[3] );
```

$$(c\ z\ +\ 1\ +\ z^3)\ (\ 2\ z^4\ +\ 3\ c\ z^2\ -\ z\ +\ c^2\ )$$

In the **gsolve** approach, we are more sure that no solutions are lost during the computation.

Our third example of a system of polynomial equations attacked by Gröbner basis methods comes from computational geodesy. Here we shall only sketch the problem and its solution by Maple; for a detailed account we refer to [69].

The relationships between the geocentric Cartesian coordinates x, y, and z of a point P on or near the surface of the earth and the geodetic coordinates h (height), λ (longitude), and ϕ (latitude) of its Helmert's projection on the geocentric reference ellipsoid are

$$x = (N + h) \cos\phi \cos\lambda,$$
$$y = (N + h) \cos\phi \sin\lambda,$$
$$z = (N(1 - e^2) + h) \sin\phi,$$

where the prime vertical radius of curvature N and the eccentricity e of the reference ellipsoid are defined by

$$N = \frac{a}{\sqrt{1 - e^2 \sin^2\phi}}$$

and

$$e = \sqrt{\frac{a^2 - b^2}{a^2}},$$

a and b being semi-major and semi-minor axes of the reference ellipsoid. With the above equations, the Cartesian coordinates x, y, and z can be computed directly from the geodetic coordinates h, λ, and ϕ. The inverse problem is more difficult: you are asked to solve the above nonlinear system of equations in the unknowns h, λ, and ϕ for given x, y, and z.

When you ask Maple to solve this system of trigonometric equations, it returns an answer for the latitude in which roots of an 8th degree polynomials are involved. But you can do better! First, associate with the system of trigonometric equations a system of polynomial equations by introducing variables for the trigonometric entities and by adding polynomial equations that originate from well-known trigonometric identities. Henceforth, we shall use the following variables: $cf = \cos\phi$, $sf = \sin\phi$,

$tf = \tan\phi$, $cl = \cos\lambda$, and $sl = \sin\lambda$. We shall also use the variable S to deal with the square root $S = \sqrt{1 - e^2\,sf^2}$ and define $d = (N + h)\,cf$. In this way, we come up with the following system of ten equations:

```
> sys := [ x - (N+h)*cf*cl, y - (N+h)*cf*sl,
>      z - (N*(1-e^2)+h)*sf, cf^2 + sf^2 - 1, cl^2 +sl^2 - 1,
>      tf*cf - sf, N*S - a, S^2 + e^2*sf^2 - 1, (N+h)*cf - d,
>      d^2 - x^2 - y^2 ];
```

$$sys := [\,x - (N + h)\ cf\ cl,\ y - (N + h)\ cf\ sl,$$
$$z - (N(1 - e^2) + h)\ sf,\ cf^2 + sf^2 - 1,$$
$$sl^2 - 1 + cl^2,\ tf\ cf - sf,\ N\ S - a,$$
$$S^2 + e^2\ sf^2 - 1,\ (N + h)\ cf - d,\ d^2 - x^2 - y^2\,]$$

We compute the Gröbner basis with respect to the following pure lexicographical ordering of the variables.

$$N > S > x > y > h > cl > sl > cf > sf > tf$$

```
> with( grobner ):
> vars := [N,S,x,y,h,cl,sl,cf,sf,tf]:
> gsys := gbasis( sys, vars, plex ):
```

The complete Gröbner basis is too big to be presented here. Besides, we are only interested in the univariate polynomial in tf, which is expected to be the last polynomial in the Gröbner basis.

```
> collect( gsys[9], tf );   # get the polynomial in tf
```

$$(-z^2 + z^2\ e^2 - d^2 + a^2\ e^4)\ tf^2$$
$$+ (-2\ z\ d\ e^2 + 2\ d\ z)\ tf^3 + (-d^2 + d^2\ e^2)\ tf^4$$
$$- z^2 + 2\ d\ z\ tf$$

```
> # rewrite the polynomial a bit
> map( convert, -", 'sqrfree' );
```

$$tf^2\ (z^2 - z^2\ e^2 + d^2 - a^2\ e^4) + 2\ d\ tf^3\ (-1 + e^2)\ z$$
$$+ d^2\ tf^4\ (1 - e^2) + z^2 - 2\ d\ z\ tf$$

```
> sort( subs( e^2*z^2 = (e^2-1)*z^2 + z^2, " ), tf );
```

$$d^2\ (1 - e^2)\ tf^4 + 2\ d\ (-1 + e^2)\ z\ tf^3$$

$$+ \ (-(-1 + e^2) \ z^2 + d^2 - a^2 \ e^4) \ tf^2 - 2 \ d \ z \ tf$$

$$+ \ z^2$$

So, we end up with a 4th degree polynomial in $\tan \phi$ which can be solved analytically (q.v., [97]).

The same answer can be found by the procedure **finduni**.

```
> finduni(tf,sys,vars);
```

$$z^2 - 2 \ d \ z \ tf + (2 \ z \ d \ e^2 - 2 \ d \ z) \ tf^3$$

$$+ \ tf^2 \ (z^2 - z^2 \ e^2 + d^2 - a^2 \ e^4)$$

$$+ \ (d^2 - d^2 \ e^2) \ tf^4$$

This procedure uses the total degree ordering of variables to compute a Gröbner basis and uses this to construct the univariate polynomial (in tf) of least degree in the ideal generated by the polynomials. In this particular case, the computing time is two and a half times longer than the previous one, which uses lexicographic ordering.

The examples in this section give you an idea of the strength of the Gröbner basis method as an alternative to the elimination method or Ritt-Wu's characteristic sets method, which is implemented and contributed by Dongming Wang [120] to the Maple share library. One warning at the end: time and memory complexity of the Gröbner basis algorithm can be a serious drawback.

15.6 Numerical Solvers

For numerical approximations of solutions of equations or systems of equations Maple offers you the procedure **fsolve**. The use of this procedure is similar to the use of **solve**.

```
> x^7 - 2*x^6 - 4*x^5 - x^3 + x^2 + 6*x + 4;
```

$$x^7 - 2 \ x^6 - 4 \ x^5 - x^3 + x^2 + 6 \ x + 4$$

```
> fsolve(");
```

$$-1.236067977, \ 1.167303978, \ 3.236067977$$

But there are additional options. For example:

```
> fsolve( "" , x , ´complex´ );
    -1.236067977, -.7648844336 - .3524715460 I,

         -.7648844336 + .3524715460 I,

         .1812324445 - 1.083954101 I,

         .1812324445 + 1.083954101 I, 1.167303978,

         3.236067977

> fsolve( """ , x , 0..2 );

                      1.167303978
```

In the latter case, Maple was told to try and find only real solutions between 0 and 2.

<table>
<tr><th colspan="2">Options of fsolve</th></tr>
<tr><th>Option</th><th>Description</th></tr>
<tr><td>complex</td><td>complex-valued root(s)</td></tr>
<tr><td>a..b</td><td>search range over the real numbers</td></tr>
<tr><td>maxsols=n</td><td>maximum number of solutions</td></tr>
<tr><td>fulldigits</td><td>use floating-point number with Digits precision</td></tr>
</table>

For polynomial equations, the procedure **fsolve** returns in general (but not always) all real solutions, and with the option `complex` all complex solutions. For equations of other types, **fsolve** is usually satisfied when one solution has been found.

```
> eqn := sin(x) = x/2;
```

$$eqn := \sin(x) = \frac{1}{2} x$$

```
> fsolve( eqn, x );
```

$$1.167303978$$

```
> fsolve( eqn, x, 0.1 .. infinity );
```

$$1.895494267$$

```
> fsolve( eqn, x, -0.1 .. 0.1 );
```

$$0$$

```
> fsolve( eqn, x, -infinity .. -0.01 );
```

$$-1.895494267$$

fsolve is based on two methods, the (multi-dimensional) Newton method and, when this fails, the (multi-dimensional) secant method [111].

The procedure **realroot** uses Descartes' rule of signs (q.v., [90]) to find a list of isolating intervals for all real roots of a univariate polynomial. The width of the interval is optional.

```
> readlib( realroot ):
> x^7 - 2*x^6 - 4*x^5 - x^3 + x^2 + 6*x + 4;
```
$$x^7 - 2 x^6 - 4 x^5 - x^3 + x^2 + 6 x + 4$$

```
> realroot(");
```
$$[[0, 2], [2, 4], [-2, -1]]$$

```
> realroot( "", 1/100 );
```
$$\left[\left[\frac{149}{128}, \frac{75}{64}\right], \left[\frac{207}{64}, \frac{415}{128}\right], \left[\frac{-159}{128}, \frac{-79}{64}\right]\right]$$

15.7 Other Solvers in Maple

isolve

With **isolve** you look for integer solutions of (systems of) equations. The next example is an application in dimensional analysis.

The drag F of a fast moving object in the air is supposed to depend upon its speed V, diameter d, the air density ρ, the velocity of sound c, and the kinematic viscosity ν. All these quantities have dimensions related to the dimensions mass m, length l, and time t. You can determine dimensional groupings of the quantities $F, V, d, \rho, c,$ and ν in the following way.

```
> nondimensional := force^f * speed^v * diameter^d
>    * density^r * acoustic_velocity^c
>    * kinematic_viscosity^m;
```
$$nondimensional := force^f \ speed^v \ diameter^d \ density^r$$
$$acoustic\_velocity^c \ kinematic\_viscosity^m$$

```
> subs( { force = M*L/T^2, speed = L/T, diameter = L,
>    density = M/L^3, acoustic_velocity = L/T,
```

```
>    kinematic_viscosity = L^2/T }, nondimensional );
```

$$\left(\frac{M\,L}{T^2} \right)^f \left(\frac{L}{T} \right)^v L^d \left(\frac{M}{L^3} \right)^r \left(\frac{L}{T} \right)^c \left(\frac{L^2}{T} \right)^m$$

```
> simplify(");
```

$$M^{(\,f\,+\,r\,)}\; L^{(\,f\,+\,v\,+\,d\,-\,3\,r\,+\,c\,+\,2\,m\,)}\; T^{(\,-2\,f\,-\,v\,-\,c\,-\,m\,)}$$

```
> eqns := { seq( op(2,i)=0, i= " ) };
```

$$eqns := \{\, f + r = 0,\;\; f + v + d - 3\,r + c + 2\,m = 0,$$
$$-2\,f - v - c - m = 0\,\}$$

```
> isolve("); # find all integral solutions
```

$$\{\, r = \_N2,\;\; d = \_N3,\;\; c = -\_N1 + \_N3,\;\; f = -\_N2,$$
$$m = 2\,\_N2 - \_N3,\;\; v = \_N1\,\}$$

```
> subs( ", nondimensional );
```

$$force^{(\,-\_N2\,)}\; speed^{\_N1}\; diameter^{\_N3}\; density^{\_N2}$$
$$acoustic\_velocity^{(\,-\_N1\,+\,\_N3\,)}$$
$$kinematic\_viscosity^{(\,2\,\_N2\,-\,\_N3\,)}$$

Some tricks enable you to group powers with the same exponent.

```
> extract_powers := proc( expression, exponents )
>    exp( combine(
>    collect( expand( ln(expression) ), exponents ), ln ) )
> end:
> extract_powers("",{_N1,_N2,_N3});
```

$$\left(\frac{speed}{acoustic\_velocity} \right)^{\_N1}$$

$$\left(\frac{density\ kinematic\_viscosity^2}{force} \right)^{\_N2}$$

$$\left(\frac{acoustic\_velocity\ diameter}{kinematic\_viscosity} \right)^{\_N3}$$

Here, you have obtained three powers of dimensionless numbers, two of which are well-known in fluid dynamics.

```
> subs(_N1=1,_N2=0,_N3=0,"); # the Mach number
```

$$\frac{speed}{acoustic\_velocity}$$

```
> subs(_N1=0,_N2=0,_N3=1,""); # the Reynold´s number
```

$$\frac{acoustic\_velocity\ diameter}{kinematic\_viscosity}$$

msolve

Modular arithmetic is also provided for. One example is a cubic analogue of Pell's equation over $\mathbb{Z}_7$.

```
> msolve( y^2 = x^3 - 28, 7 );
```

$$\{x=0,\ y=0\},\ \{x=2,\ y=6\},\ \{x=2,\ y=1\},$$

$$\{x=1,\ y=6\},\ \{x=1,\ y=1\},\ \{x=4,\ y=6\},$$

$$\{x=4,\ y=1\}$$

rsolve

Maple can also solve recurrence equations. It uses standard techniques like generating functions and z-transforms, and methods based on substitutions and characteristic equations. A few examples:

```
> rsolve( { f(n+2) = f(n+1) + f(n),
>     f(0)=0, f(1)=1 }, f(n) ); # Fibonacci numbers
```

$$-\frac{1}{5}\frac{\left(-1+\sqrt{5}\right)\sqrt{5}\left(-2\dfrac{1}{1-\sqrt{5}}\right)^{n}}{1-\sqrt{5}}$$

$$-\frac{1}{5}\sqrt{5}\left(-2\dfrac{1}{1+\sqrt{5}}\right)^{n}$$

```
> rsolve( { f(n+2) = x*f(n+1) + y*f(n),
>     f(0)=0, f(1)=1 }, f(n) );
```

$$\frac{\left(-2\dfrac{y}{x-\sqrt{x^2+4\,y}}\right)^{n}}{\sqrt{x^2+4\,y}}-\frac{\left(-2\dfrac{y}{x+\sqrt{x^2+4\,y}}\right)^{n}}{\sqrt{x^2+4\,y}}$$

```
> # 5th generalized Fibonacci polynomial
> normal( subs( n=5," " ), ´expanded´ );
```

$$x^4 + 3\ x^2\ y + y^2$$

By the way, the conjecture that $f(n)$ is irreducible if and only if n is prime number holds for $n < 100$.

```
> # complexity of Gauss elimination
> rsolve( { T(n) = T(n-1) + n^2, T(1)=0 }, T(n) );
```

$$2\ (n+1)\left(\frac{1}{2}\ n+1\right)\left(\frac{1}{3}\ n+1\right)-3\ (n+1)\left(\frac{1}{2}\ n+1\right)$$

$$+\ n$$

```
> factor(");
```

$$\frac{1}{6}\ (n-1)\ (2\ n^2+5\ n+6)$$

```
> # complexity of merge sort
> rsolve( { T(n) = 2*T(n/2) + n-1, T(1)=0}, T(n) );
```

$$n\left(\frac{\ln(n)}{\ln(2)}-1+2\left(\frac{1}{2}\right)^{\left(\frac{\ln(n)}{\ln(2)}+1\right)}\right)$$

```
> simplify(");
```

$$\frac{\ln(n)\ n-\ln(2)\ n+\ln(2)}{\ln(2)}$$

```
> # complexity of Karatsuba multiplication
> rsolve( { T(n) = 3*T(n/2) + n, T(1)=1}, T(n) );
```

$$n^{\left(\frac{\ln(3)}{\ln(2)}\right)}+n^{\left(\frac{\ln(3)}{\ln(2)}\right)}\left(-3\left(\frac{2}{3}\right)^{\left(\frac{\ln(n)}{\ln(2)}+1\right)}+2\right)$$

```
> simplify(");
```

$$3\ n^{\left(\frac{\ln(3)}{\ln(2)}\right)}-2\ n$$

Sometimes, only partial solutions of a summation problem are found.

```
> rsolve( a(n+1) = (n+1)^2*a(n) + 1, a(n) );
```

$$\Gamma(n+1)^2 \left(\left(\sum_{\_n2=0}^{n-1} \frac{1}{\Gamma(\_n2+2)^2} \right) + a(0) \right)$$

Even when **rsolve** cannot find a closed formula, it may still give you information on the asymptotic behavior. An example:

```
> rsolve( u(n+1) = ln(u(n)+1), u(n) );
```

$$rsolve(u(n+1) = \ln(u(n)+1), u(n))$$

```
> asympt(",n,4);
```

$$2\frac{1}{n} + \frac{\_C + \frac{2}{3}\ln(n)}{n^2} + O\left(\frac{1}{n^3}\right)$$

Our final example will be the solution of a problem posed by Knuth [82]. Solve the recurrence

$$x_0 = a, \quad x_1 = b, \quad x_{n+2} = x_{n+1} + x_n/(n+1), \quad \text{for } n = 0, 1, 2, \ldots$$

both analytically (in terms of familiar functions of n) and asymptotically.

```
> rsolve( { x(n+2) = x(n+1) + x(n)/(n+1),
>     x(0)=a, x(1)=b }, x(n) );
```

$$rsolve\left(\left\{ x(n+2) = x(n+1) + \frac{x(n)}{n+1}, \ x(1) = b, \ x(0) = a \right\}, \ x(n) \right)$$

```
> asympt(",n);
```

$$\_C1 \, n \left(1 + \frac{1}{n} + O\left(\frac{1}{n^6}\right) \right)$$

We were too optimistic. So let us try to assist Maple and first compute the z-transform of the recurrence equation (written in a different but equivalent way).

```
> readlib( ztrans ):   # load library function
```

```
> x(0)  := a:   x(1)  := b:
> subs( ztrans(x(n),n,z)  =  F(z),
>      ztrans(  (n+1)*x(n+2)=(n+1)*x(n+1)+x(n), n, z ) );
```

$$-z^2 \ F(z) \ - \ z^3 \left(\frac{\partial}{\partial z} \ F(z) \right) + \ a \ z^2 =$$

$$-z^2 \left(\frac{\partial}{\partial z} \ F(z) \right) + \ F(z)$$

Next we have to solve the differential equation.

```
> dsolve(",F(z));
```

$$F(z) = \frac{z \left(z \ a + e^{-\frac{1}{z}} \_C1 \right)}{z^2 \ - \ 2 \ z \ + \ 1}$$

The last step of computing the inverse z-transform is the most difficult one.

```
> expand(");
```

$$F(z) = \frac{z^2 \ a}{z^2 \ - \ 2 \ z \ + \ 1} \ + \ \frac{z \ \_C1}{(z^2 \ - \ 2 \ z \ + \ 1) \ e^{\frac{1}{z}}}$$

```
> subs( invztrans(F(z),z,n)=x(n), invztrans(",z,n) );
```

$$x(n) = a \ n + a$$

$$+ \ \_C1 \ \text{invztrans} \left(\frac{z}{e^{\frac{1}{z}} \ (z^2 \ - \ 2 \ z \ + \ 1)}, \ z, \ n \right)$$

```
> simplify( factor(") );
```

$$x(n) = a \ n + a + \_C1 \ \text{invztrans} \left(\frac{e^{-\frac{1}{z}} \ z}{(z \ - \ 1)^2}, \ z, \ n \right)$$

```
> f := subs( body = invztrans(exp(-1/z),z,k), k->body );
```

$$f := k \rightarrow \frac{(-1)^k}{k!}$$

```
> g := subs( body = invztrans(z/(z-1)^2,z,k), k->body );
```

$$g := k \to k$$

So, the inverse z-transform which remains to be computed can be found as a convolution.

```
> lhs("""") = subsop( 3 = _C1*sum(f(n-k)*g(k),k=0..n),
>     rhs(""""));
```

$$x(n) = a \, n + a + \_C1 \left(\sum_{k=0}^{n} \frac{(-1)^{(n-k)} \, k}{(n-k)!} \right)$$

```
> (eval@subs)( n=1, " );
```

$$b = 2 \, a + \_C1$$

```
> solve(",_C1);
```

$$b - 2 \, a$$

```
> subs( _C1=", """);
```

$$x(n) = a \, n + a + (b - 2 \, a) \left(\sum_{k=0}^{n} \frac{(-1)^{(n-k)} \, k}{(n-k)!} \right)$$

The *genfunc* package contains functions for manipulating rational generating functions. It is a convenient tool when you want to apply the method of generating functions manually to recurrence relations.

15.8 Exercises

1. Compute the 6th degree polynomial mapping of which the graph goes through the points $(-5, -120)$, $(-3, 48)$, $(-2, 36)$, $(1, 120)$, $(4, 2400)$, $(10, 220380)$, and $(12, 57408)$.

2. Check whether
   $$3x^2 + 3y^2 + 6xy + 6x + 6y + 2$$
   can be written in the form
   $$a(x + by + c)^n + d$$
   for suitable values of a, b, c, d, and n.

3. Consider the stoichiometry of the following two chemical reactions.
   (a) For what values of p, q, r, s, t, u, and v is the reaction equation
   $$p\,KMnO_4 + q\,H_2SO_4 + r\,H_2C_2O_4 \longrightarrow$$
   $$s\,K_2SO_4 + t\,MnSO_4 + u\,H_2O + v\,CO_2$$
   balanced?
   (b) For what values of p, q, r, s, and t is the reaction equation
   $$p\,CO + q\,CO_2 + r\,H_2 \longrightarrow s\,CH_4 + t\,H_2O$$
   balanced?

4. Solve the following equation in x by **solve** and **fsolve**.
   $$48x^5 + 8x^4 - 6x^3 + 114x^2 - 37x + 18 = 0$$

5. Solve the system $\{x^2 + y^2 = 5,\ xy = y^2 - 2\}$ with **solve** and **fsolve**.

6. Solve the following system of polynomial equations in the unknowns x, y, and z over $\mathbb{R}$ (here, a is a real constant).
   $$\{\ z^2 - x^2 - y^2 + 2ax + 2az - a^2 = \ 0,$$
   $$yz - ay - ax + \ a^2 \qquad\quad = \ 0,$$
   $$-2a + \ x + \ y \qquad\qquad\qquad = \ 0\ \}$$

7. Let f be the homogeneous polynomial $x_0^3 + x_1^3 + x_2^3 + x_3^3$. It defines the Fermat surface in the projective space $\mathbb{P}^3$ as
   $$\{x_0\!:\!x_1\!:\!x_2\!:\!x_3 \in \mathbb{P}^3 \mid f(x_0, x_1, x_2, x_3) = 0\}\,.$$
   (a) There are 27 lines on the surface; use Maple to determine these lines. Hint: the line through the two points $x_0 : x_1 : x_2 : x_3$ and $y_0\!:\!y_1\!:\!y_2\!:\!y_3$ is described in so-called Plücker coordinates by
   $$p^{ij} := x_i y_j - x_j y_i, \quad \text{with } i, j = 0, 1, 2, 3 \text{ and } i \neq j\,.$$
   In this coordinate system, a line is on the surface iff
   $$f(p^{01}u_1 + p^{02}u_2 + p^{03}u_3,\ p^{10}u_0 + p^{12}u_2 + p^{13}u_3,$$
   $$p^{20}u_0 + p^{21}u_1 + p^{23}u_3,\ p^{30}u_0 + p^{31}u_1 + p^{32}u_2) = 0$$
   for all u_0, u_1, u_2, u_3 in $\mathbb{R}$, and $p^{01}p^{23} + p^{02}p^{31} + p^{03}p^{12} = 0$.
   (b) Determine the singular points on the Fermat surface.
   Recall that a point is singular when the function values and all partial derivatives in this point are equal to zero.

8. Solve the recurrence equation $a_{n+1} = (8/5)\,a_n - a_{n-1}$, $a_0 = 0$, $a_1 = 1$.

9. Solve the recurrence equation $a_{n+2} = 3n\,a_n - 2n\,(n-1)\,a_{n-1}$, $a_3 = 5$, $a_5 = 54$.

Differential Equations

Maple can solve many ordinary differential equations analytically as explicit functions or in implicit form. Traditional techniques such as the method of Laplace transformations, integrating factors, etc., are available through the differential equation solver **dsolve**. But modern Lie symmetry methods are implemented as well for partial differential equations in the *liesymm* package. Approximate methods such as Taylor series and power series methods are also available. And if all fails, one can still use the numerical solver based on the Runge-Kutta method. Moreover, Maple provides all the tools to apply perturbation methods, like the Poincaré-Lindstedt method and the method of multiple scales up to high order. In this chapter, we shall discuss all tools available in Maple for studying differential equations. Many examples come from applied mathematics.

16.1 First Glance at ODEs

Recall that an *ordinary differential equation* (abbreviated ODE) is an equation of the form

$$F\left(y, y', y'', \cdots, y^{(n)}, x\right) = 0,$$

which holds on a particular interval, where $y', y'', \ldots, y^{(n)}$ are short notations for the derivatives of $y(x)$, and where F is a real function defined over (a subdomain of) $\mathbb{R}^{n+2}$. The ODE is of *order n*, when the function F does depend on the $(n+1)^{\text{th}}$ argument. When the function F is linear in its first $n+1$ arguments, the ODE is called *linear*; it is of the form

$$a_n(x)\, y^{(n)} + a_{n-1}(x)\, y^{(n-1)} + \cdots + a_1(x)\, y' + a_0(x)y + a(x) = 0.$$

When F is a polynomial mapping, then the *degree* of the ODE of order n is defined as the exponent of the $(n+1)^{\text{th}}$ argument in F. In short, the order of an ODE is equal to k if the kth derivative is the highest derivative that occurs in the ODE, and the degree is the exponent with which this highest derivative occurs. Some examples:

$$y'' - x^2 y - x^3 = 0 \qquad \text{a linear ODE of order 2 and degree 1,}$$

$$y'' - y^3 = 0 \qquad \text{a nonlinear ODE of order 2 and degree 1,}$$

$$\left(y''\right)^3 - y = 0 \qquad \text{a nonlinear ODE of order 2 and degree 3.}$$

Mathematicians have developed a whole range of methods for solving differential equations, some of which are implemented in Maple. Once again all methods are provided by one procedure, viz., **dsolve** (**diff**erential equation **solve**r). You can leave it up to the Maple system to chose a method for solving a differential equation or you can select one yourself. For example, when you want to apply the method of Laplace transforms or find a Taylor series solution, then you only have to say so.

To be honest, Maple's capabilities in solving ODEs are rather limited: in most cases, solutions are only found for ODEs of degree 1 and order smaller than 3. Little knowledge about special functions is incorporated in the differential equation solver (with the exception of Bessel functions). Nevertheless, Maple provides valuable facilities for solving ordinary differential equations. In the next sections we shall have a look at these facilities through many examples from applied mathematics.

16.2 Analytic Solutions

Consider the differential equation

$$xy' = y\ln(xy) - y,$$

of order 1 and degree 1. If you have no strong preference for a particular method of solving the ODE, then you call **dsolve** without all the trimmings.

```
> ODE := x*diff(y(x),x) = y(x)*ln(x*y(x)) - y(x);
```

$$ODE := x\left(\frac{\partial}{\partial x}\, y(x)\right) = y(x)\,\ln(x\,y(x)) - y(x)$$

```
> dsolve( ODE, y(x) );
```

$$x = \_C1\,\ln(x) + \_C1\,\ln(y(x))$$

A more natural and convenient notation is provided for by the **alias** construct in Maple. Let us apply it to the same example.

```
> alias( y=y(x) ):
> ODE := x*diff(y,x) = y*ln(x*y) - y;
```

$$ODE := x\left(\frac{\partial}{\partial x}\, y\right) = y\,\ln(x\,y) - y$$

```
> dsolve( ODE, y );
```

$$x = \_C1\,\ln(x) + \_C1\,\ln(y)$$

You see that Maple chose to find an implicit solution of the differential equation. If you prefer an explicit expression for the function y, you can use the procedure **solve** to this end, but **isolate** is also of help.

```
> readlib(isolate)(",y);
```

$$y = e^{-\frac{-x + \_C1 \; \ln(x)}{\_C1}}$$

However, you could have informed Maple about this right from the beginning.

```
> dsolve( ODE, y, ´explicit´ );
```

$$y = e^{\frac{x - \_C1 \; \ln(x)}{\_C1}}$$

This is not the simplest expression for the general solution.

```
> expand(");
```

$$y = \frac{e^{\frac{x}{\_C1}}}{x}$$

```
> subs( _C1=1/c, " );
```

$$y = \frac{e^{c \, x}}{x}$$

This solution of the ODE can easily be checked (and it is good advice to do this as much as you can).

```
> subs(",ODE);
```

$$x \left(\frac{\partial}{\partial x} \; \frac{e^{c \, x}}{x} \right) = \frac{e^{c \, x} \; \ln(e^{c \, x})}{x} - \frac{e^{c \, x}}{x}$$

```
> expand( lhs(") - rhs(") );
```

$$0$$

As a second example, we consider the differential equation

$$y' = \sqrt{y^2 + 1}.$$

In order to get more information about what is going on during the computation, we set a higher value to the variable `infolevel[dsolve]`.

```
> infolevel[dsolve] := 2:
```

```
> alias( y=y(x) ):
> ODE := diff(y,x) = sqrt(y^2+1);
```

$$ODE := \frac{\partial}{\partial x} \, y = \sqrt{y^2 + 1}$$

```
> dsolve(",y);
```

```
dsolve/diffeq/linbern:
determining if d.e is linear or bernoulli
dsolve/diffeq/seperable: checking if d.e. is separable
dsolve/diffeq/sepsol: solving separable d.e.
```

$$-\ln\left(y + \sqrt{y^2 + 1} \right) + x = \_C1$$

```
> readlib(isolate)(",y);
```

```
factor: polynomial factorization: number of terms    3
factor: polynomial factorization: number of terms    3
```

$$-\ln\left(y + \sqrt{y^2 + 1} \right) + x = \_C1$$

You can further simplify this result.

```
> subs( -_C1+x=z, " );
```

$$y = \frac{1}{2} \frac{(e^z)^2 - 1}{e^z}$$

```
> expand(");
```

$$y = \frac{1}{2} e^z - \frac{1}{2} \frac{1}{e^z}$$

```
> convert(", ´trig´);
```

$$y = \frac{1}{2} \cosh(z) + \frac{1}{2} \sinh(z) - \frac{1}{2} \frac{1}{\cosh(z) + \sinh(z)}$$

```
> simplify(");
```

$$y = \sinh(z)$$

```
> subs( z=-_C1+x, " );
```

$$y = \sinh(-\_C1 + x)$$

```
> (eval@subs)(",ODE); # check the answer
```

$$\cosh(-\_C1 + x) = \sqrt{\sinh(-\_C1 + x)^2 + 1}$$

```
> simplify(");
```

```
simplify: applying   trig    function to expression
simplify: applying   trig    function to expression
simplify: applying   power   function to expression
simplify: applying commonpow  function to expression
simplify: applying power   function to expression
```

$$\cosh(-\_C1 + x) = \cosh(-\_C1 + x)$$

Look what would have happened if you had immediately asked for an explicit solution.

```
> dsolve( ODE, y, ´explicit´ );
```

```
dsolve/diffeq/linbern:
determining if d.e. is linear or bernoulli
dsolve/diffeq/separable:   checking if d.e. is separable
dsolve/diffeq/sepsol:   solving separable d.e.
dsolve:   Warning: no explicit solutions found
```

No solutions found at all! The reason for this is that **solve** could not isolate the requested formula from the implicit solution, whereas **isolate** did credit to its name. Anyway, you see that different roads may lead to different answers.

A differential equation may contain several variables. For example, look at the differential equation which describes the trajectory of an object that is pulled with a rope of length a by someone who walks along the x-axis to the right.

$$y' = -\frac{y}{\sqrt{a^2 - y^2}}$$

```
> infolevel[dsolve] := 1:  alias( y=y(x) ):
> ODE := diff(y,x) = -y / sqrt(a^2-y^2);
```

$$ODE := \frac{\partial}{\partial x} y = -\frac{y}{\sqrt{a^2 - y^2}}$$

```
> solution := dsolve( ODE, y );
```

$$solution :=$$

$$\sqrt{a^2 - y^2} - a \ln\left(a + \sqrt{a^2 - y^2}\right) + a \ln(y) + x$$

$$= \_C1$$

Note that the constant function 0 is not recognized by Maple as a solution of the differential equation.

When the person starts at the origin and the object is at that time at position $(0, a)$, i.e., when the initial condition is $y(0) = a$, then you can determine the constant _C1.

```
> subs( {y=a,x=0}, solution );
```

$$0 = \_C1$$

You might be tempted to substitute as follows.

```
> subs( x=0, solution );
```

$$\sqrt{a^2 - y(0)^2} - a \ln\left(a + \sqrt{a^2 - y(0)^2}\right)$$
$$+ a \ln(y(0)) = \_C1$$

```
> subs( y(0)=0, " );
```

$$\sqrt{a^2 - y(0)^2} - a \ln\left(a + \sqrt{a^2 - y(0)^2}\right)$$
$$+ a \ln(y(0)) = \_C1$$

The reason why this does not do what it was expected to do is that y has first been aliased to $y(x)$. After the first substitution x=0 an object $y(0)$ is returned that differs from the one obtained when you enter $y(0)$.

```
> subs( subs(x=0,y) = a, " );
```

$$0 = \_C1$$

```
> subs( op(0,y)(0) = a, " );
```

$$0 = \_C1$$

These would be tricky solutions compared to the way we have chosen above. We end this example with a description of the slip curve.

```
> slipcurve := subs( _C1=0, solution );
```

$$slipcurve :=$$
$$\sqrt{a^2 - y^2} - a \ln\left(a + \sqrt{a^2 - y^2}\right) + a \ln(y) + x$$
$$= 0$$

By the way, in Maple you can immediately specify an initial value problem. We illustrate this by studying the differential equation,

$$u'' + \omega^2 u = 0,$$

of the mathematical pendulum. The same problems with aliases as described in the previous example would occur; hence we avoid them.

```
> ODE := diff(u(t),t$2) + omega^2*u(t) = 0;
```

$$ODE := \left(\frac{\partial^2}{\partial t^2} u(t) \right) + \omega^2 \, u(t) = 0$$

```
> dsolve( { ODE, u(0)=2, D(u)(0)=3 }, u(t) );
```

$$u(t) = 3 \, \frac{\sin(\omega \, t)}{\omega} + 2 \, \cos(\omega \, t)$$

You give the first derivative at zero as `D(u)(0)`. Higher derivatives $u''(0)$, $u'''(0)$, ... are given as `(D@@2)(u)(0)`, `(D@@3)(u)(0)`, ...

In Maple you can easily use the method of *Laplace transforms* for solving differential equations. As an example, we will look at the step response of a linear damped oscillator. The initial value problem is

```
> ODE := diff(u(t),t$2) + 2*damp*omega*diff(u(t),t)
>     + omega^2*u(t) = Heaviside(t);
```

$$ODE := \left(\frac{\partial^2}{\partial t^2} u(t) \right) + 2 \, damp \, \omega \left(\frac{\partial}{\partial t} u(t) \right) + \omega^2 \, u(t) =$$

$$Heaviside(t)$$

```
> initvals := u(0)=0, D(u)(0)=0:
> solution := dsolve( { ODE, initvals }, u(t),
>     `laplace` );
```

$$solution := u(t) = \frac{1}{\omega^2}$$

$$- \frac{damp \; e^{-damp \, \omega \, t} \, \sinh\left(\omega \, \sqrt{-1 + damp^2} \; t \right)}{\omega^2 \, \sqrt{-1 + damp^2}}$$

$$- \frac{e^{-damp \, \omega \, t} \, \cosh\left(\omega \, \sqrt{-1 + damp^2} \; t \right)}{\omega^2}$$

Maple does not distinguish the cases of no damping ($damp = 0$), under-damping ($0 < damp < 1$), critical damping ($damp = 1$), and overdamping ($damp > 1$). In most cases, the above formula for the solution is simplified to its most convenient form.

```
> damp := 0:   simplify( solution );
```

$$u(t) = - \frac{-1 + \cos(\omega\ t)}{\omega^2}$$

```
> damp := 1/6: simplify( solution );
```

$$u(t) = - \frac{1}{35} \left(-35 \right.$$

$$+\ e^{-\ 1/6\ \omega\ t}\ \sin\!\left(\frac{1}{6}\ \omega\ \sqrt{5}\ \sqrt{7}\ t\right) \sqrt{5}\ \sqrt{7}$$

$$\left. +\ 35\ e^{-\ 1/6\ \omega\ t}\ \cos\!\left(\frac{1}{6}\ \omega\ \sqrt{5}\ \sqrt{7}\ t\right) \right) \Big/ \omega^2$$

You can plot this solution for a range of frequency values.

```
> plot3d( rhs("), omega=2/3..4/3, t=0..20,

>    style=hidden, orientation=[-30,45], axes=BOXED );
```

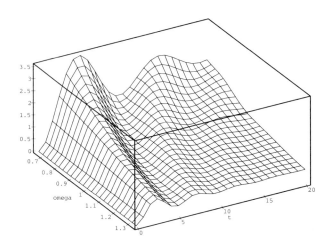

Similarly, you can plot the solutions for a fixed frequency and a range of damping values.

```
> damp := ´damp´: omega := 1:

> plot3d( rhs(solution), damp=1/5..2, t=0..20,

>    style=hidden, orientation=[-10,45], axes=BOXED );
```

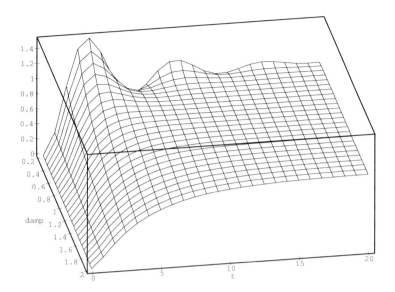

From this picture the trade-off between system damping and system response is clear; low damping values result in overshooting while high damping values are slow to respond to input signals.

Systems of linear differential equations can also be solved with **dsolve**.

```
> ODE := diff(f(t),t$2) - 6*diff(g(t),t) = 6*sin(t),
>    6*diff(g(t),t$2) + c^2*diff(f(t),t) = 6*cos(t);
```

$$ODE := \left(\frac{\partial^2}{\partial t^2}\, f(t) \right) - 6 \left(\frac{\partial}{\partial t}\, g(t) \right) = 6\, \sin(t),$$

$$6 \left(\frac{\partial^2}{\partial t^2}\, g(t) \right) + c^2 \left(\frac{\partial}{\partial t}\, f(t) \right) = 6\, \cos(t)$$

```
> initvals := f(0)= 0, g(0)=1, D(f)(0)=0, D(g)(0)=1:
> funcs := {f(t),g(t)}:
> dsolve( { ODE, initvals}, funcs, ´laplace´ );
```

$$\left\{ g(t) = \frac{\cos(t)\, c^2}{-1 + c^2} + \frac{\cos(t)}{-1 + c^2} - \frac{\sin(c\, t)}{(-1 + c^2)\, c} \right.$$

$$\left. + \frac{c\, \sin(c\, t)}{-1 + c^2} - 2\, \frac{\cos(c\, t)}{-1 + c^2},\ f(t) = 6\, \frac{1}{c^2} \right.$$

$$+ 12 \; \frac{\sin(\ t\ )}{-1 \ + \ c^2} \; - \; 12 \; \frac{c \; \sin(\ c\ t\ )}{-c^2 \ + \ c^4} \; + \; 6 \; \frac{\cos(\ c\ t\ )}{-c^2 \ + \ c^4}$$

$$\left. - \; 6 \; \frac{c^2 \; \cos(\ c\ t\ )}{-c^2 \ + \ c^4} \right\}$$

```
> collect( ",  {cos(c*t),sin(c*t)}, normal );
```

$$\left\{ g(\ t\ ) = \frac{\sin(\ c\ t\ )}{c} \; - \; 2 \; \frac{\cos(\ c\ t\ )}{-1 \ + \ c^2} \; + \; \frac{(\ c^2 \ + \ 1\ ) \; \cos(\ t\ )}{-1 \ + \ c^2} \right.$$

$$, \; f(\ t\ ) = -12 \; \frac{\sin(\ c\ t\ )}{(\ -1 \ + \ c^2\ ) \; c} \; - \; 6 \; \frac{\cos(\ c\ t\ )}{c^2}$$

$$\left. + \; 6 \; \frac{-1 \ + \ c^2 \ + \ 2 \; \sin(\ t\ ) \; c^2}{c^2 \; (\ -1 \ + \ c^2\ )} \right\}$$

We end this section by summarizing what kind of ordinary differential equations can presently be solved with **dsolve**.

First Order ODEs

Type of ODE	Shape of ODE
linear	$y' + P(x)y = Q(x)$
exact	$y' = -\dfrac{P(x,y)}{Q(x,y)}$, with $\dfrac{\partial Q}{\partial x} = \dfrac{\partial P}{\partial y}$
inexact	$F(x,y)y' + G(x,y) = 0$, when an integrating factor can be found
separable	$y' = f(x)g(y)$
homogeneous	$y' = F(xy^n)\dfrac{y}{x}$
high degree	$x = F(y, y')$
Bernoulli	$y' + P(x)y = Q(x)y^n$
Clairaut	$y = xy' + F(y')$
Riccati	$y' = P(x)y^2 + Q(x)y' + R(x)$

Second Order ODEs

Type of ODE	Shape of ODE
linear	$ay'' + by' + cy = d(x)$, where $a, b, c \in \mathbb{C}$
Euler	$x^2 y'' + axy' + by = c(x)$
Bessel	$x^2 y'' + (2k+1)xy' + (\alpha^2 x^{2r} + \beta^2)y = 0$, where $k, \alpha, r, \beta \in \mathbb{C}$ and $\alpha r \neq 0$
Bernoulli	$y' + P(x)y = Q(x)y^n$

Moreover, Kovacic's algorithm [83] has been implemented in Maple; it tries to solve linear homogeneous second order ODEs of the form

$$P(x)y'' + Q(x)y' + R(x)y = 0,$$

where $P(x)$, $Q(x)$, and $R(x)$ are rational functions.

Even if Maple recognizes the type of an ODE it may still need help.

```
> infolevel[dsolve] := 2:
> ODE := diff(y(x),x) + 2*y(x)*exp(x) - y(x)^2
>     - exp(2*x) - exp(x) = 0;
```

$$ODE := \left(\frac{\partial}{\partial x} \, y(x) \right) + 2 \, y(x) \, e^x - y(x)^2 - e^{2x} - e^x = 0$$

```
> dsolve( ODE, y(x) );

dsolve/diffeq/linbern:
determining if d.e. is linear or bernoulli
dsolve/diffeq/separable:   checking if d.e. is separable
dsolve/diffeq/exactinex:   determining if d.e. is exact
dsolve/diffeq/genhomo:  determining if d.e. is homogeneous
dsolve/diffeq/riccati:  determining if d.e. is riccati
dsolve/diffeq/riccati:  trying to solve Riccati d.e.
dsolve/diffeq/riccati:  searching for polynomial solution
dsolve/diffeq/riccati:  using Kovacic algorithm
dsolve/diffeq/riccati:
no solution found by Kovacic´s algorithm
dsolve:    Warning: no solutions found
```

It is easily checked that e^x is a solution.

```
> subs( y(x) = exp(x), ODE ):  expand(");
```

$$0 = 0$$

Write the required solution $y(x)$ as $z(x) + e^x$, derive the ODE for the function $z(x)$, and try to solve this one.

```
> subs( y(x) = z(x) + exp(x), ODE ):  expand(");
```

$$\left(\frac{\partial}{\partial x}\, z(x) \right) - z(x)^2 = 0$$

```
> dsolve( ", z(x), ´explicit´ );
```

```
dsolve/diffeq/linbern:
determining if d.e. is linear or bernoulli
dsolve/diffeq/bernsol:   trying Bernoulli solution
dsolve/diffeq/linearsol:   solving 1st order linear d.e.
```

$$z(x) = - \frac{1}{x - \_C1}$$

Check the general solution.

```
> solution := exp(x) + rhs(");
```

$$solution := e^x - \frac{1}{x - \_C1}$$

```
> subs( y(x) = solution, ODE ):  expand(");
```

$$0 = 0$$

16.3 Taylor Series Method

When an analytical solution for an ordinary differential equation cannot be found, there is still the possibility of using Maple to find a Taylor series approximation. We shall apply this method to the (large oscillation) pendulum, shown below and described by the differential equation

$$l\, \theta'' = -g \sin \theta,$$

where l is the pendulum length, g is the gravitational acceleration, and θ is the angle between the rope and the vertical.

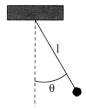

```
> ODE := l*diff(theta(t),t$2) = -g*sin(theta(t));
```

$$ODE := l\left(\frac{\partial^2}{\partial t^2}\,\theta(\,t\,)\right) = -g\,\sin(\,\theta(\,t\,)\,)$$

```
> initvals := theta(0)=0, D(theta)(0)=v0/l:
> Order := 9:
> solution := dsolve( { ODE, initvals }, theta(t),
>    ´series´ );
```

$$solution := \theta(\,t\,) = \frac{v0}{l}\,t\;-\;\frac{1}{6}\,\frac{g\;v0}{l^2}\,t^3\;+$$

$$\frac{1}{120}\,\frac{g\;v0\;(\,v0^2\;+\;g\;l\,)}{l^4}\,t^5\;-$$

$$\frac{1}{5040}\,\frac{g\;v0\;(\,11\;g\;v0^2\;l\;+\;g^2\;l^2\;+\;v0^4\,)}{l^6}\,t^7\;+\;O(\,t^9\,)$$

Below, we shall rewrite this solution in dimensionless variables. First, we check dimensions.

```
> subs( { v0=L/T, g=L/T^2, l=L }, " );
```

$$\theta(\,t\,) =$$

$$\frac{1}{T}\,t\;-\;\frac{1}{6}\,\frac{1}{T^3}\,t^3\;+\;\frac{1}{60}\,\frac{1}{T^5}\,t^5\;-\;\frac{13}{5040}\,\frac{1}{T^7}\,t^7\;+\;O(\,t^9\,)$$

Next, we determine dimensionless parameters a and b.

```
> nondimensional := v0^ev0 * g^eg * l^el * t^et;
```

$$nondimensional := v0^{ev0}\;g^{eg}\;l^{el}\;t^{et}$$

```
> simplify( subs( { v0=L/T, g=L/T^2, l=L, t=T },
>    nondimensional ) );
```

$$L^{(\,ev0\;+\;eg\;+\;el\,)}\;T^{(\,-ev0\;-\;2\;eg\;+\;et\,)}$$

```
> isolve( { seq( op(2,i)=0, i=" ) } );
```

$$\{ et = \_N1 + 2 \ \_N2, \ el = -\_N1 - \_N2, \ ev0 = \_N1, \ eg = \_N2 \}$$

```
> assign("):
> { a = subs( _N1=1, _N2=0, nondimensional),
>   b = subs( _N1=2, _N2=-1, nondimensional) };
```

$$\left\{ a = \frac{v0 \ t}{l}, \ b = \frac{v0^2}{g \ l} \right\}$$

We express the gravitation g and length l of the rod in terms of the dimensionless variables, and we substitute these expressions into the solution of the ODE.

```
> solve(",{g,l});
```

$$\left\{ g = \frac{v0 \ a}{b \ t}, \ l = \frac{v0 \ t}{a} \right\}$$

```
> subs( ", convert( rhs(solution), `polynom` ) );
```

$$a - \frac{1}{6} \frac{a^3}{b} + \frac{1}{120} \frac{a^5 \left(v0^2 + \frac{v0^2}{b} \right)}{v0^2 \ b}$$

$$- \frac{1}{5040} \frac{a^7 \left(11 \frac{v0^4}{b} + \frac{v0^4}{b^2} + v0^4 \right)}{v0^4 \ b}$$

```
> map(normal,");
```

$$a - \frac{1}{6} \frac{a^3}{b} + \frac{1}{120} \frac{a^5 \ (b + 1)}{b^2}$$

$$- \frac{1}{5040} \frac{a^7 \ (11 \ b + 1 + b^2)}{b^3}$$

Compare this with the series expansion of $\sin t$.

```
> series( sin(t), t, 9 );
```

$$t - \frac{1}{6} \ t^3 + \frac{1}{120} \ t^5 - \frac{1}{5040} \ t^7 + O(t^9)$$

16.4 Power Series Method

Naturally, in a modern computer algebra system like Maple, the method of power series to solve differential equation should not be absent. This facility resides in the *powseries* package. However, note that it only works for linear differential equations with polynomial coefficients. Our first example will be a differential equation of Bessel type.

$$xy'' + y' + 4x^2 y = 0$$

Maple can find the exact solution.

```
> eqn := x*diff(y(x),x$2) + diff(y(x),x) + 4*x^2*y(x) = 0;
```

$$eqn := x \left(\frac{\partial^2}{\partial x^2} y(x) \right) + \left(\frac{\partial}{\partial x} y(x) \right) + 4 \ x^2 \ y(x) = 0$$

```
> dsolve( eqn ,y(x) );
```

$$y(x) = \_C1 \ \text{BesselJ}\left(0, \ \frac{4}{3} \ x^{3/2}\right) + \_C2 \ \text{BesselY}\left(0, \ \frac{4}{3} \ x^{3/2}\right)$$

Below, we shall compute the power series solution for initial values $y(0) = 1$, $y'(0) = 0$.

```
> initvals := y(0)=1, D(y)(0)=0:
> with( powseries ):   # load the power series package
> solution := powsolve( { eqn, initvals } );
solution := proc(powparm) ... end
> tpsform( solution, x, 15 );   # truncated powerseries
```

$$1 - \frac{4}{9} \ x^3 + \frac{4}{81} \ x^6 - \frac{16}{6561} \ x^9 + \frac{4}{59049} \ x^{12} + O(\ x^{15}\ )$$

Maple can give you the recurrence relation of the coefficients.

```
> solution(_k);
```

$$-4 \ \frac{a(\_k - 3)}{\_k^2}$$

Interpret this as the relation

$$a_k = -4 \frac{a_{k-3}}{k^2}.$$

Our second example is a classical one in quantum mechanics — the solutions of the one-dimensional harmonic oscillator. The Schrödinger equation can be given in dimensionless units as

$$\frac{d^2 y(x)}{dx^2} + (\epsilon - x^2)\, y(x) = 0.$$

```
> alias( y=y(x), h=h(x) ):
> eqn := diff(y,x$2) + (epsilon-x^2)*y = 0;
```

$$eqn := \left(\frac{\partial^2}{\partial x^2}\, y\right) + (\, \varepsilon\, -\, x^2\,)\;\; y = 0$$

Asymptotic analysis suggests the substitution $y(x) = h(x)e^{-x^2/2}$. The differential equation for h is

```
> subs( y = exp(-x^2/2)*h, " ):
> collect( ", exp(-x^2/2) ) / exp(-x^2/2);
```

$$-h + x^2\, h - 2\, x \left(\frac{\partial}{\partial x}\, h\right) + \left(\frac{\partial^2}{\partial x^2}\, h\right) + (\, \varepsilon\, -\, x^2\,)\;\; h = 0$$

```
> eqn := collect( ", [diff(h,x$2), diff(h,x), h] );
```

$$eqn := \left(\frac{\partial^2}{\partial x^2}\, h\right) - 2\, x \left(\frac{\partial}{\partial x}\, h\right) + (\, -1\, +\, \varepsilon\,)\;\; h = 0$$

We solve this differential equation via the power series method.

```
> with(powseries):
> H := powsolve(eqn):
> h := tpsform(H,x,10); # a few terms
```

$$h := C0 + C1\; x - \frac{1}{2}\; (\, -1\, +\, \varepsilon\,)\; C0\; x^2 - \frac{1}{6}\; (\, -3\, +\, \varepsilon\,)\; C1\; x^3$$

$$+ \frac{1}{24}\; (\, -5\, +\, \varepsilon\,)\; (\, -1\, +\, \varepsilon\,)\; C0\; x^4 +$$

$$\frac{1}{120}\; (\, -7\, +\, \varepsilon\,)\; (\, -3\, +\, \varepsilon\,)\; C1\; x^5 -$$

$$\frac{1}{720}\; (\, -9\, +\, \varepsilon\,)\; (\, -5\, +\, \varepsilon\,)\; (\, -1\, +\, \varepsilon\,)\; C0\; x^6 -$$

$$\frac{1}{5040}\; (\, -11\, +\, \varepsilon\,)\; (\, -7\, +\, \varepsilon\,)\; (\, -3\, +\, \varepsilon\,)\; C1\; x^7 +$$

$$\frac{1}{40320} \ (-13 \ + \ \epsilon) \ (-9 \ + \ \epsilon) \ (-5 \ + \ \epsilon) \ (-1 \ + \ \epsilon) \ C0$$

$$x^8 \ + \ \frac{1}{362880}$$

$$(-15 \ + \ \epsilon) \ (-11 \ + \ \epsilon) \ (-7 \ + \ \epsilon) \ (-3 \ + \ \epsilon) \ C1 \ x^9$$

$$+ \ O(\ x^{10} \ )$$

```
> collect( convert(",´polynom´), [C0,C1] );
```

$$\left(1 \ - \ \frac{1}{2} \ (-1 \ + \ \epsilon) \ x^2 \ + \ \frac{1}{24} \ (-5 \ + \ \epsilon) \ (-1 \ + \ \epsilon) \ x^4 \right.$$

$$- \ \frac{1}{720} \ (-9 \ + \ \epsilon) \ (-5 \ + \ \epsilon) \ (-1 \ + \ \epsilon) \ x^6 \ + \ \frac{1}{40320}$$

$$\left. (-13 \ + \ \epsilon) \ (-9 \ + \ \epsilon) \ (-5 \ + \ \epsilon) \ (-1 \ + \ \epsilon) \ x^8 \right) C0$$

$$+ \left(x \ - \ \frac{1}{6} \ (-3 \ + \ \epsilon) \ x^3 \right.$$

$$+ \ \frac{1}{120} \ (-7 \ + \ \epsilon) \ (-3 \ + \ \epsilon) \ x^5$$

$$- \ \frac{1}{5040} \ (-11 \ + \ \epsilon) \ (-7 \ + \ \epsilon) \ (-3 \ + \ \epsilon) \ x^7 \ +$$

$$\frac{1}{362880}$$

$$\left. (-15 \ + \ \epsilon) \ (-11 \ + \ \epsilon) \ (-7 \ + \ \epsilon) \ (-3 \ + \ \epsilon) \ x^9 \right) C1$$

Let us look at the recurrence relation for the coefficients of the series h.

```
> H(_k);
```

$$- \ \frac{(3 \ + \ \epsilon \ - \ 2 \ \_k) \ a(\ \_k \ - \ 2)}{\_k \ (\ \_k \ - \ 1)}$$

This must be interpreted as

$$a_k = -\frac{(3 + \epsilon - 2k)a_{k-2}}{k(k-1)},$$

or equivalently as

$$(k+1)(k+2)a_{k+2} = (2k+1-\epsilon)a_k,$$

for all k. A finite series h is obtained if and only if $\epsilon = 2k+1$ for some integer k. This is the famous quantization of the energy levels of the harmonic oscillator. One example of a wave function:

```
> C0 := 1:   C1 := 0:   epsilon := 9:
> tpsform(H,x,10): convert(",`polynom`);
```

$$1 - 4 \ x^2 + \frac{4}{3} \ x^4$$

It is a multiple of the fourth Hermite polynomial.

```
> orthopoly[H](4,x) / 12;
```

$$1 - 4 \ x^2 + \frac{4}{3} \ x^4$$

16.5 Numerical Solutions

You can solve initial-value problems numerically in Maple by adding the key word *numeric*. The system uses a Fehlberg fourth-fifth order Runge-Kutta method also known as algorithm RKF45 [47]. First, we shall apply it to van der Pol's equation

$$y'' - (1-y^2)y' + y = 0,$$

with initial values $y(0) = 0, y'(0) = -0.1$.

To find a numerical solution of the system of differential equations, call the procedure **dsolve** with the keyword `numeric`.

```
> alias( y=y(t), y0=y(0), yp0=D(y)(0) ):
> eqn := diff(y,t$2) - (1-y^2)*diff(y,t) + y = 0;
```

$$eqn := \left(\frac{\partial^2}{\partial t^2} \ y \right) - (1 - y^2) \left(\frac{\partial}{\partial t} \ y \right) + y = 0$$

```
> initvals := y0=0, yp0=-0.1:
> F := dsolve( {eqn, initvals}, y, `numeric` );

F := proc(t) `dsolve/numeric/result2`(t,268851300,[2]) end
```

The numeric solver returns a set consisting of an equation describing the value of the independent variable t and an equation describing the value of the dependent variable y at that point. Two examples:

```
> F(0);
```
$$\{ t = 0, \ y = 0 \}$$
```
> F(1);
```
$$\{ t = 1., \ y = -.1447686136 \}$$

You get a better understanding of the solution by plotting it over a domain of interest. Let us first convert the numeric solution into a function. Because ordering of elements of sets is based on address ordering and y has been aliased to $y(t)$, you have to put some extra effort into selection of the right-hand side of the equation of the dependent variable y.

```
# The actual numerical solution
> Y := t -> rhs( op(
>     select( hastype, F(t), ´function´ )
> ) ):
```

But now you can use the **plot** command to draw the graph of the solution.

```
> plot( Y, 0..14, title=
>     `solution of van der Pol´s Equation` );
```

solution of van der Pol's Equation

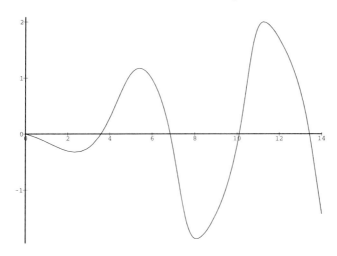

You can make it less difficult for yourself if you are satisfied with non-adaptive plotting; simply use the procedure **odeplot** from the **plots** package.

```
> plots[odeplot]( F, [t,y], 0..30, title=

>     `odeplot of the solution of van der Pol´s Equation` );

    odeplot of the solution of van der Pol's Equation
```

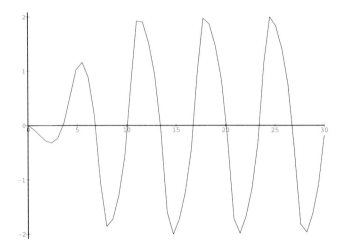

If you want to use other numerical solvers, e.g., Euler methods, and plot the numeric solution, then you can use plotting routines from the *DEtools* package.

In the second, more lengthy, example we apply the numerical ODE-solver to the system of differential equations which describe the dynamics of a frictionless, rigid, two-link robot manipulator without torque (double-pendulum).

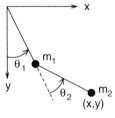

First, we derive the equations of motion via the *Euler-Lagrange* formalism. Let $\theta = (\theta_1, \theta_2)$ and $\dot{\theta} = (\dot{\theta}_1, \dot{\theta}_2)$, and define the *Lagrangian function* as

$$L(\theta, \dot{\theta}) = T(\theta, \dot{\theta}) - V(\theta),$$

where $T(\theta, \dot{\theta})$ is the kinetic energy and $V(\theta)$ is the potential energy. For the above configuration the kinetic energy is computed as the sum of the kinetic energies T_1 and T_2 of the masses m_1 and m_2, respectively. The kinetic energy of mass m_1 can be written directly as

$$T_1(\dot{\theta}) = \frac{1}{2}m_1\dot{\theta}_1^2.$$

The Cartesian coordinates (x, y) of the endpoint are given by

$$x = l_1 \sin\theta_1 + l_2 \sin(\theta_1 + \theta_2),$$
$$y = l_1 \cos\theta_1 + l_2 \cos(\theta_1 + \theta_2).$$

So, the Cartesian components of the velocity are

$$\dot{x} = l_1(\cos\theta_1)\dot{\theta}_1 + l_2 \cos(\theta_1 + \theta_2)(\dot{\theta}_1 + \dot{\theta}_2),$$
$$\dot{y} = -l_1(\sin\theta_1)\dot{\theta}_1 - l_2 \sin(\theta_1 + \theta_2)(\dot{\theta}_1 + \dot{\theta}_2).$$

Squaring the magnitude of the velocity yields

$$T_2(\theta, \dot{\theta}) = \frac{1}{2}m_2\left((l_1^2\dot{\theta}_1^2 + (l_2^2(\dot{\theta}_1 + \dot{\theta}_2)^2 + 2l_1l_2(\cos\theta_2)\dot{\theta}_1(\dot{\theta}_1 + \dot{\theta}_2)\right).$$

The potential energy is determined by the height of the mass.

$$V_1(\theta) = -m_1gl_1 \cos\theta_1,$$
$$V_2(\theta) = -m_2gl_1 \cos\theta_1 - m_2gl_2 \cos(\theta_1 + \theta_2).$$

All above formulae could have been found with Maple.

```
> alias( t1=t1(t), t2=t2(t) ):
> x1 := l1*sin(t1):   y1 := l1*cos(t1):
>   x := l1*sin(t1) + l2*sin(t1+t2):
>   y := l1*cos(t1) + l2*cos(t1+t2):
```

The kinetic energy of mass m_1 is computed by

```
> T1 := simplify( 1/2*m1*(diff(x1,t)^2 + diff(y1,t)^2) );
```

$$T1 := \frac{1}{2}\, m1\ l1^2 \left(\frac{\partial}{\partial t}\, t1\right)^2$$

The kinetic energy of mass m_2 is obtained in a similar way.

```
> T2 := expand( 1/2*m2*(diff(x,t)^2 + diff(y,t)^2),
>    cos(t1+t2), sin(t1+t2) );
```

$$T2 := \frac{1}{2}\, m2\ l1^2\ \cos(\,t1\,)^2 \left(\frac{\partial}{\partial t}\, t1\right)^2$$

$$+\ m2\ l1\ \cos(\,t1\,)\left(\frac{\partial}{\partial t}\, t1\right)^2 l2\ \cos(\,t1\ +\ t2\,)\ +$$

$$m2 \; l1 \; \cos(t1) \left(\frac{\partial}{\partial t} t1\right) l2 \; \cos(t1 + t2) \left(\frac{\partial}{\partial t} t2\right)$$

$$+ \; \frac{1}{2} \; m2 \; l2^2 \; \cos(t1 + t2)^2 \left(\frac{\partial}{\partial t} t1\right)^2$$

$$+ \; m2 \; l2^2 \; \cos(t1 + t2)^2 \left(\frac{\partial}{\partial t} t1\right) \left(\frac{\partial}{\partial t} t2\right)$$

$$+ \; \frac{1}{2} \; m2 \; l2^2 \; \cos(t1 + t2)^2 \left(\frac{\partial}{\partial t} t2\right)^2$$

$$+ \; \frac{1}{2} \; m2 \; l1^2 \; \sin(t1)^2 \left(\frac{\partial}{\partial t} t1\right)^2$$

$$+ \; m2 \; l1 \; \sin(t1) \left(\frac{\partial}{\partial t} t1\right)^2 l2 \; \sin(t1 + t2) \; +$$

$$m2 \; l1 \; \sin(t1) \left(\frac{\partial}{\partial t} t1\right) l2 \; \sin(t1 + t2) \left(\frac{\partial}{\partial t} t2\right)$$

$$+ \; \frac{1}{2} \; m2 \; l2^2 \; \sin(t1 + t2)^2 \left(\frac{\partial}{\partial t} t1\right)^2$$

$$+ \; m2 \; l2^2 \; \sin(t1 + t2)^2 \left(\frac{\partial}{\partial t} t1\right) \left(\frac{\partial}{\partial t} t2\right)$$

$$+ \; \frac{1}{2} \; m2 \; l2^2 \; \sin(t1 + t2)^2 \left(\frac{\partial}{\partial t} t2\right)^2$$

```
> simplify(");
```

$$m2 \; l1 \; \cos(t1) \left(\frac{\partial}{\partial t} t1\right)^2 l2 \; \cos(t1 + t2) \; +$$

$$m2 \; l1 \; \cos(t1) \left(\frac{\partial}{\partial t} t1\right) l2 \; \cos(t1 + t2) \left(\frac{\partial}{\partial t} t2\right)$$

$$+ \; \frac{1}{2} \; m2 \; l1^2 \left(\frac{\partial}{\partial t} t1\right)^2$$

$$+ \; m2 \; l1 \; \sin(t1) \left(\frac{\partial}{\partial t} t1\right)^2 l2 \; \sin(t1 + t2) \; +$$

$$m2 \; l1 \; \sin(t1) \left(\frac{\partial}{\partial t} t1\right) l2 \; \sin(t1 + t2) \left(\frac{\partial}{\partial t} t2\right)$$

$$+ \frac{1}{2} \ m2 \ 12^2 \ \left(\frac{\partial}{\partial t} \ t1 \right)^2 \ + \ m2 \ 12^2 \ \left(\frac{\partial}{\partial t} \ t1 \right) \left(\frac{\partial}{\partial t} \ t2 \right)$$

$$+ \frac{1}{2} \ m2 \ 12^2 \ \left(\frac{\partial}{\partial t} \ t2 \right)^2$$

More simplification is needed, such as computing the finite Fourier series.

```
> map( combine, collect(",diff(t1,t)), ´trig´ ):
> T2 := collect( ", [l1,l2,m2,cos(t2)], factor );
```

$$T2 \ := \ \frac{1}{2} \ m2 \ 11^2 \ \left(\frac{\partial}{\partial t} \ t1 \right)^2 \ +$$

$$\left(\frac{\partial}{\partial t} \ t1 \right) \left(\left(\frac{\partial}{\partial t} \ t1 \right) \ + \ \left(\frac{\partial}{\partial t} \ t2 \right) \right) \cos(\ t2 \ ) \ m2 \ 12 \ 11$$

$$+ \frac{1}{2} \ \left(\left(\frac{\partial}{\partial t} \ t1 \right) \ + \ \left(\frac{\partial}{\partial t} \ t2 \right) \right)^2 \ m2 \ 12^2$$

The Euler-Lagrange equations are

$$\frac{d}{dt} \left(\frac{\partial L}{\partial \dot{\theta}_i} \right) - \frac{\partial L}{\partial \theta_i} = 0,$$

for $i = 1, 2$, which yield in this case the vector equation

$$M(\theta)\ddot{\theta} + C(\theta, \dot{\theta}) + G(\theta) = 0,$$

where $\ddot{\theta} = (\ddot{\theta}_1, \ddot{\theta}_2)$,

$$M(\theta) = \begin{pmatrix} m_1 l_1^2 + m_2 l_1^2 + m_2 l_2^2 + 2m_2 l_1 l_2 \cos \theta_2 & m_2 l_2^2 + m_2 l_1 l_2 \cos \theta_2 \\ m_2 l_2^2 + m_2 l_1 l_2 \cos \theta_2 & m_2 l_2^2 \end{pmatrix},$$

the centripetal or Coriolis term $C(\theta, \dot{\theta})$ is defined as

$$\begin{pmatrix} -m_2 l_1 l_2 \sin(\theta_2)\dot{\theta}_2(2\dot{\theta}_1 + \dot{\theta}_2) \\ m_2 l_1 l_2 \sin(\theta_2)\dot{\theta}_1^2 \end{pmatrix},$$

and the gravitational term $G(\theta)$ is defined as

$$\begin{pmatrix} m_1 g l_1 \sin \theta_1 + m_2 g l_1 \sin \theta_1 + m_2 g l_2 \sin(\theta_1 + \theta_2) \\ m_2 g l_2 \sin(\theta_1 + \theta_2) \end{pmatrix}.$$

Let us see how this can be computed by Maple. First, we compute the potential energy of masses m_1 and m_2, respectively.

```
> V1 := - m1*g*l1*cos(t1):

> V2 := - m2*g*l1*cos(t1) - m2*g*l2*cos(t1+t2):

> L := T1+T2-V1-V2: # Lagrangian
```

Because of our aliases, we cannot easily compute the derivatives $\dfrac{\partial L}{\partial \dot{\theta}_i}$ and $\dfrac{\partial L}{\partial \theta_i}$. We solve this problem by introducing some auxiliary variables.

```
> L := subs( { t1=t_1, t2=t_2, diff(t1,t)=t1p,

>     diff(t2,t)=t2p }, L ):

> dL_dt1p := diff(L,t1p):

> dL_dt2p := diff(L,t2p):

> dL_dt1 := diff(L,t_1):

> dL_dt2 := diff(L,t_2):

> dL_dt1p := subs( {t_1=t1, t_2=t2, t1p=diff(t1,t),

>    t2p=diff(t2,t)}, dL_dt1p ):

> dL_dt2p := subs( {t_1=t1, t_2=t2, t1p=diff(t1,t),

>    t2p=diff(t2,t)}, dL_dt2p ):

> dL_dt1  := subs( {t_1=t1, t_2=t2, t1p=diff(t1,t),

>    t2p=diff(t2,t)}, dL_dt1 ):

> dL_dt2  := subs( {t_1=t1, t_2=t2, t1p=diff(t1,t),

>    t2p=diff(t2,t)}, dL_dt2 ):
```

Now, we are ready to compute the differential equations via the Euler-Lagrange equations.

```
> eqn1 := collect( diff( dL_dt1p, t ) - dL_dt1 = 0,

>    [diff(t1,t$2),diff(t2,t$2),diff(t1,t),diff(t2,t)] );
```

$$eqn1 :=$$

$$(m1\ l1^2 + m2\ l1^2 + m2\ l2^2 + 2\cos(t2)\ m2\ l2\ l1)$$

$$\left(\frac{\partial^2}{\partial t^2}\ t1 \right) + (m2\ l2^2 + \cos(t2)\ m2\ l2\ l1)\left(\frac{\partial^2}{\partial t^2}\ t2 \right)$$

$$- 2\left(\frac{\partial}{\partial t}\ t1 \right)\sin(t2)\left(\frac{\partial}{\partial t}\ t2 \right)m2\ l2\ l1$$

$$- \left(\frac{\partial}{\partial t}\ t2 \right)^2 \sin(t2)\ m2\ l2\ l1$$

$$+ \; m2 \; g \; l2 \; \sin(\; t1 \; + \; t2 \;) \; + \; m1 \; g \; l1 \; \sin(\; t1 \;)$$

$$+ \; m2 \; g \; l1 \; \sin(\; t1 \;) = 0$$

```
> eqn2 := collect( diff( dL_dt2p, t ) - dL_dt2 = 0,
>      [diff(t1,t$2),diff(t2,t$2),diff(t1,t),diff(t2,t)] );
```

$$eqn2 := (\; m2 \; l2^2 \; + \; \cos(\; t2 \;) \; m2 \; l2 \; l1 \;) \left(\frac{\partial^2}{\partial t^2} \; t1 \right)$$

$$+ \left(\frac{\partial^2}{\partial t^2} \; t2 \right) m2 \; l2^2 \; + \; \sin(\; t2 \;) \; m2 \; l2 \; l1 \left(\frac{\partial}{\partial t} \; t1 \right)^2$$

$$+ \; m2 \; g \; l2 \; \sin(\; t1 \; + \; t2 \;) = 0$$

For simplicity, we shall consider the case that both masses and lengths are equal, say $m_1 = m_2 = m$ and $l_1 = l_2 = l$. Then the equations of motion are as follows.

```
> m1 := m2:    m2 := m:    l1 := l2:    l2 := l:
> map( x -> x/(m*l^2), lhs(eqn1) ):
> eqn1 := map( normal, " ) = 0;
```

$$eqn1 := (\; 3 \; + \; 2 \; \cos(\; t2 \;) \;) \left(\frac{\partial^2}{\partial t^2} \; t1 \right)$$

$$+ \; (\; 1 \; + \; \cos(\; t2 \;) \;) \left(\frac{\partial^2}{\partial t^2} \; t2 \right)$$

$$- \; 2 \left(\frac{\partial}{\partial t} \; t1 \right) \sin(\; t2 \;) \left(\frac{\partial}{\partial t} \; t2 \right)$$

$$- \left(\frac{\partial}{\partial t} \; t2 \right)^2 \sin(\; t2 \;) \; + \; \frac{g \; \sin(\; t1 \; + \; t2 \;)}{l}$$

$$+ \; 2 \; \frac{g \; \sin(\; t1 \;)}{l} = 0$$

```
> map( x -> x/(m*l^2), lhs(eqn2) ):
> eqn2 := map( normal, " ) = 0;
```

$$eqn2 := (\; 1 \; + \; \cos(\; t2 \;) \;) \left(\frac{\partial^2}{\partial t^2} \; t1 \right) + \left(\frac{\partial^2}{\partial t^2} \; t2 \right)$$

$$+ \; \sin(\; t2 \;) \left(\frac{\partial}{\partial t} \; t1 \right)^2 \; + \; \frac{g \; \sin(\; t1 \; + \; t2 \;)}{l} = 0$$

Let us take $l = 1$ and $g = 9.8$. As initial values we choose

$$\theta_1(0) = 0.04, \; \theta_2(0) = 0.04, \; \dot{\theta}_1 = 0, \; \dot{\theta}_2 = 0.$$

Now we are ready to solve the initial value problem numerically.

```
> l := 1:    g := 9.8:
> alias( t1_0=t1(0), t2_0=t2(0),
>    t1p_0=D(t1)(0), t2p_0=D(t2)(0) ):
```

Once again, all we have to do is to call the procedure **dsolve** with the keyword numeric.

```
> F := dsolve( {eqn1, eqn2, t1_0=0.04, t2_0=0.04,
>    t1p_0=0, t2p_0=0}, {t1,t2}, ´numeric´ );

F := proc(t) `dsolve/numeric/result2`(t,268691948,[2,2])

end

> F(2);   # an example

     { t = 2.,  t1 = -.0007027305568,  t2 = .01244036248 }
```

The numeric solver returns a set consisting of an equation describing the value of the independent variable t and two equations describing the value of the dependent variables θ_1 and θ_2 at t. Unfortunately, in Maple you are not initially sure in what order these variables are stored, so you have to put some extra work into the construction of the numerical functions.

```
> alias( t1=t1, t2=t2 ):
```

We unalias these variables so that we can use them below in the procedure **select** as a name.

```
> theta[1] := t -> rhs( op( select( has, F(t), t1 ) ) ):
> theta[2] := t -> rhs( op( select( has, F(t), t2 ) ) ):
```

We plot the approximations of θ_1 and θ_2 to get an impression of the solution found.

```
> plot( theta[1], 0 .. 6, title = ´theta_1´ );
```

theta_1

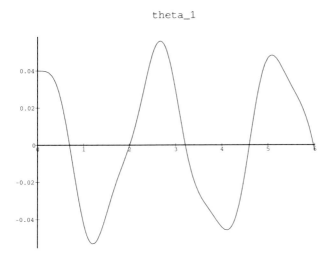

```
> plot( theta[2], 0 .. 6, title = 'theta_2' );
```

theta_2

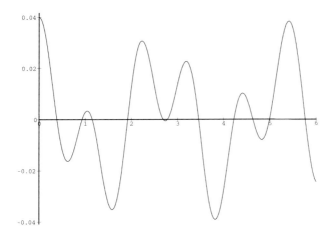

Is this what you expected for the angles? A three-dimensional solution curve can be plotted with **odeplot** from the *plots* package. By modifying the orientation of the three-dimensional plot, it is possible instead to obtain the above two-dimensional projections of the solution curve.

Better insight into the motion of the double-pendulum can be obtained from an animation. Below, we give the commands that generate such an animation. Note that this is a continuation of the previous computation. You are invited to mimic the session.

First, we define functions which describe the position of the kink and the tip of thetwo-link robot arm.

```
> x1 := t -> sin( theta[1](t) ):
> y1 := t -> cos( theta[1](t) ):
> x2 := t -> sin( theta[1](t) ) +
>    sin( theta[1](t) + theta[2](t) ):
> y2 := t -> cos( theta[1](t) ) +
>    cos( theta[1](t) + theta[2](t) ):
```

Secondly, we generate a table of plots that describe the robot-arm at different times in the interval $(0, 6)$.

```
> for i from 0 to 60 do
>    P[i] := plot( [ [0,0], [x1(i/10),y1(i/10)],
>    [x2(i/10),y2(i/10)] ], style=line,
>    view=[-0.2..0.2,0..2] )
> od:
```

Thirdly, we display them in sequence with the **display** routine from the *plots* package, i.e., we produce the animation.

```
> plots[display]( [ seq( P[i], i=0..60 ) ],
>    insequence=true );
```

We end with the remark that the procedure **phaseportrait** from the *DEtools* package produces a plot of the integral curves for a system of first order differential equations of the form $x' = f_1(t, x, y)$, $y' = f_2(t, x, y)$ with given initial conditions.

16.6 Perturbation Methods

When you want to apply perturbation methods to find approximate solutions of ODEs, computer algebra systems are most valuable computational tools. In this section, we shall describe two classical methods, viz., the Poincaré-Lindstedt method and the method of multiple scales; and we shall apply them to van der Pol's equation. The interested reader is also referred to [102, 103], which contain many examples of the use of

MACSYMA in perturbation and bifurcation theory. Mathematical background can be found in [93].

Poincaré-Lindstedt Method

Recall van der Pol's equation,

$$y'' - \epsilon\left(1 - y^2\right) y' + y = 0.$$

For $\epsilon = 0$ it is the ODE of the mathematical pendulum. For any ϵ, this differential equation possesses an asymptotically stable periodic solution called the *limit cycle*.

We want to compute a good approximation of the limit cycle for small ϵ. Because there are no explicit time dependent terms in van der Pol's equation we can choose without loss of generality the point that corresponds with $t = 0$; we shall choose the initial value $y(0) = 0$. In the Poincaré-Lindstedt method, time is stretched via the transformation

$$\tau = \omega t,$$

where

$$\omega = 1 + \omega_1 \epsilon + \omega_2 \epsilon^2 + \omega_3 \epsilon^3 + \dots$$

Then van der Pol's equation for $y(\tau)$ becomes

$$\omega^2 y'' - \omega \epsilon \left(1 - y^2\right) y' + y = 0.$$

We assume that the solution $y(\tau)$ can expanded in a Taylor series in ϵ,

$$y(\tau) = y_0(\tau) + y_1(\tau)\epsilon + y_2(\tau)\epsilon^2 + y_3(\tau)\epsilon^3 + \dots$$

Then we substitute the expansions of $y(\tau)$ and $\omega(\epsilon)$ in van der Pol's equation, collect terms in ϵ, and equate to zero the coefficient of each power of ϵ. The equations for small orders of ϵ are

$$y_0'' + y_0 = 0$$
$$y_1'' + y_1 = y_0'\left(1 - y_0^2\right) - 2\omega_1 y_0''$$
$$y_2'' + y_2 = \left(1 - y_0^2\right) y_1' - 2y_0 y_1 y_0' - 2\omega_1 y_1''$$
$$- \left(2\omega_2 + \omega_1^2\right) y_0'' + \omega_1(1 - y_0) x_0'$$

The initial value $y(0) = 0$ translates into

$$y_0(0) = 0, \quad y_1(0) = 0, \quad y_2(0) = 0, \quad y_3(0) = 0, \dots$$

Let us check some of the differential equations with Maple, at the same time setting the notation for the rest of the session.

```
> alias( omega=w, epsilon=e, tau=T ):
> ODE := w^2*diff(y(T),T$2) -
>    w*e*(1-y(T)^2)*diff(y(T),T) + y(T) = 0;
```

$$ODE := \omega^2 \left(\frac{\partial^2}{\partial\tau^2} \, y(\tau) \right) - \omega \, \varepsilon \left(1 - y(\tau)^2 \right) \left(\frac{\partial}{\partial\tau} \, y(\tau) \right)$$

$$+ \, y(\tau) = 0$$

```
> e_order := 6:
> e := () -> e: # introduce e as a constant function
> for i from 0 to e_order do
>    y.i := T -> y.i(T)
> od:
> w := 1 + sum( ´w.i*e^i´, ´i´=1..e_order );
```

$$\omega := 1 + w1 \, \varepsilon + w2 \, \varepsilon^2 + w3 \, \varepsilon^3 + w4 \, \varepsilon^4 + w5 \, \varepsilon^5 + w6 \, \varepsilon^6$$

```
> y := sum( ´y.i*e^i´,´i´=0..e_order);
```

$$y := y0 + y1 \, \varepsilon + y2 \, \varepsilon^2 + y3 \, \varepsilon^3 + y4 \, \varepsilon^4 + y5 \, \varepsilon^5 + y6 \, \varepsilon^6$$

```
> deqn := simplify( collect(ODE,e), {e^(e_order+1)=0} ):
> for i from 0 to e_order do
>    eqn.i:=coeff( lhs(deqn), e, i ) = 0
> od:
> print( ´eqn0´=eqn0, ´eqn1´=eqn1, ´eqn2´=eqn2 );
```

$$eqn0 = (\%1 + y0(\tau) = 0), \quad eqn1 = \left(\left(\frac{\partial}{\partial\tau} \, y0(\tau) \right) y0(\tau)^2 \right.$$

$$+ \left(\frac{\partial^2}{\partial\tau^2} \, y1(\tau) \right) + y1(\tau) + 2 \, w1 \, \%1 - \left(\frac{\partial}{\partial\tau} \, y0(\tau) \right) =$$

$$\left. 0 \right), \quad eqn2 = \left(\left(\frac{\partial^2}{\partial\tau^2} \, y2(\tau) \right) + y2(\tau) \right.$$

$$+ \left(\frac{\partial}{\partial\tau} \, y1(\tau) \right) y0(\tau)^2 - \left(\frac{\partial}{\partial\tau} \, y0(\tau) \right) w1$$

$$+ 2 \, w1 \left(\frac{\partial^2}{\partial\tau^2} \, y1(\tau) \right) + 2 \, \%1 \, w2 + \%1 \, w1^2$$

$$- \left(\frac{\partial}{\partial\tau} \, y1(\tau) \right) + 2 \left(\frac{\partial}{\partial\tau} \, y0(\tau) \right) y0(\tau) \, y1(\tau)$$

$$+ \left(\frac{\partial}{\partial \tau} \, y0\,(\,\tau\,) \right) w1 \; y0\,(\,\tau\,)^2 = 0 \right)$$

$$\%1 := \frac{\partial^2}{\partial \tau^2} \, y0\,(\,\tau\,)$$

The initial value problem for $y_0(\tau)$ can easily be solved.

```
> dsolve( { eqn0, y0(0)=0 }, y0(T) );
```

$$y0\,(\,\tau\,) = \_C1 \; \sin(\,\tau\,)$$

We assign this function and proceed with the differential equation for $y_1(\tau)$.

```
> y0 := unapply( rhs("), T );
```

$$y0 := T \to \_C1 \; \sin(\,T\,)$$

```
> eqn1;
```

$$\_C1^3 \; \cos(\,\tau\,) \; \sin(\,\tau\,)^2 + \left(\frac{\partial^2}{\partial \tau^2} \, y1\,(\,\tau\,) \right) + y1\,(\,\tau\,)$$

$$- \; 2 \; w1 \; \_C1 \; \sin(\,\tau\,) \; - \; \_C1 \; \cos(\,\tau\,) = 0$$

We compute the finite Fourier series with **combine**($\ldots$,$'$trig$'$).

```
> map( combine, eqn1, ´trig´ );
```

$$\frac{1}{4} \; \_C1^3 \; \cos(\,\tau\,) \; - \; \frac{1}{4} \; \_C1^3 \; \cos(\,3\;\tau\,) \; + \left(\frac{\partial^2}{\partial \tau^2} \, y1\,(\,\tau\,) \right)$$

$$+ \; y1\,(\,\tau\,) \; - \; 2 \; w1 \; \_C1 \; \sin(\,\tau\,) \; - \; \_C1 \; \cos(\,\tau\,) = 0$$

```
> eqn1 := map( collect, ", [sin(T),cos(T)] );
```

$$eqn1 := -2 \; w1 \; \_C1 \; \sin(\,\tau\,) + \left(\frac{1}{4} \; \_C1^3 \; - \; \_C1 \right) \cos(\,\tau\,)$$

$$- \; \frac{1}{4} \; \_C1^3 \; \cos(\,3\;\tau\,) \; + \left(\frac{\partial^2}{\partial \tau^2} \, y1\,(\,\tau\,) \right) + y1\,(\,\tau\,) = 0$$

The $\sin \tau$ and $\cos \tau$ terms are called the *resonant terms* or *secular terms*; they are responsible for nonperiodic behavior of the approximation — as is clear from the general solution below.

```
> dsolve( { eqn1, y1(0)=0 }, y1(T), 'laplace' );
```

$$y1(\tau) = -\frac{1}{32}\_C1^3 \cos(3\ \tau)\ +\ D(\ y1\ )(\ 0\ )\ \sin(\tau)$$

$$+\ \frac{1}{32}\_C1^3 \cos(\tau)\ -\ \tau \cos(\tau)\ \_C1\ w1$$

$$-\ \frac{1}{8}\ \tau \sin(\tau)\ \_C1^3\ +\ \frac{1}{2}\ \tau \sin(\tau)\ \_C1$$

$$+\ w1\ \_C1\ \sin(\tau)$$

```
> map( collect, ", [sin(T),cos(T),T] );
```

$$y1(\tau) = \left(\left(-\frac{1}{8}\_C1^3 + \frac{1}{2}\_C1\right)\tau\ +\ D(\ y1\ )(\ 0\ )\ +\ w1\ \_C1\right)$$

$$\sin(\tau)\ +\ \left(\frac{1}{32}\_C1^3\ -\ \tau\ \_C1\ w1\right)\cos(\tau)$$

$$-\ \frac{1}{32}\_C1^3 \cos(3\ \tau)$$

So, we choose ω_1 such that these terms vanish.

```
> solve( { coeff( lhs(eqn1), sin(T) ) = 0,
>    coeff( lhs(eqn1), cos(T) ) = 0}, {_C1,w1} );
```

$$\{\ \_C1 = 0,\ w1 = w1\ \},\ \{\ \_C1 = 0,\ w1 = 0\ \},\ \{\ w1 = 0,\ \_C1 = 2\ \},$$

$$\{\ w1 = 0,\ \_C1 = -2\ \}$$

Because we want to compare it with the numerical method that was discussed in the previous section, we choose a negative amplitude _C1.

```
> assign("[4]):
> eqn1;
```

$$2\ \cos(3\ \tau)\ +\ \left(\frac{\partial^2}{\partial \tau^2}\ y1(\tau)\right)\ +\ y1(\tau) = 0$$

We solve the differential equation for $y_1(\tau)$ with initial values $y_1(0) = 0$.

```
> dsolve( {eqn1, y1(0)=0, D(y1)(0)=_C2}, y1(T),
>    'laplace' );
```

$$y1(\tau) = \_C2 \; \sin(\tau) \; - \; \frac{1}{4} \; \cos(\tau) \; + \; \frac{1}{4} \; \cos(3 \; \tau)$$

```
> y1 := unapply( rhs("), T );
```

$$y1 \; := \; T \rightarrow \_C2 \; \sin(T) \; - \; \frac{1}{4} \; \cos(T) \; + \; \frac{1}{4} \; \cos(3 \; T)$$

Similarly, we deal with c_2 and $y_2(\tau)$. We omit comments.

```
> eqn2;
```

$$\left(\frac{\partial^2}{\partial \tau^2} \; y2(\tau) \right) + y2(\tau) + 4$$

$$\left(\_C2 \; \cos(\tau) \; + \; \frac{1}{4} \; \sin(\tau) \; - \; \frac{3}{4} \; \sin(3 \; \tau) \right) \sin(\tau)^2$$

$$+ \; 4 \; \sin(\tau) \; w2 \; - \; \_C2 \; \cos(\tau) \; - \; \frac{1}{4} \; \sin(\tau)$$

$$+ \; \frac{3}{4} \; \sin(3 \; \tau) \; + \; 8 \; \cos(\tau) \; \sin(\tau)$$

$$\left(\_C2 \; \sin(\tau) \; - \; \frac{1}{4} \; \cos(\tau) \; + \; \frac{1}{4} \; \cos(3 \; \tau) \right) = 0$$

```
> map( combine, eqn2, ´trig´ ):
> eqn2 := map( collect, ",
>    [ sin(T), sin(3*T), cos(T), cos(3*T) ] );
```

$$eqn2 \; := \; \left(\frac{1}{4} \; + \; 4 \; w2 \right) \sin(\tau) \; + \; \left(\frac{\partial^2}{\partial \tau^2} \; y2(\tau) \right) + y2(\tau)$$

$$+ \; 2 \; \_C2 \; \cos(\tau) \; - \; 3 \; \_C2 \; \cos(3 \; \tau) \; - \; \frac{3}{2} \; \sin(3 \; \tau)$$

$$+ \; \frac{5}{4} \; \sin(5 \; \tau) = 0$$

```
> solve( {coeff( lhs(eqn2), sin(T) ) = 0,
>    coeff( lhs(eqn2), cos(T) ) = 0}, {_C2,w2} );
```

$$\left\{ \_C2 = 0, \; w2 = \frac{-1}{16} \right\}$$

```
> assign("):
```

```
> dsolve( { eqn2, y2(0)=0, D(y2)(0)=_C3 }, y2(T),
>      'laplace' ):
> collect( ", [ sin(T), sin(3*T), sin(5*T),
>      cos(T), cos(3*T), cos(5*T) ] ):
> y2 := unapply( rhs("), T );
```

$$y2 := T \rightarrow$$

$$\left(\frac{29}{96} + \_C3 \right) \sin(T) + \frac{5}{96} \sin(5\ T) - \frac{3}{16} \sin(3\ T)$$

We assume that you understand the pattern for finding the higher order terms and compute them repetitively.

```
> for i from 3 to e_order do
>    map( combine, eqn.i, 'trig' ):
>    eqn.i := map( collect, ",
>       [ seq(sin((2*j+1)*T),j=0..i),
>       seq(cos((2*j+1)*T),j=0..i) ] ):
>    solve( {coeff( lhs(eqn.i), sin(T) ) = 0,
>    coeff( lhs(eqn.i), cos(T) ) = 0}, {_C.i,w.i} ):
>    assign("):
>    dsolve( { eqn.i, y.i(0)=0, D(y.i)(0)=_C.(i+1) },
>       y.i(T), 'laplace' ):
>    collect( ", [ seq(sin((2*j+1)*T),j=0..i),
>       seq(cos((2*j+1)*T),j=0..i) ] ):
>    y.i := unapply( rhs("), T )
> od:
```

Let us look at the final results.

```
> w;
```

$$1 - \frac{1}{16} \varepsilon^2 + \frac{17}{3072} \varepsilon^4 + \frac{35}{884736} \varepsilon^6$$

```
> y(T);
```

$$-2 \sin(\tau) + \left(- \frac{1}{4} \cos(\tau) + \frac{1}{4} \cos(3\ \tau) \right) \varepsilon$$

$$+ \left(\frac{5}{96} \sin(5\ \tau)\ -\ \frac{3}{16} \sin(3\ \tau) \right) \varepsilon^2 + \Bigg($$

$$-\ \frac{7}{576} \cos(7\ \tau)\ +\ \frac{19}{768} \cos(\tau)\ +\ \frac{5}{72} \cos(5\ \tau)$$

$$-\ \frac{21}{256} \cos(3\ \tau) \Bigg) \varepsilon^3 + \left(-\ \frac{11}{4096} \sin(\tau) \right.$$

$$+\ \frac{29}{768} \sin(3\ \tau)\ +\ \frac{2555}{110592} \sin(7\ \tau)$$

$$-\ \frac{61}{20480} \sin(9\ \tau)\ -\ \frac{1385}{27648} \sin(5\ \tau) \Bigg) \varepsilon^4 + \Bigg($$

$$\frac{153251}{6635520} \cos(7\ \tau)\ -\ \frac{5807}{4423680} \cos(\tau)$$

$$+\ \frac{5533}{7372800} \cos(11\ \tau)\ -\ \frac{9013}{1228800} \cos(9\ \tau)$$

$$-\ \frac{77915}{2654208} \cos(5\ \tau)\ +\ \frac{4175}{294912} \cos(3\ \tau) \Bigg) \varepsilon^5 + \Bigg($$

$$\left(-\ \frac{148447039}{55738368000}\ +\ \_C7 \right) \sin(\tau)$$

$$+\ \frac{690583}{73728000} \sin(9\ \tau)\ +\ \frac{469795}{31850496} \sin(5\ \tau)$$

$$-\ \frac{143191}{35389440} \sin(3\ \tau)\ +\ \frac{715247}{3715891200} \sin(13\ \tau)$$

$$-\ \frac{6017803}{2654208000} \sin(11\ \tau)\ -\ \frac{6871193}{398131200} \sin(7\ \tau) \Bigg)$$

$$\varepsilon^6$$

The constant _C7 would be determined in the next step. We shall only consider $y(\tau)$ up to order 5; results of computations up to order 164 can be found in [2].

```
> y := unapply( simplify( y(T), {eê_order=0} ), T );
```

$$y := T \rightarrow \left(\frac{5}{6} \cos(T)^4 \sin(T)\ -\ \frac{11}{8} \cos(T)^2 \sin(T) \right.$$

$$\left. + \frac{23}{96} \sin(T) \right) \varepsilon^2 + \left(\frac{89}{36} \cos(T)^5 - \frac{7}{9} \cos(T)^7 \right.$$

$$\left. + \frac{45}{64} \cos(T) - \frac{1381}{576} \cos(T)^3 \right) \varepsilon^3 + \Bigg($$

$$- \frac{64487}{552960} \sin(T) - \frac{323}{96} \cos(T)^4 \sin(T)$$

$$+ \frac{365}{256} \cos(T)^2 \sin(T) + \frac{1519}{540} \cos(T)^6 \sin(T)$$

$$\left. - \frac{61}{80} \cos(T)^8 \sin(T) \right) \varepsilon^4 + \left(- \frac{114941}{28800} \cos(T)^9 \right.$$

$$- \frac{471671}{1105920} \cos(T) + \frac{9894757}{3317760} \cos(T)^3$$

$$- \frac{1853173}{259200} \cos(T)^5 + \frac{5533}{7200} \cos(T)^{11}$$

$$\left. + \frac{1012987}{129600} \cos(T)^7 \right) \varepsilon^5 - 2 \sin(T)$$

$$+ \left(\cos(T)^3 - \cos(T) \right) \varepsilon$$

vskip 5ptLet us plot this function for $\epsilon = 1$.

```
> e := 1: y(T);
```

$$- \frac{81}{32} \cos(\tau)^4 \sin(\tau) + \frac{13}{256} \cos(\tau)^2 \sin(\tau)$$

$$- \frac{1037927}{552960} \sin(\tau) - \frac{1212373}{259200} \cos(\tau)^5$$

$$+ \frac{912187}{129600} \cos(\tau)^7 - \frac{799991}{1105920} \cos(\tau)$$

$$+ \frac{5257957}{3317760} \cos(\tau)^3 + \frac{1519}{540} \cos(\tau)^6 \sin(\tau)$$

$$- \frac{61}{80} \cos(\tau)^8 \sin(\tau) - \frac{114941}{28800} \cos(\tau)^9$$

$$+ \frac{5533}{7200} \cos(\tau)^{11}$$

```
> plot( y(T), T=0..14 );
```

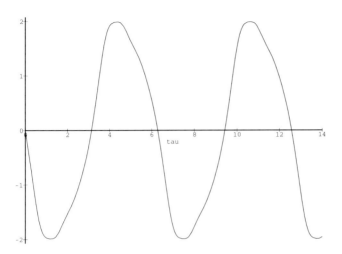

Comparing this with the numerical solution found in the previous section, both results are plotted in the picture below.

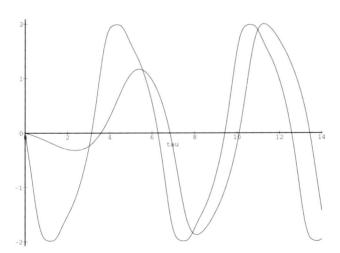

Method of Multiple Scales

The Poincaré-Lindstedt method is useful for finding periodic solutions of ODEs, but it does not help to approximate general solutions of ODEs in the neighborhood of a limit cycle. In the method of multiple scales, the solution of an ODE is not viewed as a function of one variable t but as a function of two or more independent variables $t_1, t_2, t_3, \ldots$ defined as

$$t_1 = t, \quad t_2 = \epsilon t, \quad t_3 = \epsilon^2 t, \quad \ldots$$

Then:

$$\frac{d}{dt} = \frac{\partial}{\partial t_1} + \epsilon \frac{\partial}{\partial t_2} + \epsilon^2 \frac{\partial}{\partial t_3} + \cdots,$$

$$\frac{d^2}{dt^2} = \frac{\partial^2}{\partial t_1^2} + 2\epsilon \frac{\partial^2}{\partial t_1 t_2} + \epsilon^2 \left(\frac{\partial}{\partial t_2^2} + 2\frac{\partial}{\partial t_3} \right) + \cdots.$$

You can check this with Maple. (you can compute higher order terms by increasing the variable e_order.)

```
> alias( epsilon=e ):

> e_order := 2:

> e := subs( variables = seq( t.j, j=0..e_order),

>    body=e, (variables -> body) );
```

$$\varepsilon := (t0, \ t1, \ t2) \rightarrow \varepsilon$$

```
> subs( D = sum( ´e^(i-1)*D[i]´, ´i´=1..e_order+1 ),

>    (D@@2)(y) ):

> simplify( collect(",e), {e^(e_order+1)=0} );
```

$$\left(2\ D_{[\ 1,\ 3\ ]}(\ y\ ) \ + \ D_{[\ 2,\ 2\ ]}(\ y\ ) \right) \varepsilon^2 \ + \ D_{[\ 1,\ 1\ ]}(\ y\ )$$

$$+ \ 2\ \varepsilon\ D_{[\ 1,\ 2\ ]}(\ y\ )$$

In the method of multiple scales, the solution y of an ODE is expanded in a power series of ϵ as

$$y = y_0(t_1, t_2, t_3, \ldots) + \epsilon y_1(t_1, t_2, t_3, \ldots) + \epsilon^2 y_2(t_1, t_2, t_3, \ldots) + \cdots.$$

This leads to differential equations for y_0, y_1, y_2, etc.

We shall apply the three variable method to van der Pol's equation

$$y'' - \epsilon(1 - y^2)y' + y = 0,$$

with initial values $y(0) = 0, y'(0) = -1/10$. We shall actually redo work of Noble and Husain [94].

First, we derive the differential equations for $y_0(t_0, t_1, t_2)$, $y_1(t_0, t_1, t_2)$, and $y_2(t_0, t_1, t_2)$ with Maple.

```
> ODE := (D@@2)(y) - e*(1-y^2)*D(y) + y=0;
```

$$ODE := D^{(2)}(y) - \varepsilon\ (1 - y^2)\ D(y) + y = 0$$

```
> subs( D = sum(´e^(i-1)*D[i]´,´i´=1..e_order+1), ODE ):
> y := sum( ´y.i*e^i´,´i´=0..e_order);
```

$$y := y0 + y1\ \varepsilon + y2\ \varepsilon^2$$

```
> diffeqn := simplify( collect("",e), {e^(e_order+1)=0} ):
> for i from 0 to e_order do
>       eqn.i := coeff( lhs(diffeqn), e, i ) = 0
> od;
```

$$eqn0 := D_{[\,1,\ 1\,]}(\,y0\,) + y0 = 0$$

$$eqn1 := D_{[\,1,\ 1\,]}(\,y1\,) + 2\ D_{[\,1,\ 2\,]}(\,y0\,) + y1 - D_{[\,1\,]}(\,y0\,)$$
$$+ D_{[\,1\,]}(\,y0\,)\ y0^2 = 0$$

$$eqn2 := -D_{[\,1\,]}(\,y1\,) - D_{[\,2\,]}(\,y0\,) + y0^2\ D_{[\,1\,]}(\,y1\,)$$
$$+ y0^2\ D_{[\,2\,]}(\,y0\,) + 2\ y0\ y1\ D_{[\,1\,]}(\,y0\,)$$
$$+ 2\ D_{[\,1,\ 2\,]}(\,y1\,) + y2 + D_{[\,2,\ 2\,]}(\,y0\,)$$
$$+ D_{[\,1,\ 1\,]}(\,y2\,) + 2\ D_{[\,1,\ 3\,]}(\,y0\,) = 0$$

So, the required differential equations are:

$$\frac{\partial^2 y_0}{\partial t_1^2} + y_0 = 0$$

$$\frac{\partial^2 y_0}{\partial t_1^2} + y_1 = -2\frac{\partial^2 y_0}{\partial t_1 t_2} + (1 - y_0^2)\frac{\partial y_0}{\partial t_1}$$

$$\frac{\partial^2 y_2}{\partial t_1^2} + y_2 = -2\frac{\partial^2 y_0}{\partial t_1 t_2} - \frac{\partial^2 y_0}{\partial t_2^2} - 2\frac{\partial^2 y_0}{\partial t_1 t_3} +$$
$$(1 - y_0^2)\left(\frac{\partial y_1}{\partial t_1} + \frac{\partial y_0}{\partial t_2}\right) - 2 y_0 y_1 \frac{\partial y_0}{\partial t_1}$$

The first equation has the general solution

$$y_0(t_1, t_2, t_3) := A(t_2, t_3)\sin(t_1 + B(t_2, t_3)).$$

Substituting this in the next equation we get the following differential equations for $A(t_2, t_3)$ and $B(t_2, t_3)$, if we insist on removal of resonant terms.

$$\frac{\partial B(t_2, t_3)}{\partial t_2} = 0$$

$$\frac{\partial A(t_2, t_3)}{\partial t_2} = \frac{1}{2} A(t_2, t_3) - \frac{1}{8} A(t_2, t_3)$$

Let us check this with Maple.

```
> eqn1 := convert( eqn1(t1,t2,t3), diff );
```

$$eqn1 := \left(\frac{\partial^2}{\partial t1^2} \, y1(\, t1, \ t2, \ t3\,) \right)$$

$$+ \ 2 \left(\frac{\partial^2}{\partial t2 \, \partial t1} \, y0(\, t1, \ t2, \ t3\,) \right) + y1(\, t1, \ t2, \ t3\,)$$

$$- \left(\frac{\partial}{\partial t1} \, y0(\, t1, \ t2, \ t3\,) \right)$$

$$+ \left(\frac{\partial}{\partial t1} \, y0(\, t1, \ t2, \ t3\,) \right) y0(\, t1, \ t2, \ t3\,)^2 = 0$$

```
> y0 := (t1,t2,t3) -> A(t2,t3) * sin(t1 + B(t2,t3));
```

$$y0 := (\, t1, \ t2, \ t3\,) \rightarrow A(\, t2, \ t3\,) \, \sin(\, t1 + B(\, t2, \ t3\,)\,)$$

```
> combine( eqn1, `trig` ):
> eqn1 := collect( ",
>    [ sin(t1+B(t2,t3)), cos(t1+B(t2,t3)) ] );
```

$$eqn1 := -2 \, A(\, t2, \ t3\,) \, \sin(\, t1 + B(\, t2, \ t3\,)\,)$$

$$\left(\frac{\partial}{\partial t2} \, B(\, t2, \ t3\,) \right) + \Bigg($$

$$2 \left(\frac{\partial}{\partial t2} \, A(\, t2, \ t3\,) \right) - A(\, t2, \ t3\,) + \frac{1}{4} A(\, t2, \ t3\,)^3 \Bigg)$$

$$\cos(\, t1 + B(\, t2, \ t3\,)\,) + \left(\frac{\partial^2}{\partial t1^2} \, y1(\, t1, \ t2, \ t3\,) \right)$$

$$- \frac{1}{4} A(\, t2, \ t3\,)^3 \cos(\, 3 \, t1 + 3 \, B(\, t2, \ t3\,)\,)$$

$$+ \, y1(\, t1, \ t2, \ t3\,) = 0$$

The resonant terms are

$$\sin\left(t_1 + B(t_2, t_3)\right),\ \cos\left(t_1 + B(t_2, t_3)\right).$$

By insisting that coefficients of resonant terms are equal to zero we get the following differential equations.

```
> restrictions := {
>    coeff( lhs(eqn1), cos(t1+B(t2,t3)) ) = 0,
>    coeff( lhs(eqn1), sin(t1+B(t2,t3)) ) = 0 };
```

$$restrictions := \left\{ \begin{array}{l} 2\left(\dfrac{\partial}{\partial t2}\ A(\ t2,\ t3\ )\right) - A(\ t2,\ t3\ ) + \dfrac{1}{4}\ A(\ t2,\ t3\ )^3 \\[3mm] = 0,\ -2\ A(\ t2,\ t3\ )\left(\dfrac{\partial}{\partial t2}\ B(\ t2,\ t3\ )\right) = 0 \end{array} \right\}$$

These differential equations are easily solved. From

```
> 2*diff(F(t),t) - F(t) + 1/4*F(t)^3 = 0;
```

$$2\left(\frac{\partial}{\partial t}\ F(\ t\ )\right) - F(\ t\ ) + \frac{1}{4}\ F(\ t\ )^3 = 0$$

```
> map( simplify, [dsolve( ", F(t), ´explicit´ )] );
```

$$\left[F(\ t\ ) = 2\ \frac{1}{\sqrt{1\ +\ 4\ e^{-t}\ \_C1}}, \right.$$

$$\left. F(\ t\ ) = -2\ \frac{1}{\sqrt{1\ +\ 4\ e^{-t}\ \_C1}} \right]$$

it follows that we can take

$$A(t_2, t_3) = \frac{-2}{\sqrt{1 + C(t_3)e^{-t_2}}}.$$

Moreover, we can take $B(t_2, t_3) = B(t_3)$. Then, the differential equation satisfied by y_1 becomes

```
> simplify( eqn1, restrictions,
>    [D[1](B)(t2, t3),D[1](A)(t2, t3),A(t2, t3)]):
> combine( ", ´trig´ );
```

$$- \frac{1}{4} \, \text{A}(\, t2, \ t3 \,)^{3} \, \cos(\, 3 \ t1 \, + \, 3 \ \text{B}(\, t2, \ t3 \,) \,)$$

$$+ \left(\frac{\partial^2}{\partial t1^2} \, \text{y1}(\, t1, \ t2, \ t3 \,) \right) + \text{y1}(\, t1, \ t2, \ t3 \,) = 0$$

Now comes a tricky point in the computation: we ignore the solution of the homogeneous differential equation and choose a particular solution y_1 which has a simple form.

```
> y1 := (t1,t2,t3) -> 1/32 * A(t2,t3)^3
>    * sin(3*t1+3*B(t2,t3)+3/2*Pi);
```

$$y1 := (\, t1, \ t2, \ t3 \,) \to$$

$$\frac{1}{32} \, \text{A}(\, t2, \ t3 \,)^{3} \, \sin\!\left(3 \ t1 \, + \, 3 \ \text{B}(\, t2, \ t3 \,) \, + \, \frac{3}{2} \, \pi \right)$$

```
> ""; # check the solution
```

$$0 = 0$$

We take into account that B does not depend on t_2 and substitute y_1 into the third differential equation:

```
> y1 := 'y1': y0 := 'y0':
> eqn2 := convert( eqn2(t1,t2,t3), diff ):
> y1:= (t1,t2,t3)-> 1/32 * A(t2,t3)^3
>    * sin(3*t1+3*B(t3)+3/2*Pi);
```

$$y1 := (\, t1, \ t2, \ t3 \,) \to$$

$$\frac{1}{32} \, \text{A}(\, t2, \ t3 \,)^{3} \, \sin\!\left(3 \ t1 \, + \, 3 \ \text{B}(\, t3 \,) \, + \, \frac{3}{2} \, \pi \right)$$

```
> y0 := (t1,t2,t3) -> A(t2,t3) * sin(t1 + B(t3));
```

$$y0 := (\, t1, \ t2, \ t3 \,) \to \text{A}(\, t2, \ t3 \,) \, \sin(\, t1 \, + \, \text{B}(\, t3 \,) \,)$$

```
> combine( eqn2, 'trig' ):
> eqn2 := collect( ", [ sin(t1+B(t3)), cos(t1+B(t3)) ] ):
> conditions := { coeff( lhs(eqn2), cos(t1+B(t3)) ) = 0,
>    coeff( lhs(eqn2), sin(t1+B(t3)) ) = 0 };
```

$$conditions := \left\{ 2 \left(\frac{\partial}{\partial t3} A(t2, t3) \right) = 0, \right.$$

$$- \frac{1}{128} A(t2, t3)^5 + \left(\frac{\partial^2}{\partial t2^2} A(t2, t3) \right)$$

$$- \left(\frac{\partial}{\partial t2} A(t2, t3) \right)$$

$$+ \frac{3}{4} A(t2, t3)^2 \left(\frac{\partial}{\partial t2} A(t2, t3) \right)$$

$$\left. - 2 A(t2, t3) \left(\frac{\partial}{\partial t3} B(t3) \right) = 0 \right\}$$

The first condition means that $A(t_2, t_3)$ does not depend on t_3 (so, $C(t_3)$ is a constant). From the earlier restrictions, we can derive a necessary condition for $\dfrac{\partial^2 A(t_2, t_3)}{\partial t_2^2}$.

```
> restrictions[1];
```

$$2 \left(\frac{\partial}{\partial t2} A(t2, t3) \right) - A(t2, t3) + \frac{1}{4} A(t2, t3)^3 = 0$$

```
> diff(",t2);
```

$$2 \left(\frac{\partial^2}{\partial t2^2} A(t2, t3) \right) - \left(\frac{\partial}{\partial t2} A(t2, t3) \right)$$

$$+ \frac{3}{4} A(t2, t3)^2 \left(\frac{\partial}{\partial t2} A(t2, t3) \right) = 0$$

Together with the first restriction, we can rewrite the second condition.

```
> simplify( conditions[1], { ", restrictions[1] },
>    [ D[1,1](A)(t2,t3), D[1](A)(t2,t3), A(t2,t3) ] );
```

$$\frac{1}{4} A(t2, t3)^3 - \frac{7}{128} A(t2, t3)^5$$

$$+ \left(-2 \left(\frac{\partial}{\partial t3} B(t3) \right) - \frac{1}{4} \right) A(t2, t3) = 0$$

```
> readlib(isolate)( ", diff(B(t3),t3) );
```

$$\frac{\partial}{\partial t3} B(t3) = \frac{1}{8} A(t2, t3)^2 - \frac{7}{256} A(t2, t3)^4 - \frac{1}{8}$$

Because $A(t_2, t_3)$ does not really depend on t_3 we get

$$B(t_3) = -\frac{1}{8}\left(1 - A(t_2, t_3) + \frac{7}{32}A(t_2, t_3)^4\right)t_3 + B_0,$$

where B_0 is a constant. Strictly speaking, the formula for $B(t_3)$ contradicts an earlier restriction, viz., B does not depend on t_2. But A depends on t_2! However, the formula for A shows that it is a slowly varying function of t, and as long as t is not too large we may assume that A is a constant. For a more thorough discussion of how to avoid this contradiction, the interested reader is referred to [94].

Let us see what the approximation is for the initial values

$$y(0) = 0, \quad y'(0) = -0.1,$$

if we only consider the approximation $y = y_0 + \epsilon y_1$ and set ϵ equal to one.

```
> y := y0 + e*y1;
```

$$y := y0 + \varepsilon\ y1$$

```
> y0 := t -> A(t)*sin(t+B(t));
```

$$-\ln\left(y + \sqrt{y^2 + 1}\right) + x = \_C1$$

```
> y1 := t -> -1/32*A(t)^3*cos(3*t+3*B(t));
```

$$y1 := t \to \frac{1}{32}\ A(\ t\ )^3\ \sin\left(3\ t\ +\ 3\ B(\ t\ )\ +\ \frac{3}{2}\ \pi\right)$$

```
> B := t-> -1/8*(1-A(t)^2+7/32*A(t)^4)*e^2*t+b;
```

$$B := t \to -\ \frac{1}{8}\left(1\ -\ A(\ t\ )^2\ +\ \frac{7}{32}\ A(\ t\ )^4\right)t\ +\ b$$

```
> A := t-> -2/(1+c*exp(-e*t));
```

$$A := t \to -2\ \frac{1}{1\ +\ c\ e^{-t}}$$

```
> e := 1:
> y := unapply( y(t), t ):
> fsolve( { y(0)=0, D(y)(0)=-0.1 }, {b,c},
>    {b=-0.1..0.1} );
```

$$\{\ b =\ .0004073638406,\quad c =\ 16.51715658\ \}$$

```
> assign("):
```

Let us plot this function.

```
> plot( y(t), t=0..20 );
```

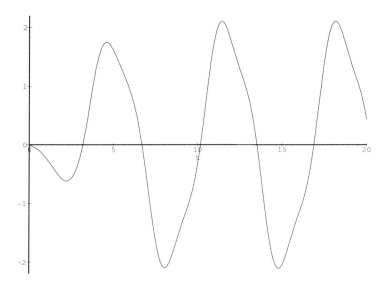

The agreement with the numerical approximation of the previous section is striking.

16.7 Liesymm

One of the most useful techniques for studying differential equations is the Lie symmetry method. In Maple, the *liesymm* package provides tools to apply Lie symmetry methods in the formalism described by Harrison and Estabrook [13, 67]. In this section, we shall use the package for finding the Lie symmetries of the Korteweg-de Vries equation

$$u_t + u\,u_t + u_{xxx} = 0,$$

using the abbreviated notation for partial derivatives.

```
> with(liesymm):
> KdV_eqn := Diff(u(t,x),t) + u(t,x)*Diff(u(t,x),x)
>     + Diff(u(t,x),x$3)=0;
```

$$KdV\_eqn := \left(\frac{\partial}{\partial t}\, u(t,\ x) \right) + u(t,\ x)\, \left(\frac{\partial}{\partial x}\, u(t,\ x) \right)$$

$$+ \left(\frac{\partial^3}{\partial x^3}\, u(t,\ x) \right) = 0$$

The general idea of Lie symmetry methods for partial differential equations (PDEs) is the following [96, 107, 109]. A *Lie point symmetry* for the PDE

$$\omega(t, x, u, u_t, u_x, u_{tt}, u_{tx}, u_{xx}, \ldots) = 0$$

is a mapping

$$t \to \bar{t}(t, x, u), \quad x \to \bar{x}(t, x, u), \quad u \to \bar{u}(t, x, u)$$

such that the new variables obey the original equation. Usually, one considers only one-parameter groups of Lie point symmetries. In this case, the infinitesimal mappings are,

$$t \to t + \epsilon \tau, \quad x \to x + \epsilon \xi, \quad u \to u + \epsilon \eta.$$

The PDE is unchanged if

$$X\omega = 0$$

for the operator

$$X = \tau \partial_t + \xi \partial_x + \eta \partial_u + \ldots.$$

This property leads to a system of linear homogeneous PDEs for the functions τ, ξ, and *eta*. This is called the *determining system*. In Maple, you can compute it with the procedure **determine**.

```
> eqns1 := determine( KdV_eqn, V, u(t,x), w );
```

$$eqns1 := \left\{ \frac{\partial}{\partial x} V1(t, x, u) = 0, \quad \frac{\partial}{\partial u} V1(t, x, u) = 0, \right.$$

$$\frac{\partial}{\partial u} V2(t, x, u) = 0, \quad \frac{\partial^3}{\partial u^2 \partial x} V1(t, x, u) = 0,$$

$$\frac{\partial^2}{\partial x^2} V1(t, x, u) = 0, \quad \frac{\partial^2}{\partial u^2} V1(t, x, u) = 0,$$

$$\frac{\partial^3}{\partial u^2 \partial x} V2(t, x, u) = \frac{1}{3} \left(\frac{\partial^3}{\partial u^3} V3(t, x, u) \right),$$

$$\frac{\partial^2}{\partial u \partial x} V2(t, x, u) = \frac{1}{3} \left(\frac{\partial^2}{\partial u^2} V3(t, x, u) \right),$$

$$\frac{\partial^3}{\partial u \partial x^2} V2(t, x, u) = \frac{\partial^3}{\partial u^2 \partial x} V3(t, x, u),$$

$$\frac{\partial^2}{\partial x^2} V2(t, x, u) = \frac{\partial^2}{\partial u \partial x} V3(t, x, u),$$

$$\frac{\partial}{\partial t} V1(t, x, u) =$$

$$3 \left(\frac{\partial}{\partial x} \mathit{V2}(t, x, u) \right) - \left(\frac{\partial^3}{\partial x^3} \mathit{V1}(t, x, u) \right),$$

$$\frac{\partial^3}{\partial u\, \partial x^2} \mathit{V1}(t, x, u) = 0, \quad \frac{\partial^3}{\partial x^3} \mathit{V3}(t, x, u) =$$

$$-\left(\frac{\partial}{\partial t} \mathit{V3}(t, x, u) \right) - u \left(\frac{\partial}{\partial x} \mathit{V3}(t, x, u) \right),$$

$$\frac{\partial}{\partial t} \mathit{V2}(t, x, u) = 3 \left(\frac{\partial^3}{\partial u\, \partial x^2} \mathit{V3}(t, x, u) \right)$$

$$- \left(\frac{\partial^3}{\partial x^3} \mathit{V2}(t, x, u) \right) + 2 \left(\frac{\partial}{\partial x} \mathit{V2}(t, x, u) \right) u$$

$$+ \mathit{V3}(t, x, u), \quad \frac{\partial^3}{\partial u^3} \mathit{V1}(t, x, u) = 0,$$

$$\frac{\partial^2}{\partial u\, \partial x} \mathit{V1}(t, x, u) = 0, \quad \frac{\partial^2}{\partial u^2} \mathit{V2}(t, x, u) = 0,$$

$$\left. \frac{\partial^3}{\partial u^3} \mathit{V2}(t, x, u) = 0 \right\}$$

Here, the following change of notation has been used.

$$\mathit{V1} = \tau, \quad \mathit{V2} = \xi, \quad \mathit{V3} = \eta$$

Maple provides the procedure **autosimp** to simplify the determining system, or if you are lucky, to solve it completely. Let us see what happens in our case.

```
> eqns2 := autosimp( eqns1 );
```

$$\mathit{eqns2} := \{\ \} \ \&where \ \Big\{$$

$$\mathit{V1}(t, x, u) = \mathit{C9} - \frac{3}{2} t^2\, \mathit{C5} + 3\, \mathit{C8}\, t,$$

$$\mathit{V2\_2}(t) = -t\, \mathit{C5} + \mathit{C8}, \quad \mathit{V3\_4}(t) = -\mathit{C5},$$

$$\mathit{V3\_5}(t) = \mathit{C3}, \quad \mathit{V3\_2}(t, x) = -x\, \mathit{C5} + \mathit{C3},$$

$$\mathit{V2}(t, x, u) = x\ (-t\, \mathit{C5} + \mathit{C8}) + t\, \mathit{C3} + \mathit{C4},$$

$$\mathit{V2\_1}(t, x) = x\ (-t\, \mathit{C5} + \mathit{C8}) + t\, \mathit{C3} + \mathit{C4},$$

$$\mathit{V3}(t, x, u) = u\ (t\, \mathit{C5} + \mathit{C6}) - x\, \mathit{C5} + \mathit{C3},$$

$$t\ C5\ -\ C6\ -\ 2\ C8 = 0, \quad V3\_1(\ t,\ x\ ) = t\ C5\ +\ C6,$$

$$V1\_2(\ t\ ) = C9\ -\ \frac{3}{2}\ t^2\ C5\ +\ 3\ C8\ t,$$

$$V3\_3(\ t\ ) = t\ C5\ +\ C6, \quad V2\_3(\ t\ ) = t\ C3\ +\ C4 \Bigg\}$$

Maple has solved the determining system of equations. But the solution contains the equation

$$t\, C5 - C6 - 2\, C8 = 0,$$

which can only be satisfied for all values of t if $C5 = 0$ and $C6 = -2\, C8$. When we do this substitution, we obtain the following expressions for $V1$, $V2$, and $V3$.

```
> eqns := subs( C5=0,C6=-2*C8, eqns ):
> select( has, eqns, {V1,V2,V3} );
```

$$\{\ V1(\ t,\ x,\ u\ ) = C9\ +\ 3\ C8\ t,$$

$$V2(\ t,\ x,\ u\ ) = x\ C8\ +\ t\ C3\ +\ C4,$$

$$V3(\ t,\ x,\ u\ ) = -2\ u\ C8\ +\ C3\ \}$$

We were lucky and have found the general solution

$$\tau = c_9 + c_8 t,$$
$$\xi = c_4 + c_3 t + c_8 x,$$
$$\eta = c_3 - 2c_8 u,$$

where c_3, c_4 c_8, and c_9 are arbitrary constants. So, the four-dimensional symmetry algebra of the Korteweg-de Vries equation is spanned by the symmetries tabulated below

Lie Point Symmetries of KdV-Equation	
Symmetry	**Meaning**
∂_t	time translation
∂_x	space translation
$t\partial_x + \partial_u$	Galilean boost
$x\partial_x + 3t\partial_t - 2u\partial_u$	scaling

The benefit of the above Lie symmetries is that if $u = f(t,x)$ is a solution of the Korteweg-de Vries equation, so are

$$u_1 = f(t - \epsilon, x),$$
$$u_2 = f(t, x - \epsilon),$$
$$u_3 = f(t, x - \epsilon t) + \epsilon,$$
$$u_4 = e^{-2\epsilon} f(e^{-3\epsilon} t, e^{-\epsilon} x),$$

for all real ϵ.

Despite the above success it must be remarked that the current integration capabilities in *liesymm* for solving the determining system automatically are limited. Therefore, quite some work must still be done manually.

16.8 Exercises

1. Solve the following ODEs with Maple. Try several methods, try to find the solutions in their simplest form, and check if Maple finds all solutions.

   (a) $3y^2 y' + 16x = 12xy^3$

   (b) $y' = 2\dfrac{y}{x} - \left(\dfrac{y}{x}\right)^2$

   (c) $xy' - y = x \tan\left(\dfrac{y}{x}\right)$.

2. Some ODEs of degree larger than one can be solved with Maple. Consider the following two examples.

   (a) Solve $y'^2 - y^2 = 0$.

   (b) Solve $y'^2 + xy = y^2 + xy'$.

   Do these two examples give you any clue of how Maple attacks higher degree ODEs?

3. Consider the initial value problem.

   $$y'' - y = 0,$$
   $$y(0) = 1,\ y'(0) = 0.$$

   (a) Find the solutions via the method of Laplace transforms.

   (b) Redo part (a) after you have given `printlevel` the value 3.

   (c) Repeat task (a), but now with `printlevel` equal to 33.

4. Compute the first ten terms in a Taylor series solution of the following initial value problem.

$$y' = yz$$
$$z' = xz + y$$
$$y(0) = 1, \ z(0) = 0$$

5. Consider Airy's differential equation,

$$y'' + xy = 0.$$

   (a) Find the solution for initial values $y(0) = 1$ and $y'(0) = 0$ via the power series method. Which terms of degree less than 30 occur in the solution?

   (b) What recurrence relation holds for the coefficients of the power series found in (a)?

   (c) Find the solution for initial values $y(0) = 0$ and $y'(0) = 1$ via the power series method. Which terms of degree less than 30 occur in the solution?

6. Consider Duffing's differential equation,

$$x'' + x + \epsilon x^3 = \epsilon F \cos \omega t.$$

   Apply the Poincaé-Lindstedt method to find an approximation of a periodic solution of the ODE which satisfies the initial values

$$x(0) = A \quad \text{and} \quad x'(0) = 0.$$

   What are the results when you apply the method of multiple scales and how do both methods compare to a numerical approximation?

7. Compute the determining system for the Boltzmann equation,

$$u_{tx} + u_x + u^2 = 0,$$

   and try to compute the symmetry algebra.
   (Hint: you may have to load the procedure **pdintegrate** of the "hidden" package `liesymm/difftools`.)

Linear Algebra: Basics

In this chapter, we shall look at Maple's basic facilities for computing with matrices. Not only elementary matrix operations like addition and multiplication, but also high-level computations like determinants, inverses, eigenvalues, and eigenvectors will pass in review. Furthermore, the last name evaluation concept for arrays, tables, and procedures will be explained in detail.

17.1 Basic Operations on Matrices

Before you start calculating with matrices it is wise to load the *linalg* package, which is especially designed for computations in linear algebra.

```
> with(linalg):
Warning: new definition for    norm
Warning: new definition for    trace
```

The warnings after loading the package remind you that the functions **norm** and **trace** already existed in Maple and that they are replaced by procedures from the *linalg* package with the same names. You can get back to previous definition of a procedure by explicitly reloading it. For example, to get back the original definition of **norm**, which is for computing the norm of a polynomial, you can enter the following command.

```
> readlib( norm ):
proc(p,n,v) ... end
```

In the third section, we shall look at the main facilities of the *linalg* package. Here, we shall only concentrate on basic calculations with matrices: multiplication, addition, and powers of matrices.

Let us first define some matrices. (See §12.4 for details.)

```
> A := matrix( 2, 2, [ a, b, c, d ] );
```

$$A := \begin{bmatrix} a & b \\ c & d \end{bmatrix}$$

```
> B := toeplitz( [ alpha, beta ] );
```

$$B := \begin{bmatrix} \alpha & \beta \\ \beta & \alpha \end{bmatrix}$$

```
> C := matrix( 3, 2, (i,j) -> i+j-1 );
```

$$C := \begin{bmatrix} 1 & 2 \\ 2 & 3 \\ 3 & 4 \end{bmatrix}$$

The most convenient way to calculate with matrices is to use the Maple procedure **evalm** (**eval**uate using **m**atrix arithmetic).

```
> evalm( A + B );
```

$$\begin{bmatrix} a + \alpha & b + \beta \\ c + \beta & d + \alpha \end{bmatrix}$$

```
> evalm( 3*A - 2/7*B );
```

$$\begin{bmatrix} 3\,a - \dfrac{2}{7}\,\alpha & 3\,b - \dfrac{2}{7}\,\beta \\ 3\,c - \dfrac{2}{7}\,\beta & 3\,d - \dfrac{2}{7}\,\alpha \end{bmatrix}$$

Addition of scalars is also possible; the main diagonal is increased by the scalar value.

```
> evalm( A - 1 );
```

$$\begin{bmatrix} a - 1 & b \\ c & d - 1 \end{bmatrix}$$

```
> evalm( C + 10 );
```

$$\begin{bmatrix} 11 & 2 \\ 2 & 13 \\ 3 & 4 \end{bmatrix}$$

You cannot use the operator * for matrix multiplication; this operator is reserved in Maple as the *commutative* multiplication operator.

```
> A*B + 2*B*A;
```

$$3 \ A \ B$$

```
> A*A + B*C*B;
```

$$A^2 \ + \ B^2 \ C$$

As you see, Maple does not take into account the data type of the names A, B, and C when it carries out automatic simplification operations. And, when you want to compute the matrix product with **evalm**, Maple does not always compute what you think it should.

```
> evalm( B * A );
```

$$\begin{bmatrix} a \ \alpha \ + \ b \ \beta & a \ \beta \ + \ b \ \alpha \\ c \ \alpha \ + \ d \ \beta & c \ \beta \ + \ d \ \alpha \end{bmatrix}$$

Maple has in fact computed the product $A \, B$. You must use the multiplication operator &* for multiplication of matrices.

```
> evalm( B &* A );
```

$$\begin{bmatrix} a \ \alpha \ + \ c \ \beta & b \ \alpha \ + \ d \ \beta \\ a \ \beta \ + \ c \ \alpha & b \ \beta \ + \ d \ \alpha \end{bmatrix}$$

```
> evalm( A &* B );
```

$$\begin{bmatrix} a \ \alpha \ + \ b \ \beta & a \ \beta \ + \ b \ \alpha \\ c \ \alpha \ + \ d \ \beta & c \ \beta \ + \ d \ \alpha \end{bmatrix}$$

The multiplication operator &* can also be used for multiplication of matrices with vectors. Column vectors are represented in Maple as objects of type *array* of dimension $n \times 1$ or as objects of type *vector*.

```
> columnvector := matrix( 2, 1, [ x, y ] );
```

$$columnvector \ := \ \begin{bmatrix} x \\ y \end{bmatrix}$$

```
> type( columnvector, 'matrix' );
```

$$true$$

```
> type( columnvector, 'vector' );
```

$$false$$

```
> columnvector := vector( [ x, y ] );
```
$$columnvector := [x \quad y]$$

```
> type( columnvector, `vector` );
```
$$true$$

```
> evalm( A &* columnvector );
```
$$[a\ x + b\ y \quad c\ x + d\ y]$$

Row vectors are represented as $1 \times n$ matrices.

```
> rowvector := matrix( 1, 3, [ alpha, beta, gamma ] );
```
$$rowvector := \begin{bmatrix} \alpha & \beta & \gamma \end{bmatrix}$$

```
> evalm( rowvector &* C );
```
$$\begin{bmatrix} \alpha + 2\ \beta + 3\ \gamma & 2\ \alpha + 3\ \beta + 4\ \gamma \end{bmatrix}$$

Matrix powers can be computed with the usual operator ^.

```
> evalm( B^3 );
```
$$\begin{bmatrix} \alpha^3 + 3\ \alpha\ \beta^2 & 3\ \alpha^2\ \beta + \beta^3 \\ 3\ \alpha^2\ \beta + \beta^3 & \alpha^3 + 3\ \alpha\ \beta^2 \end{bmatrix}$$

With the **map** procedure, you can simplify all matrix entries at the same time.

```
> map( factor, " );
```
$$\begin{bmatrix} \alpha \left(\alpha^2 + 3\ \beta^2 \right) & \beta \left(3\ \alpha^2 + \beta^2 \right) \\ \beta \left(3\ \alpha^2 + \beta^2 \right) & \alpha \left(\alpha^2 + 3\ \beta^2 \right) \end{bmatrix}$$

Not only natural numbers are accepted by Maple as exponents; negative integral exponents can also be used, provided that the matrix is not singular.

```
> evalm( B^(-3) );
```
$$\begin{bmatrix} -\dfrac{\alpha \left(\alpha^2 + 3\ \beta^2 \right)}{\%1^3} & \dfrac{\beta \left(3\ \alpha^2 + \beta^2 \right)}{\%1^3} \\ \dfrac{\beta \left(3\ \alpha^2 + \beta^2 \right)}{\%1^3} & -\dfrac{\alpha \left(\alpha^2 + 3\ \beta^2 \right)}{\%1^3} \end{bmatrix}$$

$$\%1 := -\alpha^2 + \beta^2$$

```
> evalm(" &* """);
```

$$\begin{bmatrix} 1 & 0 \\ 0 & 1 \end{bmatrix}$$

Make sure that you enter a space after the `&*` operator; otherwise the operator is not recognized.

Automatic simplification may sometimes surprise you.

```
> evalm( A^0 );
```

$$1$$

```
> whattype(");
```

integer

Furthermore, because the `&*` operator has the same priority as the multiplication and division operators `*` and `/`, you should be cautious about precedence of operators. Sometimes you have to use parentheses.

```
> evalm( A &* 1/A);

Error, (in evalm/amperstar)
&* is reserved for matrix multiplication

> evalm( A &* (1/A) );
```

$$\&*(\quad)$$

Maple uses `&*()` for the identity matrix. With **lprint** you can see what is going on here.

```
> lprint(A &* 1/A );

&*(A,1)/A

> lprint(A1 &* (1/A1));

&*(A,1/A)
```

17.2 Last Name Evaluation

As was noted in §12.4, evaluation of *arrays* is different from the usual concept of *full evaluation*.

```
> R := matrix( [ [ cos(alpha), -sin(alpha) ],
>    [ sin(alpha), cos(alpha) ] ] );
```

$$R := \begin{bmatrix} \cos(\alpha) & -\sin(\alpha) \\ \sin(\alpha) & \cos(\alpha) \end{bmatrix}$$

```
> R; # evaluation to a name
```

$$R$$

```
> whattype(R);
```

$$string$$

```
> eval(R); # full evaluation to an array
```

$$\begin{bmatrix} \cos(\alpha) & -\sin(\alpha) \\ \sin(\alpha) & \cos(\alpha) \end{bmatrix}$$

The individual matrix entries are not evaluated in the last command, as can be seen from the following continuation of the session.

```
> alpha := 1:
> eval(R);
```

$$\begin{bmatrix} \cos(\alpha) & -\sin(\alpha) \\ \sin(\alpha) & \cos(\alpha) \end{bmatrix}$$

```
> map( eval, R );
```

$$\begin{bmatrix} \cos(1) & -\sin(1) \\ \sin(1) & \cos(1) \end{bmatrix}$$

By the way, the same is true for *tables* and *procedures*.

```
> Laplace := table( [ erf(sqrt(t)) = 1/s/sqrt(s+1),
>    1/2/sqrt(Pi*t^3)*(exp(-q*t)-exp(-p*t)) =
>    sqrt(s+p)-sqrt(s+q) ] );
```

$$Laplace := table([$$

$$\frac{1}{2}\frac{e^{-q\,t} - e^{-p\,t}}{\sqrt{\pi}\ t^{3/2}} = \sqrt{s + p} - \sqrt{s + q}$$

$$\mathrm{erf}\left(\sqrt{t}\right) = \frac{1}{s\sqrt{s + 1}}$$

$$])$$

```
> Laplace;
```

$$Laplace$$

```
> Laplace[ erf(sqrt(t)) ];
```

$$\frac{1}{s\sqrt{s+1}}$$

```
> eval( Laplace );
```

$$Laplace := \text{table}([$$

$$\frac{1}{2}\frac{e^{-q\,t}-e^{-p\,t}}{\sqrt{\pi}\;t^{3/2}} = \sqrt{s+p}-\sqrt{s+q}$$

$$\text{erf}\!\left(\sqrt{t}\right) = \frac{1}{s\sqrt{s+1}}$$

$$])$$

```
> s := u;
> eval(Laplace);
```

$$Laplace := \text{table}([$$

$$\frac{1}{2}\frac{e^{-q\,t}-e^{-p\,t}}{\sqrt{\pi}\;t^{3/2}} = \sqrt{s+p}-\sqrt{s+q}$$

$$\text{erf}\!\left(\sqrt{t}\right) = \frac{1}{s\sqrt{s+1}}$$

$$])$$

```
> map( eval, Laplace );
```

$$\text{table}([$$

$$\frac{1}{2}\frac{e^{-q\,t}-e^{-p\,t}}{\sqrt{\pi}\;t^{3/2}} = \sqrt{u+p}-\sqrt{u+q}$$

$$\text{erf}\!\left(\sqrt{t}\right) = \frac{1}{u\sqrt{u+1}}$$

$$])$$

```
> f := x -> sqrt(x+1):
```

```
> f; # evaluation to a name
```

$$f$$

```
> f(t);
```

$$\sqrt{t + 1}$$

```
> eval(f); # full evaluation to a procedure
```

$$x \rightarrow \text{sqrt}(\ x + 1\ )$$

For these three types of Maple objects, *last name evaluation* takes place instead of *full evaluation*. This means that the result of evaluation is the last name in the chain of values just before the final object of type *table*, *array*, or *procedure* is reached. So, in the above examples, Maple evaluates R, Laplace, and f just to their own name of type *string*.

```
> map( whattype, [ R, Laplace, f ] );
```

$$[\ string,\ string,\ string\ ]$$

As you have seen earlier, full evaluation can be forced by **eval**, or even further by **map**ping **eval**.

Back to matrix arithmetic. The effect of *last name evaluation* of arrays can of course be shown better by an example in which a variable does not evaluate itself to an array but to a name of an array.

```
> T := S;
```

$$T := S$$

```
> S := R;
```

$$S := R$$

```
> eval(T,1); # value of T
```

$$S$$

```
> eval(T,2); # value of S
```

$$R$$

```
> eval(T,3); # value of R
```

$$\begin{bmatrix} \cos(\ \alpha\ ) & -\sin(\ \alpha\ ) \\ \sin(\ \alpha\ ) & \cos(\ \alpha\ ) \end{bmatrix}$$

```
> map( eval, T );
```

$$\begin{bmatrix} \cos(1) & -\sin(1) \\ \sin(1) & \cos(1) \end{bmatrix}$$

```
> T; # evaluation of T to last name
```

$$R$$

The internal data structure looks as follows.

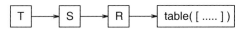

It is clear that R, S, and T all point to the same array. When you refer to the matrix element R[1,2], you get the same result as when you had chosen S[1,2] or T[1,2].

```
> alpha := ´alpha´:   # reset alpha to its name
> R[1,2], S[1,2], T[1,2];
```

$$-\sin(\alpha), \ -\sin(\alpha), \ -\sin(\alpha)$$

When you change the matrix element S[1,2], all three matrices are simultaneously changed in the same way.

```
> print(R);
```

$$\begin{bmatrix} \cos(\alpha) & -\sin(\alpha) \\ \sin(\alpha) & \cos(\alpha) \end{bmatrix}$$

```
> S[2,1] := 0:
> eval(R), eval(S), eval(T);
```

$$\begin{bmatrix} \cos(\alpha) & -\sin(\alpha) \\ 0 & \cos(\alpha) \end{bmatrix}, \begin{bmatrix} \cos(\alpha) & -\sin(\alpha) \\ 0 & \cos(\alpha) \end{bmatrix},$$

$$\begin{bmatrix} \cos(\alpha) & -\sin(\alpha) \\ 0 & \cos(\alpha) \end{bmatrix}$$

If you want to make a copy of the matrix and then change this copy without disturbing the original matrix, you should use the procedure **copy**.

```
> S := copy(R):    S[1,2] := 0:
> eval(R), eval(S);
```

$$\begin{bmatrix} \cos(\alpha) & -\sin(\alpha) \\ 0 & \cos(\alpha) \end{bmatrix}, \begin{bmatrix} \cos(\alpha) & 0 \\ 0 & \cos(\alpha) \end{bmatrix}$$

17.3 The Linear Algebra Package

An easy way to carry out computations in linear algebra is to use procedures in the *linalg* package.

```
> with(linalg);
```

   [*BlockDiagonal*, *GramSchmidt*, *JordanBlock*, *Wronskian*,

         add, *addcol*, *addrow*, *adj*, *adjoint*, *angle*,

         augment, *backsub*, *band*, *basis*, *bezout*,

         blockmatrix, *charmat*, *charpoly*, *col*, *coldim*,

         colspace, *colspan*, *companion*, *concat*, *cond*,

         copyinto, *crossprod*, *curl*, *definite*, *delcols*,

         delrows, *det*, *diag*, *diverge*, *dotprod*,

         eigenvals, *eigenvects*, *entermatrix*, *equal*,

         exponential, *extend*, *ffgausselim*, *fibonacci*,

         frobenius, *gausselim*, *gaussjord*, *genmatrix*,

         grad, *hadamard*, *hermite*, *hessian*, *hilbert*,

         htranspose, *ihermite*, *indexfunc*, *innerprod*,

         intbasis, *inverse*, *ismith*, *iszero*, *jacobian*,

         jordan, *kernel*, *laplacian*, *leastsqrs*, *linsolve*,

         matrix, *minor*, *minpoly*, *mulcol*, *mulrow*,

         multiply, *norm*, *normalize*, *nullspace*, *orthog*,

         permanent, *pivot*, *potential*, *randmatrix*,

         randvector, *range*, *rank*, *ratform*, *row*, *rowdim*,

         rowspace, *rowspan*, *rref*, *scalarmul*,

         singularvals, *smith*, *stack*, *submatrix*,

         subvector, *sumbasis*, *swapcol*, *swaprow*,

         sylvester, *toeplitz*, *trace*, *transpose*,

         vandermonde, *vecpotent*, *vectdim*, *vector*]

From this list of available functions, it is clear that most popular matrix operations are available: multiplication and addition of matrices, row and column operations on matrices, Gauss elimination and row-reduced echelon form, determinant, trace and inverse of a matrix, characteristic polynomial, characteristic matrix, eigenvectors and eigenvalues, and so on. Information about individual *linalg* functions can be obtained from the on-line help system. In this section, we shall only present a couple of examples by which the most popular matrix calculations are covered. More examples can be found in [75]. In the next chapter, we shall look at advanced applications of linear algebra. But practicing yourself will be the best way to learn about the linear algebra facilities and their usefulness.

The procedures **trace** and **det** compute the trace and the determinant of a matrix, respectively. Let us apply them to the following Toeplitz matrix.

```
> toeplitz( [1,2,3] );
```
$$\begin{bmatrix} 1 & 2 & 3 \\ 2 & 1 & 2 \\ 3 & 2 & 1 \end{bmatrix}$$

```
> trace(");
```
$$3$$

```
> det("");
```
$$8$$

The row- and column-rank of a matrix, bases for the row- and column-spaces, and a basis for the kernel of a matrix can be easily computed.

```
> A := matrix( [ [1,0,0,1], [1,0,1,1], [0,0,1,0] ] );
```
$$A := \begin{bmatrix} 1 & 0 & 0 & 1 \\ 1 & 0 & 1 & 1 \\ 0 & 0 & 1 & 0 \end{bmatrix}$$

```
> rank(A);
```
$$2$$

```
> rowspace(A), colspace(A);
```
$$\{ [0 \ \ 0 \ \ 1 \ \ 0], [1 \ \ 0 \ \ 0 \ \ 1] \},$$
$$\{ [0 \ \ 1 \ \ 1], [1 \ \ 0 \ \ -1] \}$$

```
> kernel(A);
```

```
{ [ 0   1   0   0 ],  [ -1   0   0   1 ] }
```

Computation of the characteristic polynomial, eigenvalues, and eigenvectors is in principle possible; but exact calculus may of course come to the deadlock of an unsolvable characteristic equation.

```
> A := matrix( [ [-2,2,3], [3,7,-8], [10,-4,-3] ] );
```

$$A := \begin{bmatrix} -2 & 2 & 3 \\ 3 & 7 & -8 \\ 10 & -4 & -3 \end{bmatrix}$$

```
> cp := charpoly( A, lambda );
```

$$cp := \lambda^3 - 2\,\lambda^2 - 97\,\lambda + 282$$

The Cayley-Hamilton theorem states that substitution of the matrix A in its characteristic polynomial yields the zero matrix. Let us check this.

```
> evalm( subs( lambda=A, cp ) );
```

$$\begin{bmatrix} 0 & 0 & 0 \\ 0 & 0 & 0 \\ 0 & 0 & 0 \end{bmatrix}$$

The characteristic equation must be solved to obtain the eigenvalues of A.

```
> solve( cp );
```

$$3, \; -\frac{1}{2} + \frac{1}{2}\sqrt{377}, \; -\frac{1}{2} - \frac{1}{2}\sqrt{377}$$

The eigenvalues could have been obtained straight away with the **eigenvalues** procedure.

```
> eigenvals( A );
```

$$\left[\text{RootOf}(\_Z^2 + \_Z - 94), \; 1, \right.$$

$$\left\{ \left[\frac{-1}{2} - \frac{1}{4}\,\text{RootOf}(\_Z^2 + \_Z - 94) - 2 \quad 1 \right] \right\} \Big],$$

$$\left[3, \; 1, \; \left\{ \left[\frac{14}{13} \quad \frac{31}{26} \quad 1 \right] \right\} \right]$$

Eigenvectors can be computed with **eigenvect**.

```
> eigenvects( A );
```

$$\left[\left[-\frac{1}{2}+\frac{1}{2}\sqrt{377},\ 1,\ \left\{\left[\frac{-1}{2}\ -\frac{15}{8}-\frac{1}{8}\sqrt{377}\ \ 1\right]\right\}\right],\right.$$

$$\left[-\frac{1}{2}-\frac{1}{2}\sqrt{377},\ 1,\ \left\{\left[\frac{-1}{2}\ -\frac{15}{8}+\frac{1}{8}\sqrt{377}\ \ 1\right]\right\}\right]$$

$$\left.,\left[3,\ 1,\ \left\{\left[\frac{14}{13}\ \frac{31}{26}\ \ 1\right]\right\}\right]\right]$$

You get a sequence of lists. Each list consists of an eigenvalue, its multiplicity, and a basis of the eigenspace. Note that Maple uses the **RootOf** construction in the eigenvalues and eigenvectors. You can compute all values with **allvalues**.

```
> readlib( allvalues ):
> map( allvalues, [""], ´d´ );
```

$$\left[\left[-\frac{1}{2}+\frac{1}{2}\sqrt{377},\ 1,\ \left\{\left[\frac{-1}{2}\ -\frac{15}{8}-\frac{1}{8}\sqrt{377}\ \ 1\right]\right\}\right],\right.$$

$$\left[-\frac{1}{2}-\frac{1}{2}\sqrt{377},\ 1,\ \left\{\left[\frac{-1}{2}\ -\frac{15}{8}+\frac{1}{8}\sqrt{377}\ \ 1\right]\right\}\right]$$

$$\left.,\left[3,\ 1,\ \left\{\left[\frac{14}{13}\ \frac{31}{26}\ \ 1\right]\right\}\right]\right]$$

This could have been found immediately with the option `radical` in the **eigenvals** procedure.

```
> eigenvects( A, ´radical´ );
```

$$\left[3,\ 1,\ \left\{\left[\frac{14}{13}\ \frac{31}{26}\ \ 1\right]\right\}\right],$$

$$\left[-\frac{1}{2}+\frac{1}{2}\sqrt{377},\ 1,\ \left\{\left[\frac{-1}{2}\ -\frac{15}{8}-\frac{1}{8}\sqrt{377}\ \ 1\right]\right\}\right]$$

$$,$$

$$\left[-\frac{1}{2}-\frac{1}{2}\sqrt{377},\ 1,\ \left\{\left[\frac{-1}{2}\ -\frac{15}{8}+\frac{1}{8}\sqrt{377}\ \ 1\right]\right\}\right]$$

Until now, most of our matrices had rational coefficients. In fact, all procedures in the *linalg* package work for matrices over the ring of polynomials with rational coefficients. But for many procedures, coefficients may come from a wider class; complex numbers, algebraic numbers, and algebraic functions are allowed in many cases. Below is one example of a Toeplitz matrix.

```
> A := toeplitz( [ sqrt(2), alpha, beta ] );
```

$$A := \begin{bmatrix} \sqrt{2} & \alpha & \beta \\ \alpha & \sqrt{2} & \alpha \\ \beta & \alpha & \sqrt{2} \end{bmatrix}$$

```
> factor( det(A), sqrt(2) );
```

$$-\sqrt{2} \left(\beta + \sqrt{2} - \sqrt{2}\, \alpha^2 \right) \left(-\sqrt{2} + \beta \right)$$

```
> charpoly( A, lambda );
```

$$\lambda^3 - 3\, \lambda^2 \sqrt{2} + 6\, \lambda - 2\, \lambda\, \alpha^2 - 2\, \sqrt{2} + 2\, \sqrt{2}\, \alpha^2$$
$$- 2\, \alpha^2\, \beta - \beta^2\, \lambda + \beta^2 \sqrt{2}$$

```
> factor( ", sqrt(2) );
```

$$-\left(\beta\, \lambda - \beta \sqrt{2} + 2\, \lambda \sqrt{2} - \lambda^2 - 2 + 2\, \alpha^2 \right)$$
$$\left(-\sqrt{2} + \beta + \lambda \right)$$

```
> eigenvals(A);
```

$$\frac{1}{2}\, \beta + \sqrt{2} - \frac{1}{2} \sqrt{\beta^2 + 8\, \alpha^2} ,$$

$$\frac{1}{2}\, \beta + \sqrt{2} + \frac{1}{2} \sqrt{\beta^2 + 8\, \alpha^2} , \quad \sqrt{2} - \beta$$

```
> eigenvects(A);
```

$$\left[\frac{1}{2}\, \beta + \sqrt{2} - \frac{1}{2}\, \%1, \ 1, \right.$$

$$\left\{ \left[\frac{1}{2}\, \frac{\frac{1}{2}\, \beta - \frac{1}{2}\, \%1}{\alpha} \quad 1 \quad \frac{1}{2}\, \frac{\frac{1}{2}\, \beta - \frac{1}{2}\, \%1}{\alpha} \right] \right\} \right], \ [$$

$$\frac{1}{2}\, \beta + \sqrt{2} + \frac{1}{2}\, \%1, \ 1,$$

$$\left\{\left[\begin{array}{ccc} \dfrac{\frac{1}{2}\beta + \frac{1}{2}\%1}{\alpha} & 1 & \dfrac{\frac{1}{2}\beta + \frac{1}{2}\%1}{\alpha} \\ \frac{1}{2} & & \frac{1}{2} \end{array}\right]\right\},$$

$$\left[\sqrt{2} - \beta,\ 1,\ \{\ [\ -1\quad 0\quad 1\ ]\ \}\right]$$

$$\%1 := \sqrt{\beta^2 + 8\,\alpha^2}$$

17.4 Exercises

1. Consider the following matrices.

$$A = \begin{pmatrix} 1 & 0 & 2 \\ 2 & -1 & 3 \\ 4 & 1 & 8 \end{pmatrix}, \quad B = \begin{pmatrix} -3 & 2 \\ 0 & 1 \\ 7 & 4 \end{pmatrix}$$

   Compute:
   (a) A^{-1}
   (b) AA^t
   (c) $B^t AB$
   (d) $(2A + BB^t)\,A^t$

2. Let $a, b \in \mathbb{R}$ with $0 \le a \le 1$, $b^2 = 2a(1-a)$, and

$$A = \begin{pmatrix} a & a-1 & b \\ a-1 & a & b \\ -b & -b & 2a-1 \end{pmatrix}.$$

   (a) Check with Maple that A is an orthogonal matrix with determinant equal to one.
   (b) From (a) follows that A is matrix which describes a rotation in the standard basis of $\mathbb{R}^3$. Determine the rotation axis.

3. Let $a, b \in \mathbb{R}$ and

$$A = \begin{pmatrix} 0 & a & 1 & 0 & b \\ 1 & 0 & 0 & b & 0 \\ 0 & 1 & b & 0 & 1 \\ b & 0 & 0 & 1 & 0 \\ 0 & b & 1 & 0 & b \end{pmatrix}.$$

   (a) For what values of a and b is the matrix A singular?
   (b) Determine the inverse of A (for those values of a and b for which A is invertible).

4. (a) Compute det $\begin{pmatrix} x^2+1 & x & 0 & 0 \\ x & x^2+1 & x & 0 \\ 0 & x & x^2+1 & x \\ 0 & 0 & x & x^2+1 \end{pmatrix}$.

(b) Compute det $\begin{pmatrix} x^2+1 & x & 0 & 0 & 0 \\ x & x^2+1 & x & 0 & 0 \\ 0 & x & x^2+1 & x & 0 \\ 0 & 0 & x & x^2+1 & x \\ 0 & 0 & 0 & x & x^2+1 \end{pmatrix}$.

(c) Looking at the results of (a) and (b), do you have any idea what the determinant of a general matrix of the above form is? If so, check your conjecture for a 8×8-matrix. If not, compute the determinants for matrices of dimension 6 and 7 to get an idea.

5. For each natural number n, the $n \times n$-matrix A_n is defined as

$$A_n(i,j) = \begin{cases} 0, & \text{if } i = j, \\ 1, & \text{if } i \neq j. \end{cases}$$

Carry out the following computations for $n = 3$, 4, and 5.
(a) Compute the determinant of A_n.
(b) Compute the characteristic polynomial of A_n.
(c) Determine all eigenvalues of A_n and determine for each eigenvalue a basis of the corresponding eigenspace.

6. For each natural number n, the $n \times n$-matrix A_n is defined as

$$A_n(i,j) = \gcd(i,j).$$

(a) Compute the determinant of A_n for $n = 1, 2, \ldots, 15$.
(b) (for the mathematicians amongst us) Try to find a closed formula for the general case.

Linear Algebra: Applications

In this chapter, matrix arithmetic is illustrated with five practical examples. They are:

- Kinematics of the Stanford manipulator.
- A 3-compartmental model of cadmium transfer through the human body.
- Molecular-orbital Hückel theory.
- Prolate spheroidal coordinates.
- Moore-Penrose inverse.

In all sessions we shall assume that the *linalg* package has been loaded.

18.1 Kinematics of the Stanford Manipulator

The matrices below are so-called Denavit-Hartenberg matrices used in kinematics studies of robot manipulators; actually, we shall use the matrices A_1, A_2, ..., A_6 defining the Stanford Manipulator [98]. Henceforth, we shall use in Maple sessions t1, t2,... instead of θ_1, θ_2, ..., and the abbreviations c1 $= \cos$ t1, c2 $= \cos$ t2,..., s1 $= \sin($t1$)$, s2 $= \sin($t2$)$,...

```
> alias( seq( c.i = cos(t.i), i=1..6 ),
>    seq( s.i = sin(t.i), i=1..6 ) ):
> M := (a,alpha,d,theta) -> matrix( 4, 4, [cos(theta),
>    -sin(theta)*cos(alpha), sin(theta)*sin(alpha),
>    a*cos(theta), sin(theta), cos(theta)*cos(alpha),
>    -cos(theta)*sin(alpha), a*sin(theta), 0, sin(alpha),
>    cos(alpha), d, 0, 0, 0, 1 ] ):
> M(a,alpha,d,theta);
```

$[\cos(\theta)$, $-\sin(\theta)\cos(\alpha)$, $\sin(\theta)\sin(\alpha)$,

$a\cos(\theta)]$

$[\sin(\theta)$, $\cos(\theta)\cos(\alpha)$, $-\cos(\theta)\sin(\alpha)$,

$a\sin(\theta)]$

$[0$, $\sin(\alpha)$, $\cos(\alpha)$, $d]$

$[0$, 0 , 0 , $1]$

```
> # link length
> a := vector([0$6]):
> # link twist
> alpha := vector([-Pi/2,Pi/2,0,-Pi/2,Pi/2,0]):
> # offset distance
> d := vector([0,d2,d3,0,0,0]):
> # joint angle
> theta := vector([t1,t2,0,t4,t5,t6]):
> for i to 6 do
>   A[i] := M( a[i], alpha[i], d[i], theta[i] )
> od;
```

$$A_{[1]} := \begin{bmatrix} c1 & 0 & -s1 & 0 \\ s1 & 0 & c1 & 0 \\ 0 & -1 & 0 & 0 \\ 0 & 0 & 0 & 1 \end{bmatrix}$$

$$A_{[2]} := \begin{bmatrix} c2 & 0 & s2 & 0 \\ s2 & 0 & -c2 & 0 \\ 0 & 1 & 0 & d2 \\ 0 & 0 & 0 & 1 \end{bmatrix}$$

$$A_{[3]} := \begin{bmatrix} 1 & 0 & 0 & 0 \\ 0 & 1 & 0 & 0 \\ 0 & 0 & 1 & d3 \\ 0 & 0 & 0 & 1 \end{bmatrix}$$

$$A_{[4]} := \begin{bmatrix} c4 & 0 & -s4 & 0 \\ s4 & 0 & c4 & 0 \\ 0 & -1 & 0 & 0 \\ 0 & 0 & 0 & 1 \end{bmatrix}$$

$$A_{[5]} := \begin{bmatrix} c5 & 0 & s5 & 0 \\ s5 & 0 & -c5 & 0 \\ 0 & 1 & 0 & 0 \\ 0 & 0 & 0 & 1 \end{bmatrix}$$

$$A_{[6]} := \begin{bmatrix} c6 & -s6 & 0 & 0 \\ s6 & c6 & 0 & 0 \\ 0 & 0 & 1 & 0 \\ 0 & 0 & 0 & 1 \end{bmatrix}$$

The position and orientation of the tip of the manipulator is determined by the Denavit-Hartenberg parameters; it is the product of the matrices $A_1, \ldots, A_6$.

```
> Tip := evalm( `&*`( seq( A[i], i=1..6 ) ) ):

  ( ( -s6 s4 + c6 c5 c4 ) c2 - c6 s2 s5 ) c1

      + ( -s6 c4 - c6 c5 s4 ) s1
```

Let us look at the entry in the upper left corner.

```
> collect( Tip[1,1], [c1,c2,s1] );

  T := [ c1 s2 d3 - s1 d2   s1 s2 d3 + c1 d2   c2 d3 ]
```

This is in agreement with formula 2.55 in [98]. By hand, such matrix computations take much time and are error-prone; the computer algebra system really does its work here as symbol cruncher.

An example of how computer algebra can help to solve the inverse kinematics problem, i.e., how to compute the link parameters for a given position and orientation of the tip of a robot arm, can be found in [58].

In this section, we shall study the forward kinematics problem, and more precisely, the velocities of the tip of the Stanford manipulator. Once the physical geometry of the robot arm is fixed, i.e., once d_2 and d_3 are fixed, the tip of the robot arm is a function of θ_1, θ_2, θ_4, θ_5, and θ_6. We shall determine the translational velocity v and rotational velocity ω of the tip as a function of θ_1', θ_2', θ_4', θ_5', and θ_6'.

First, we split the translation part T and rotational part R of the matrix which describe the location and orientation of the tip of the robot arm. This is easily done with the procedures **subvector** and **submatrix**.

```
> T := subvector( Tip, 1..3, 4 );

    T := [ c1 s2 d3 - s1 d2   s1 s2 d3 + c1 d2   c2 d3 ]

> R := submatrix( Tip, 1..3, 1..3 ):
```

$$Jv := \begin{bmatrix} -s1\ s2\ d3\ -\ c1\ d2\ , & c1\ c2\ d3\ , & 0\ , & 0\ , & 0 \\ c1\ s2\ d3\ -\ s1\ d2\ , & s1\ c2\ d3\ , & 0\ , & 0\ , & 0 \\ 0\ , & -s2\ d3\ , & 0\ , & 0\ , & 0 \end{bmatrix}$$

The information about the translational and rotational velocity is contained in the Jacobian matrix

$$J = \begin{pmatrix} J_1^v & J_2^v & \cdots & J_5^v \\ J_1^\omega & J_2^\omega & \cdots & J_5^\omega \end{pmatrix},$$

where $J = (\ J_1^v \quad J_2^v \quad \cdots \quad J_5^v\ )$ is the Jacobian matrix of the vector function which maps the kinematic parameters θ_1, θ_2, θ_4, θ_5, and θ_6 into the translational submatrix T. The J_i^ω's are 3×1 vectors defined as

$$J_i^\omega = \begin{pmatrix} \omega_{x_i} \\ \omega_{y_i} \\ \omega_{z_i} \end{pmatrix},$$

where the components can be found with respect to the kinematic parameters from the relation

$$\frac{\partial R}{\partial \theta_i} \cdot R^T = \begin{pmatrix} 0 & -\omega_{z_i} & \omega_{y_i} \\ \omega_{z_i} & 0 & -\omega_{x_i} \\ -\omega_{y_i} & \omega_{x_i} & 0 \end{pmatrix}.$$

First, we shall consider the translational part. In the *linalg* package the procedure **jacobian** already exists for computing the Jacobian matrix of a vector valued function.

```
> Jv := jacobian( T, [t1,t2,t4,t5,t6] );
```

$$Jv := \begin{bmatrix} -s1\ s2\ d3\ -\ c1\ d2\ , & c1\ c2\ d3\ , & 0\ , & 0\ , & 0 \\ c1\ s2\ d3\ -\ s1\ d2\ , & s1\ c2\ d3\ , & 0\ , & 0\ , & 0 \\ 0\ , & -s2\ d3\ , & 0\ , & 0\ , & 0 \end{bmatrix}$$

Next, we shall consider the rotational velocity of the tip. We start with computing the derivatives $\frac{\partial R}{\partial \theta_i}$ by mapping the procedure **diff** to all matrix coefficients.

```
> R1 := map( diff, R, t1 ):    R2 := map( diff, R, t2):
> R3 := map( diff, R, t4 ):    R4 := map( diff, R, t5):
> R5 := map( diff, R, t6 ):
```

The transpose of a matrix can be computed with — to no-one's surprise — **transpose**.

```
> Rtranspose := transpose( R ):
```

Now we have all ingredients for computing the matrices J_1^ω, J_2^ω, ..., J_5^ω. As an example, we show the results for J_1^ω.

```
> evalm( R1 &* Rtranspose ):   omega := map( simplify, " );
```

$$\omega := \begin{bmatrix} 0 & -1 & 0 \\ 1 & 0 & 0 \\ 0 & 0 & 0 \end{bmatrix}$$

```
> Jomega1 := vector([omega[3,2],-omega[3,1],omega[2,1]]);
```

$$Jomega1 := [\, 0 \quad 0 \quad 1 \,]$$

All other vectors may be computed in a loop; and finally we can concatenate them into the requested submatrix of J with **concat** or **augment**.

```
> for i from 1 to 5 do
>    evalm( R.i &* Rtranspose ):
>    omega := map( simplify, " ):
>    Jomega.i := vector( [ omega[3,2], -omega[3,1],
>      omega[2,1] ] ):
>    print( Jomega.i = eval(Jomega.i) )
> od:
```

$$Jomega1 = [\, 0 \quad 0 \quad 1 \,]$$

$$Jomega2 = [\, -s1 \quad c1 \quad 0 \,]$$

$$Jomega3 = [\, c1 \; s2 \quad s1 \; s2 \quad c2 \,]$$

$$Jomega4 =$$

$$[\, -c1 \; s4 \; c2 - s1 \; c4 \quad -s1 \; s4 \; c2 + c1 \; c4 \quad s4 \; s2 \,]$$

$$Jomega5 = [\, s5 \; c1 \; c2 \; c4 - s5 \; s1 \; s4 + c1 \; s2 \; c5$$

$$s5 \; s1 \; c2 \; c4 + s5 \; c1 \; s4 + s1 \; s2 \; c5$$

```
                  -s2 c4 s5 + c2 c5 ]

  > Jomega := concat( seq( Jomega.i, i=1..5 ) ):
```

The translational and rotational part of J can be placed below each other in one matrix with the *linalg* procedure **stack**.

```
  > J := stack( Jv, Jomega );

     Jomega :=

              [ 0 , -s1 , c1 s2 , -c1 s4 c2 - s1 c4 ,

              s5 c1 c2 c4 - s5 s1 s4 + c1 s2 c5 ]

              [ 0 , c1 , s1 s2 , -s1 s4 c2 + c1 c4 ,

              s5 s1 c2 c4 + s5 c1 s4 + s1 s2 c5 ]

              [ 1 , 0 , c2 , s4 s2 , -s2 c4 s5 + c2 c5 ]
```

Consider the translational part of the Jacobian matrix.

```
  > print( Jv = eval(Jv) );

     J :=

              [ -s1 s2 d3 - c1 d2 , c1 c2 d3 , 0 , 0 , 0 ]

              [ c1 s2 d3 - s1 d2 , s1 c2 d3 , 0 , 0 , 0 ]

              [ 0 , -s2 d3 , 0 , 0 , 0 ]

              [ 0 , -s1 , c1 s2 , -c1 s4 c2 - s1 c4 ,

              s5 c1 c2 c4 - s5 s1 s4 + c1 s2 c5 ]

              [ 0 , c1 , s1 s2 , -s1 s4 c2 + c1 c4 ,

              s5 s1 c2 c4 + s5 c1 s4 + s1 s2 c5 ]

              [ 1 , 0 , c2 , s4 s2 , -s2 c4 s5 + c2 c5 ]
```

The maximum rank is equal to two. If for some kinematic parameters the maximum rank is not reached, then we say that the manipulator is in a singular state. Singular states are forbidden configurations of the robot arm. Let us try to find such parameter values. What happens when $s2 = 0$ (i.e., when $\theta_2 \in \{0, \pi\}$)?

```
  > subs( s2=0, eval(Jv) );
```

$$\begin{bmatrix} -c1\ d2 & c1\ c2\ d3 & 0 & 0 & 0 \\ -s1\ d2 & s1\ c2\ d3 & 0 & 0 & 0 \\ 0 & 0 & 0 & 0 & 0 \end{bmatrix}$$

```
> submatrix( ", 1..2, 1..2 );
```

$$\begin{bmatrix} -c1\ d2 & c1\ c2\ d3 \\ -s1\ d2 & s1\ c2\ d3 \end{bmatrix}$$

The determinant of this submatrix can be computed with **det**.

```
> det(");
```

$$0$$

So, the rank is less than two and the manipulator is in a singular state. When $s2 \neq 0$ we can use elementary row operations to inspect the row space. For example, we can add $c2\ c1/s2$ times the third row to the first row with **addrow**.

```
> addrow( Jv, 3, 1, c2*c1/s2 );
```

$$\begin{bmatrix} -s1\ s2\ d3\ -\ c1\ d2\ , & 0\ , & 0\ , & 0\ , & 0 \\ c1\ s2\ d3\ -\ s1\ d2\ , & s1\ c2\ d3\ , & 0\ , & 0\ , & 0 \\ 0\ , & -s2\ d3\ , & 0\ , & 0\ , & 0 \end{bmatrix}$$

```
> addrow( ", 3, 2, s1*c2/s2 );
```

$$\begin{bmatrix} -s1\ s2\ d3\ -\ c1\ d2\ , & 0\ , & 0\ , & 0\ , & 0 \\ c1\ s2\ d3\ -\ s1\ d2\ , & 0\ , & 0\ , & 0\ , & 0 \\ 0\ , & -s2\ d3\ , & 0\ , & 0\ , & 0 \end{bmatrix}$$

The rank is less than two if and only if the first column is equal to zero.

```
> { "[1,1]=0, "[2,1]=0 };
```

$$\{\ c1\ s2\ d3\ -\ s1\ d2 = 0,\ -s1\ s2\ d3\ -\ c1\ d2 = 0\ \}$$

```
> solve( ", {s1,c1} );
```

$$\{\ s1 = 0,\ c1 = 0\ \}$$

This can only be true when both $\cos\theta_1$ and $\sin\theta_1$ are equal to zero, which is by definition impossible. No additional singular states of the manipulator are detected.

18.2 A 3-Compartment Model of Cadmium Transfer

The next example comes from a case study in linear system theory. In [16, 70], structural identifiability of several time-invariant, continuous-time, compartmental models, which describe the transfer of cadmium through the human body, have been studied. Here, we shall only consider the following 3-compartment model.

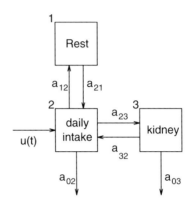

The corresponding mathematical model is a system of differential equations.

$$\frac{dx(t)}{dt} = A\,x(t) + B\,u(t)$$
$$y(t) = C\,x(t)$$

where

$$A = \begin{pmatrix} -a_{21} & a_{12} & 0 \\ a_{21} & -(a_{02} + a_{12} + a_{32}) & a_{23} \\ 0 & a_{32} & -(a_{03} + a_{23}) \end{pmatrix}$$

and

$$B = \begin{pmatrix} 0 \\ 1 \\ 0 \end{pmatrix}, \qquad C = \begin{pmatrix} 0 & 0 & c_3 \\ 0 & a_{02} & a_{03} \end{pmatrix}.$$

All parameters are nonnegative. Two measurements of cadmium concentrations are done: measurements in the kidney are described by

$$y_1(t) = c_3 x_3(t)$$

and measurements in urine are described by

$$y_2(t) = a_{02} x_2(t) + a_{03} x_3(t).$$

The parameter c_3 is supposed to be known and positive.

In general, a time-invariant, continuous-time, linear n-compartment model $M(\theta)$ which depends on parameters θ is described by

$$\frac{dx(t)}{dt} = A(\theta) \cdot x(t) + B(\theta) \cdot u(t), \quad x(t_0) = x_0,$$
$$y(t) = C(\theta) \cdot x(t) + D(\theta) \cdot u(t),$$

where $A(\theta)$ is an $n \times n$ matrix, $B(\theta)$ is an $n \times m$ matrix, $C(\theta)$ is an $k \times n$ matrix, $D(\theta)$ is an $k \times m$ matrix, $x = (x_1, x_2, \cdots, x_n)^T$ is the state vector in $\mathbf{R}_+^n$, $u = (u_1, u_2, \cdots, u_m)^T$ is the input vector in $\mathbf{R}_+^m$, $y = (y_1, y_2, \cdots, y_k)^T$ is the output vector in $\mathbf{R}_+^k$, and $\theta = (\theta_1, \cdots, \theta_r)$ is the parameter vector. Here, $\mathbf{R}_+$ denotes the set of nonnegative real numbers. The coefficients in the system matrix $A(\theta)$ satisfy

$$A_{ij} \geq \text{ if } i \neq j, \quad A_{ii} \leq 0, \quad \text{and} \quad \sum_j A_{ji} \leq 0.$$

The coefficients in the input distribution matrix $B(\theta)$, the output connection matrix $C(\theta)$, and $D(\theta)$ are all nonnegative real numbers. The input and output are related through the so-called *external behavior* of the compartmental system which is defined as

$$y(t) = C(\theta) \, e^{(t-t_0)A(\theta)} \, x_0 + \int_{t_0}^t W_\theta(t - \tau) \, u(\tau) \, d\tau,$$

where

$$W_\theta(t) = C(\theta) \, e^{tA(\theta)} \, B(\theta) + D(\theta) \, \delta(t).$$

W_θ is called the *impulse response function* of the compartmental system. It is completely characterized by the so-called *Markov parameter matrices* $M_j(\theta)$, $j = 1, 2, \ldots$ defined as

$$M_0(\theta) = D$$
$$M_j(\theta) = \frac{d^{k-1}}{dt^{k-1}} W_\theta(t)\Big|_{x=0}$$
$$= C(\theta) \, A(\theta)^k \, B(\theta), \quad \text{for } k = 1, 2, \ldots$$

Henceforth, we shall assume $D(\theta) = 0$.

Three notions in system theory are relevant in the study of theoretical (a priori) identifiability: *controllability*, *observability*, and *structural identifiability*. For a short introduction and the application of computer algebra, the interested reader is referred to [86, 101]. The following criteria hold:

Kalman's criterion for controllability. *The linear system is controllable iff the controllability matrix*

$$M_C = \left(B \,\Big|\, AB \,\Big|\, A^2 B \,\Big|\, \cdots \,\Big|\, A^{n-rb} B \right),$$

where $rb = \text{rank}(B)$, has maximum rank n.

Kalman's criterion for observability. *The linear system is observable iff the observability matrix*

$$M_O = \begin{pmatrix} C \\ CA \\ CA^2 \\ \vdots \\ CA^{n-rc} \end{pmatrix},$$

where $rc = \mathrm{rank}(C)$, *has maximum rank* n.

Remark: You may always take $rb = rc = 1$ in the above criteria (e.g., if you do not know or cannot compute the rank of matrix C).

Now, the main question in parameter identifiability is roughly stated as follows.

" Is it in principle possible, given the observations of input and output, to uniquely determine the parameter values?"

Recall that the set of common zeroes of a set of polynomials is called an algebraic set. We will use the following definitions of structural identifiability.

A model $M(\theta)$ is structurally locally identifiable at θ if there is an open neighborhood Ω around θ such that there is no $\theta' \in \Omega$ different from θ with the same external behavior for all identification experiments (t_0, x_0, u).

A model $M(\theta)$ is structurally locally identifiable if it is structurally locally identifiable for all θ outside an algebraic set.

A model $M(\theta)$ is structurally globally identifiable at θ if there is no θ' different from θ with the same external behavior for all identification experiments (t_0, x_0, u).

A model $M(\theta)$ is structurally locally identifiable if for almost all θ the θ' such that $y(t, \theta', u) = y(t, \theta, u)$ for all $t \in \mathbb{R}^+$ and all u form a finite set; when this set reduces to a singleton $\theta' = \theta$ we call the model structurally globally identifiable. Below we mention three methods to determine structural identifiability.

In our model for cadmium transfer in the human body we have assumed that the system is stable and that the time horizon is relatively long compared to the dynamics of the system. So, the effect of the initial condition may be neglected. Below we mention three methods to determine structural identifiability.

Markov parameter matrix approach to identifiability. *Use the Markov parameter matrices $M_1(\theta),\ M_2(\theta),\cdots, M_{2n}(\theta)$ to build up the matrix*

$$M_\theta = \begin{pmatrix} C(\theta)\, B(\theta) \\ C(\theta)\, A(\theta)\, B(\theta) \\ C(\theta)\, A(\theta)^2\, B(\theta) \\ \vdots \\ C(\theta)\, A(\theta)^{2n-1}\, B(\theta) \end{pmatrix}.$$

The linear system is structurally globally identifiable iff for all θ outside an algebraic set $M_{\theta'} = M_\theta$ implies $\theta' = \theta$. The linear system is structurally locally identifiable iff the $2nrm \times p$ Jacobian matrix

$$\begin{pmatrix} \dfrac{\partial M_1}{\partial \theta_1} & \cdots & \dfrac{\partial M_1}{\partial \theta_p} \\ \vdots & & \vdots \\ \dfrac{\partial \dot{M}_{2n}}{\partial \theta_1} & \cdots & \dfrac{\partial \dot{M}_{2n}}{\partial \theta_p} \end{pmatrix}$$

has maximum rank p for all θ outside an algebraic set.

Transfer function approach. *Define the transfer function matrix $H_\theta(s)$ as*

$$H_\theta(s) = C(\theta)\big[sI - A(\theta)\big]^{-1} B(\theta).$$

The linear system is structurally globally identifiable iff, for all θ outside an algebraic set, $H_{\theta'}(s) = H_\theta(s)$ implies $\theta' = \theta$. The linear compartmental system is structurally locally identifiable iff the $(2n-1)km \times r$ Jacobian matrix of the mapping of θ into the coefficients of the numerator and denominator of matrix elements of $H(s,\theta)$ has maximum rank r for all θ outside an algebraic set.

WARNING: The very popular *similarity transformation approach* only holds for general time-invariant continuous-time finite-dimensional linear systems, where state, input, and output vectors are from **R**-spaces and A, B, C, and D are matrices with coefficients in **R**. The similarity approach is of limited use in compartmental systems, where state, input, and output vectors are positive vectors. The following criterion is the best you can get in this approach.

Similarity-transformation method. Let the compartmental system be
structurally controllable and structurally observable for all parameters out-
side an algebraic set, and let the system have less than four compartments.
Under these conditions the compartmental system is structurally globally
identifiable at θ iff for all θ' and for all nonsingular T the system of equa-
tions

$$T A(\theta') = A(\theta)\, T$$
$$T B(\theta') = B(\theta)$$
$$C(\theta') = C(\theta)\, T$$

has a unique solution (I, θ). If the system of equations has a finite set of
solutions (T, θ), then the model is structurally locally identifiable at θ.

For systems with four or more compartments the above criterion is sufficient
but not necessary. This limits its usefulness enormously.

In all the above criteria, computer algebra is the appropriate computational tool. We shall apply the criteria to our example of cadmium
transfer.

```
> A := matrix( 3, 3, [ -a21, a12, 0, a21,

>     -(a02+a12+a32), a23, 0, a32, -(a03+a23) ] );
```

$$A := \begin{bmatrix} -a21 & a12 & 0 \\ a21 & -a02 - a12 - a32 & a23 \\ 0 & a32 & -a03 - a23 \end{bmatrix}$$

```
> B := matrix(3,1,[0,1,0]);
```

$$B := \begin{bmatrix} 0 \\ 1 \\ 0 \end{bmatrix}$$

```
> C := matrix(2,3,[0,0,c3,0,a02,a03]);
```

$$C := \begin{bmatrix} 0 & 0 & c3 \\ 0 & a02 & a03 \end{bmatrix}$$

```
> AB := evalm( A &* B ):    A2B := evalm( A &* AB ):
> MC := augment(B,AB,A2B);
```

$$MC :=$$

$$[\, 0\;,\; a12\;,\; -a21\ a12 - a12\ a02 - a12^2 - a12\ a32\,]$$

$$[\, 1\;,\; -a02 - a12 - a32\;,\; a21\ a12 + a02^2$$

```
                   + 2 a12 a02 + 2 a02 a32 + a12² + 2 a12 a32

                   + a32² + a23 a32 ]

               [ 0 , a32 ,

               -a02 a32 - a12 a32 - a32² - a32 a03 - a23 a32 ]
```

It is tempting to compute the rank of the controllability matrix M_C with the Maple procedure **rank**.

```
> rank(MC);
                              3
```

But this gives only the generic rank for the matrix considered as a matrix with coefficients in the quotient field $\mathbf{Q}(a_{12}, a_{21}, \ldots, a_{32})$. This is not what we wanted! Another way of computing the rank is by fraction free **Gauss elim**ination, carried out by the procedure **ffgausselim**.

```
> ffgausselim(MC);
            [ 1 , -a02 - a12 - a32 , a21 a12 + a02²

            + 2 a12 a02 + 2 a02 a32 + a12² + 2 a12 a32

            + a32² + a23 a32 ]

            [ 0 , a12 , -a21 a12 - a12 a02 - a12² - a12 a32 ]

            [ 0 , 0 ,

            -a12 a32 a03 - a12 a23 a32 + a32 a21 a12 ]

> map(factor,");
            [ 1 , -a02 - a12 - a32 , a21 a12 + a02²

            + 2 a12 a02 + 2 a02 a32 + a12² + 2 a12 a32

            + a32² + a23 a32 ]

            [ 0 , a12 , -a12 ( a12 + a21 + a02 + a32 ) ]

            [ 0 , 0 , a12 a32 ( -a03 - a23 + a21 ) ]
```

It follows immediately that the system is controllable iff $a_{12} \neq 0$, $a_{32} \neq 0$, and $a_{21} \neq a_{03} + a_{23}$. However, recall that Maple considers the matrix coefficients as elements in $\mathbf{Q}(a_{12}, a_{21}, \ldots, a_{32})$ so that, at each step of the fraction free Gauss elimination, it is possible that in each row the previous pivot is divided out or that the gcd of the polynomials in the row are divided out. The latter operation is not implemented in the procedure **ffgauselim**, and the former operation of dividing out previous pivots is of no harm as these pivots must be nonzero anyway in order to reach the maximum rank. If you don't want to rely on these implementation issues, then you can use the following equivalent controllability criterion.

Criterion for controllability. *The linear system is controllable iff for the controllability matrix M_C holds $\det\bigl(M_C\,M_C^T\bigr) \neq 0$ (or $\det(M_C) \neq 0$ when M_C is a square matrix).*

```
> factor(det(MC));
```

$$-a12 \ a32 \ (\ -a03 \ - \ a23 \ + \ a21\ )$$

But, in general this criterion will give trickier conditions.

Observability can be checked in the same way. We shall assume that $a_{02} \neq 0$ so that the matrix C has rank 2.

```
> CA := evalm( C &* A ):
> MO := stack( C, CA );
```

    MO :=

$$[\ 0\ ,\ 0\ ,\ c3\ ]$$

$$[\ 0\ ,\ a02\ ,\ a03\ ]$$

$$[\ 0\ ,\ c3\ a32\ ,\ -c3\ (\ a03\ +\ a23\ )\ ]$$

$$[\ a02\ a21\ ,\ -a02^2\ -\ a12\ a02\ -\ a02\ a32\ +\ a32\ a03$$

$$,\ a02\ a23\ -\ a03^2\ -\ a03\ a23\ ]$$

```
> ffgausselim(MO);
```

$$[\ a02\ a21\ ,\ -a02^2\ -\ a12\ a02\ -\ a02\ a32\ +\ a32\ a03$$

$$,\ a02\ a23\ -\ a03^2\ -\ a03\ a23\ ]$$

$$[\ 0\ ,\ a02^2\ a21\ ,\ a03\ a02\ a21\ ]$$

$$[\ 0\ ,\ 0\ ,\ c3\ a02^2\ a21\ ]$$

$$[\ 0\ ,\ 0\ ,\ 0\ ]$$

So, the system is observable if $a_{02} \neq 0$ and $a_{21} \neq 0$.

In our example, the next criterion for observability leads to more difficult, but equivalent conditions.

Criterion for observability. *The linear system is observable iff for the observability matrix M_O holds* $\det(M_O^T M_O) \neq 0$ *(or* $\det(M_O) \neq 0$ *when M_O is a square matrix).*

```
> factor( det( transpose(MO) &* MO ) );
```

$$a02^2\ a21^2\ c3^2\ (\ a02^2 + 2\ a02\ a32\ a03\ a23 + a32^2\ a03^2$$

$$+\ c3^2\ a32^2 + 2\ a02\ a03\ a23 + 2\ a02\ a32\ a03^2$$

$$+\ a02^2\ a23^2 + a02^2\ a03^2\ )$$

It looks as if an extra condition follows from the fourth factor. But when you consider it as a second degree polynomial in a_{32} and compute the discriminant, then you come to the conclusion that this term is always negative.

```
> collect( op(4,"), a32 );
```

$$(\ a03^2 + c3^2\ )\ a32^2 + (\ 2\ a02\ a03\ a23 + 2\ a02\ a03^2\ )\ a32$$

$$+\ a02^2 + a02^2\ a23^2 + a02^2\ a03^2 + 2\ a02^2\ a03\ a23$$

```
> discrim(",a32);
```

$$-4\ (\ c3^2\ a03^2 + a03^2 + 2\ c3^2\ a03\ a23 + c3^2\ a23^2 + c3^2\ )$$

$$a02^2$$

Next, we shall study structural local identifiability via the Markov parameter matrix. First, we must introduce the matrix and its Jacobian in Maple.

```
> n := rowdim(A);
```

$$n := 3$$

```
> CA0B := evalm(C&*B):
> for i from 1 to 5 do CA.i.B := evalm( C &* Aî &* B ) od:
> J := stack( seq(CA.i.B, i=0..2*n-1) ):
> J12 := map( diff, J, a12):   J21 := map( diff, J, a21):
> J23 := map( diff, J, a23):   J32 := map( diff, J, a32):
> J02 := map( diff, J, a02):   J03 := map( diff, J, a03):
> JM := augment( J21, J12, J02, J23, J32, J03 ):
> ffgausselim(JM):
```

```
> map(factor,");
```

$$[\, a12\ a02\ ,\ a02\ a21 + 2\ a02^2 + 2\ a12\ a02$$

$$+\ 2\ a02\ a32 - a32\ a03\ ,\ a21\ a12 + 3\ a02^2$$

$$+\ 4\ a12\ a02 + 4\ a02\ a32 + a12^2 + 2\ a12\ a32$$

$$+\ a32^2 + a23\ a32 - a32\ a03\ ,\ a32\ (\,-a03 + a02\,)$$

$$,\ 2\ a02^2 + 2\ a12\ a02 + 2\ a02\ a32 + a02\ a23$$

$$-\ a02\ a03 - a12\ a03 - 2\ a32\ a03 - a03^2$$

$$-\ a03\ a23\ ,$$

$$-a32\ (\, a32 + a02 + a12 + 2\ a03 + a23\,)\,]$$

$$[\,0\ ,\ -a12\ a02^2\ ,\ -(\,2\ a02 + a12 + a32\,)\ a12\ a02$$

$$,\ 0\ ,\ -a12\ a02\ (\,-a03 + a02\,)\ ,\ a12\ a02\ a32\,]$$

$$[\,0\ ,\ 0\ ,\ -a12\ a02^2\ ,\ 0\ ,\ 0\ ,\ 0\,]$$

$$[\,0\ ,\ 0\ ,\ 0\ ,\ c3\ a32\ a12\ a02^2\ ,\ a12\ c3\ a02\ (\,a02^2$$

$$+\ a12\ a02 + a02\ a23 + a02\ a32 + a02\ a03$$

$$+\ a32\ a03\,)\ ,\ a12\ a02\ c3\ a32\ (\, a32 + a02\,)\,]$$

$$[\,0\ ,\ 0\ ,\ 0\ ,\ 0\ ,\ c3^2\ a32\ a02^2\ a12\ ,\ 0\,]$$

$$[\,0\ ,\ 0\ ,\ 0\ ,\ 0\ ,\ 0\ ,\ a12\ a02^2\ c3^2\ a32^2$$

$$(\,-a23 - a03 + a21\,)\ (\, a21 + a12 - a03 - a23\,)\,]$$

$$[\,0\ ,\ 0\ ,\ 0\ ,\ 0\ ,\ 0\ ,\ 0\,]$$

$$[\,0\ ,\ 0\ ,\ 0\ ,\ 0\ ,\ 0\ ,\ 0\,]$$

$$[\,0\ ,\ 0\ ,\ 0\ ,\ 0\ ,\ 0\ ,\ 0\,]$$

$$[\,0\ ,\ 0\ ,\ 0\ ,\ 0\ ,\ 0\ ,\ 0\,]$$

$$[\,0\ ,\ 0\ ,\ 0\ ,\ 0\ ,\ 0\ ,\ 0\,]$$

$$[\,0\ ,\ 0\ ,\ 0\ ,\ 0\ ,\ 0\ ,\ 0\,]$$

The system is structurally locally identifiable iff a_{12}, a_{02}, and a_{32} are nonzero, $a_{21} \neq a_{03} + a_{23}$, and $a_{12} + a_{21} \neq a_{03} + a_{23}$

We shall also study structural global identifiability via the transfer function method.

```
> H := evalm( C &* (s-A)^(-1) &* B ):
> evalm( denom(H[1,1]) * H ) / collect(denom(H[1,1]),s);
```

$$(\qquad [c3 \ (a21 + s) \ a32]$$

$$[(a21 + s)$$

$$(a02 \ a03 + a02 \ a23 + a02 \ s + a32 \ a03)]] \Big/ (s^3$$

$$+ (a02 + a12 + a21 + a23 + a03 + a32) \ s^2 + ($$

$$a32 \ a21 + a03 \ a21 + a02 \ a21 + a02 \ a23 + a12 \ a03$$

$$+ a12 \ a23 + a32 \ a03 + a02 \ a03 + a23 \ a21) \ s$$

$$+ a03 \ a32 \ a21 + a02 \ a23 \ a21 + a03 \ a02 \ a21)$$

```
> collect( numer(H[1,1]), s );
```

$$c3 \ a32 \ s + c3 \ a32 \ a21$$

```
> collect( numer(H[2,1]), s );
```

$$a02 \ s^2 + (a02 \ a21 + a02 \ a03 + a02 \ a23 + a32 \ a03) \ s$$

$$+ a21 \ (a02 \ a03 + a02 \ a23 + a32 \ a03)$$

According to the transfer function criterion, structural global identifiability is equivalent to the uniqueness of the solution of the system of equations which is generated as follows.

```
> cfs1 := { coeffs( expand(numer(H[1,1])), s ) };
```

$$cfs1 := \{ c3 \ a32, \ c3 \ a32 \ a21 \}$$

```
> cfs2 := { coeffs( expand(numer(H[2,1])), s ) };
```

$$cfs2 := \{ a02, \ a02 \ a21 + a02 \ a03 + a02 \ a23 + a32 \ a03,$$

$$a03 \ a32 \ a21 + a02 \ a23 \ a21 + a03 \ a02 \ a21 \}$$

```
> cfs3 := { coeffs( expand(denom(H[1,1])), s ) }
>     minus {1};
```

$$cfs3 := \{ a02 + a12 + a21 + a23 + a03 + a32, \ a32 \ a21$$

$$+ \; a03 \; a21 \; + \; a02 \; a21 \; + \; a02 \; a23 \; + \; a12 \; a03$$

$$+ \; a12 \; a23 \; + \; a32 \; a03 \; + \; a02 \; a03 \; + \; a23 \; a21,$$

$$a03 \; a32 \; a21 \; + \; a02 \; a23 \; a21 \; + \; a03 \; a02 \; a21 \}$$

```
> cfs := `union`( cfs.(1..3) ):
> eqns := map( x -> x = subs( a12=b12, a21=b21, a23=b23,
>    a32=b32, a23=b23, a03=b03, a02=b02, x ), cfs );
```

$$eqns := \{ \, a03 \; a32 \; a21 \; + \; a02 \; a23 \; a21 \; + \; a03 \; a02 \; a21 =$$

$$b03 \; b32 \; b21 \; + \; b02 \; b23 \; b21 \; + \; b03 \; b02 \; b21,$$

$$a02 = b02, \; a02 \; a21 \; + \; a02 \; a03 \; + \; a02 \; a23 \; + \; a32 \; a03$$

$$= b02 \; b21 \; + \; b02 \; b03 \; + \; b02 \; b23 \; + \; b32 \; b03,$$

$$c3 \; a32 = c3 \; b32, \; c3 \; a32 \; a21 = c3 \; b32 \; b21,$$

$$a02 \; + \; a12 \; + \; a21 \; + \; a23 \; + \; a03 \; + \; a32 =$$

$$b02 \; + \; b12 \; + \; b21 \; + \; b23 \; + \; b03 \; + \; b32, \; a32 \; a21$$

$$+ \; a03 \; a21 \; + \; a02 \; a21 \; + \; a02 \; a23 \; + \; a12 \; a03$$

$$+ \; a12 \; a23 \; + \; a32 \; a03 \; + \; a02 \; a03 \; + \; a23 \; a21 =$$

$$b32 \; b21 \; + \; b03 \; b21 \; + \; b02 \; b21 \; + \; b02 \; b23 \; + \; b12 \; b03$$

$$+ \; b12 \; b23 \; + \; b32 \; b03 \; + \; b02 \; b03 \; + \; b23 \; b21 \}$$

```
> vars := {b12,b21,b23,b32,b02,b03}:
> solve(eqns,vars);
```

$$\{ \, b32 = a32, \; b02 = a02, \; b21 = a21, \; b23 = a23, \; b12 = a12,$$

$$b03 = a03 \, \}, \; \{ \, b32 = a32, \; b02 = a02, \; b21 = a21,$$

$$b12 = -a21 \; + \; a03 \; + \; a23, \; b23 = (\, -a02 \; a03 \; - \; a32 \; a03$$

$$+ \; a12 \; a02 \; + \; a02 \; a21 \; - \; a02 \; a23 \; + \; a12 \; a32$$

$$+ \; a32 \; a21 \,) \big/ a32, \; b03 = - \, ($$

$$-a02 \; a03 \; - \; a32 \; a03 \; + \; a12 \; a02 \; + \; a02 \; a21 \; - \; a02 \; a23$$

$$) \big/ a32 \, \}$$

There are two solutions. Thus, the system is not structurally globally identifiable; it is only structurally locally identifiable.

The last result will be checked by the similarity-transformation method. First we introduce the matrices AA, BB, and CC corresponding to the same model M but with parameter values $b_{12}, b_{21}, \ldots$ instead of $a_{12}, a_{21}, \ldots$

```
> AA := subs( a12=b12, a21=b21, a23=b23, a32=b32,
>    a23=b23, a03=b03, a02=b02, eval(A) );
```

$$AA := \begin{bmatrix} -b21 & b12 & 0 \\ b21 & -b02 - b12 - b32 & b23 \\ 0 & b32 & -b03 - b23 \end{bmatrix}$$

```
> BB := copy(B):
> CC := subs( a02=b02, a03=b03, eval(C) );
```

$$CC := \begin{bmatrix} 0 & 0 & c3 \\ 0 & b02 & b03 \end{bmatrix}$$

Introduce the similarity transformation T.

```
> T := matrix( 3, 3, (i,j)->t.i.j );
```

$$T := \begin{bmatrix} t11 & t12 & t13 \\ t21 & t22 & t23 \\ t31 & t32 & t33 \end{bmatrix}$$

From the matrix operation

```
> evalm( T&*BB - B );
```

$$\begin{bmatrix} t12 \\ t22 - 1 \\ t32 \end{bmatrix}$$

follows that $t_{12} = t_{32} = 0$ and $t_{22} = 1$. Then the matrix equation
CC - C T = 0 looks as follows.

```
> t12 := 0:  t32:= 0:  t22 := 1:
> evalm( CC - C&*T );
```

```
    [ -c3 t31 ,  -c3 t32 ,  c3 - c3 t33 ]

    [ -a02 t21 - a03 t31 ,  b02 - a02 t22 - a03 t32

    , b03 - a02 t23 - a03 t33 ]
```

```
> map( factor, " );
```

$$[-c3 \; t31 \;, \; 0 \;, \; -c3 \; (-1 + t33)]$$

$$[-a02 \; t21 \; - \; a03 \; t31 \;, \; b02 \; - \; a02 \;,$$

$$b03 \; - \; a02 \; t23 \; - \; a03 \; t33]$$

Because $c_3 \neq 0$, it follows immediately that $t_{31} = 0$, $t_{33} = 1$, and $b_{02} = a_{02}$.

```
> t31 := 0:   t33 := 1:   b02 := a02:
> evalm( CC - C&*T ):   map( factor, " );
```

$$\begin{bmatrix} 0 & 0 & 0 \\ -a02 \; t21 & 0 & b03 - a02 \; t23 - a03 \end{bmatrix}$$

If $a_{02} \neq 0$ (as is the case when the system is observable), then $t_{21} = 0$, and we have one equation left.

```
> t21 := 0:
> eqn1 := evalm(CC - C&*T)[2,3];
```

$$eqn1 := b03 - a02 \; t23 - a03$$

Now we derive the non-trivial equations obtained from the similarity transformation of the A matrix.

```
> evalm( T&*AA - A&*T );
```

$$[t11 \; (-b21 + a21) \;, \; t11 \; b12 + t13 \; b32 \; - \; a12 \;,$$

$$-t13 \; b03 \; - \; t13 \; b23 + a21 \; t13 \; - \; a12 \; t23]$$

$$[b21 \; - \; a21 \; t11 \;,$$

$$-b12 \; - \; b32 + t23 \; b32 + a12 + a32 \;, \; b23 \; - \; t23 \; b03$$

$$- \; t23 \; b23 \; - \; a21 \; t13 + a02 \; t23 + a12 \; t23$$

$$+ \; t23 \; a32 \; - \; a23]$$

$$[0 \;, \; b32 \; - \; a32 \;,$$

$$-b03 \; - \; b23 \; - \; t23 \; a32 + a03 + a23]$$

```
> eqn2 := map( op, convert(",´listlist´) ):
> eqns := { eqn1, op(eqn2) } minus {0};
```

$$eqns := \{ b03 - a02 \; t23 \; - \; a03,$$

```
        -t13 b03 - t13 b23 + a21 t13 - a12 t23,

        b32 - a32, t11 ( -b21 + a21 ),

        t11 b12 + t13 b32 - a12, b23 - t23 b03 - t23 b23

         - a21 t13 + a02 t23 + a12 t23 + t23 a32 - a23,

        -b03 - b23 - t23 a32 + a03 + a23,

        b21 - a21 t11, -b12 - b32 + t23 b32 + a12 + a32

        }
```

> solve(eqns, {b12,b32,b23,b03,b21,t11,t13,t23});

$\{\, t23=0,\ b03=a03,\ b12=a12,\ b21=a21,\ t13=0,$

$b23=a23,\ b32=a32,\ t11=1\,\},$

$t23=-\dfrac{a21 - a03 - a23 + a12}{a32},\ b21=a21,\ b03=-\,($

$a02\ a21 - a02\ a03 - a02\ a23 + a02\ a12 - a03\ a32$

$)\big/a32,\ b12=-a21 + a03 + a23,\ b23=(\,a02\ a21$

$- a02\ a03 - a02\ a23 + a02\ a12 + a21\ a32$

$- a03\ a32 + a32\ a12\,)\big/a32,$

$t13=\dfrac{a21 - a03 - a23 + a12}{a32},\ b32=a32,\ t11=1\,\}$

There are two distinct solutions, which proves again that the system is not structurally globally identifiable; it is only locally identifiable.

For more complicated systems, the analysis of controllability, observability, and structural identifiability via the outlined methods will not be as easy as above. Appropriate polynomial equation solvers like elimination, characteristic sets, or Gröbner basis methods must be used to find the answers. But at least the computational work is done by the computer algebra system with its linear algebra package, equation solvers, and so on.

18.3 Molecular-orbital Hückel Theory

The next example, molecular-orbital Hückel theory for the computation of π-electron energies and electronic charge distributions in molecules, comes from quantum chemistry. This method can be found in any book on quantum chemistry, e.g., in [11]; here we only sketch the method.

The particular molecule we shall use is Azulene $C_{10}H_{10}$, a skeleton of ten Carbon atoms linked by so-called σ-bonds.

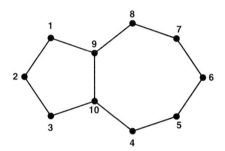

Each σ-bond contains 2 electrons; what remains are 10 electrons, which are called π-electrons. These π-electrons form π-bonds, which are constructed from the $2p_z$ Carbon orbitals. We number each Carbon atom and denote its $2p_z$ orbital as ϕ_i. The molecular orbitals are constructed from these atomic orbitals as linear combinations $\psi = c_1\phi_1 + c_2\phi_2 + \ldots + c_{10}\phi_{10}$. The coefficients $c_1, c_2 \ldots, c_{10}$ are determined by a variational method such that the energy is as low as possible. This leads to a generalized eigenvalue problem: $(H - ES)C = 0$, where H is the Hamiltonian matrix with matrix elements $< \phi_i | H | \phi_j >$, S is the overlap matrix with coefficients $< \phi_i | \phi_j >$, and C is a generalized eigenvector with generalized eigenvalue E. The following assumptions are made in Hückel theory.
- All matrix coefficients H_{ii} are equal, and are given the symbol α.
- All matrix coefficients H_{ij} are equal when atoms i and j are neighbors, and are denoted as β. When atoms i and j are not directly bonded, then $H_{ij} = 0$.
- Overlap is neglected, i.e., S is the identity matrix.

Under these assumptions we get an ordinary eigenvalue problem. The symmetric matrix H, which is called the *Hückel matrix*, for Azulene is as follows.

$$\begin{pmatrix} \alpha & \beta & 0 & 0 & 0 & 0 & 0 & 0 & \beta & 0 \\ \beta & \alpha & \beta & 0 & 0 & 0 & 0 & 0 & 0 & 0 \\ 0 & \beta & \alpha & 0 & 0 & 0 & 0 & 0 & 0 & \beta \\ 0 & 0 & 0 & \alpha & \beta & 0 & 0 & 0 & 0 & \beta \\ 0 & 0 & 0 & \beta & \alpha & \beta & 0 & 0 & 0 & 0 \\ 0 & 0 & 0 & 0 & \beta & \alpha & \beta & 0 & 0 & 0 \\ 0 & 0 & 0 & 0 & 0 & \beta & \alpha & \beta & 0 & 0 \\ 0 & 0 & 0 & 0 & 0 & 0 & \beta & \alpha & \beta & 0 \\ \beta & 0 & 0 & 0 & 0 & 0 & 0 & \beta & \alpha & \beta \\ 0 & 0 & \beta & \beta & 0 & 0 & 0 & 0 & \beta & \alpha \end{pmatrix}$$

Instead of the eigenvalue problem for the Hückel matrix, we shall solve the eigenvalue problem for the corresponding topological matrix,

$$\begin{pmatrix} 0 & 1 & 0 & 0 & 0 & 0 & 0 & 0 & 1 & 0 \\ 1 & 0 & 1 & 0 & 0 & 0 & 0 & 0 & 0 & 0 \\ 0 & 1 & 0 & 0 & 0 & 0 & 0 & 0 & 0 & 1 \\ 0 & 0 & 0 & 0 & 1 & 0 & 0 & 0 & 0 & 1 \\ 0 & 0 & 0 & 1 & 0 & 1 & 0 & 0 & 0 & 0 \\ 0 & 0 & 0 & 0 & 1 & 0 & 1 & 0 & 0 & 0 \\ 0 & 0 & 0 & 0 & 0 & 1 & 0 & 1 & 0 & 0 \\ 0 & 0 & 0 & 0 & 0 & 0 & 1 & 0 & 1 & 0 \\ 1 & 0 & 0 & 0 & 0 & 0 & 0 & 1 & 0 & 1 \\ 0 & 0 & 1 & 1 & 0 & 0 & 0 & 0 & 1 & 0 \end{pmatrix}$$

The relation between an eigenvalue x of the topological matrix and the eigenvalue E is simple, viz., $E = \alpha + \beta x$; the corresponding eigenvectors are the same.

Let us start computing. First, we tabulate the directly bonded Carbon atom pairs.

```
> `number of C-atoms` := 10:
> Azulene_skeleton :=
>   [ [1,2], [1,9], [2,3], [3,10], [4,5], [4,10],
>     [4,10], [5,6], [6,7], [7,8], [8,9], [9,10] ]:
```

We define the Hückel matrix as a sparse symmetric matrix.

```
> Hueckel_matrix := array( sparse,
>   1..`number of C-atoms`, 1..`number of C-atoms` ):
> for i from 1 to nops( Azulene_skeleton ) do
>   Hueckel_matrix[ op( Azulene_skeleton[i] ) ] := beta
> od:
```

```
> Hueckel_matrix := evalm( alpha + Hueckel_matrix

>    + transpose( Hueckel_matrix ) ):

> topological_matrix := subs( alpha=0, beta=1,

>    eval( Hueckel_matrix ) ):
```

The characteristic polynomial of the topological matrix can be computed with the *linalg* procedure **charpoly**; the characteristic matrix can be computed by **charmat**.

```
> factor( charpoly( topological_matrix, x ) );
```

$$(x^4 + x^3 - 3 \ x^2 - x + 1)$$

$$(x^6 - x^5 - 7 \ x^4 + 5 \ x^3 + 13 \ x^2 - 6 \ x - 4)$$

```
> charmat( topological_matrix, x );
```

$$
\begin{bmatrix}
x & , -1 & , 0 & , 0 & , 0 & , 0 & , 0 & , 0 & , -1 & , 0 \\
-1 & , x & , -1 & , 0 & , 0 & , 0 & , 0 & , 0 & , 0 & , 0 \\
0 & , -1 & , x & , 0 & , 0 & , 0 & , 0 & , 0 & , 0 & , -1 \\
0 & , 0 & , 0 & , x & , -1 & , 0 & , 0 & , 0 & , 0 & , -1 \\
0 & , 0 & , 0 & , -1 & , x & , -1 & , 0 & , 0 & , 0 & , 0 \\
0 & , 0 & , 0 & , 0 & , -1 & , x & , -1 & , 0 & , 0 & , 0 \\
0 & , 0 & , 0 & , 0 & , 0 & , -1 & , x & , -1 & , 0 & , 0 \\
0 & , 0 & , 0 & , 0 & , 0 & , 0 & , -1 & , x & , -1 & , 0 \\
-1 & , 0 & , 0 & , 0 & , 0 & , 0 & , 0 & , -1 & , x & , -1 \\
0 & , 0 & , -1 & , -1 & , 0 & , 0 & , 0 & , 0 & , -1 & , x
\end{bmatrix}
$$

```
> factor( det(") );
```

$$(x^4 + x^3 - 3 \ x^2 - x + 1)$$

$$(x^6 - x^5 - 7 \ x^4 + 5 \ x^3 + 13 \ x^2 - 6 \ x - 4)$$

Eigenvalues and eigenvectors can be computed with **eigenvals** and **eigenvects**, respectively.

```
> eigenvals( topological_matrix );
```

$$-\frac{1}{4} + \frac{1}{4} \sqrt{5} + \frac{1}{4} \sqrt{11 - \sqrt{5}} \ \sqrt{2} \ ,$$

$$-\frac{1}{4} + \frac{1}{4} \sqrt{5} - \frac{1}{4} \sqrt{11 - \sqrt{5}} \ \sqrt{2} \ ,$$

$$-\frac{1}{4} - \frac{1}{4} \sqrt{5} + \frac{1}{4} \sqrt{11 + \sqrt{5}} \ \sqrt{2} \ ,$$

$$- \frac{1}{4} - \frac{1}{4} \sqrt{5} - \frac{1}{4} \sqrt{11 + \sqrt{5}} \sqrt{2} , \quad \text{RootOf}($$

$$\_Z^6 - \_Z^5 - 7 \_Z^4 + 5 \_Z^3 + 13 \_Z^2 - 6 \_Z - 4)$$

```
> eigenvects( topological_matrix );
```

$$\left[\%2, \ 1, \ \left\{ \left[1 - \frac{11}{2} \%2^2 + \frac{3}{2} \%2^4 + \frac{3}{2} \%2^3 - \frac{1}{2} \%2^5 + \frac{1}{2} \%2 \right. \right. \right.$$

$$- \frac{9}{2} \%2 - \frac{1}{2} \%2^3 + \frac{1}{2} \%2^5 - \frac{3}{2} \%2^4 + \frac{11}{2} \%2^2 - 2$$

$$1 - \frac{11}{2} \%2^2 + \frac{3}{2} \%2^4 + \frac{3}{2} \%2^3 - \frac{1}{2} \%2^5 + \frac{1}{2} \%2 \quad 1$$

$$- \frac{3}{2} \%2 + \frac{5}{2} \%2^3 - \frac{3}{2} \%2^2 + \frac{1}{2} \%2^4 - \frac{1}{2} \%2^5$$

$$-3 + 5 \%2^2 - \%2^4 + \%2^3 - 3 \%2$$

$$- \frac{3}{2} \%2 + \frac{5}{2} \%2^3 - \frac{3}{2} \%2^2 + \frac{1}{2} \%2^4 - \frac{1}{2} \%2^5 \quad 1$$

$$\frac{5}{2} \%2 - \frac{5}{2} \%2^3 + \frac{3}{2} \%2^2 - \frac{1}{2} \%2^4 + \frac{1}{2} \%2^5$$

$$\left. \left. \frac{5}{2} \%2 - \frac{5}{2} \%2^3 + \frac{3}{2} \%2^2 - \frac{1}{2} \%2^4 + \frac{1}{2} \%2^5 \right] \right\} \right], \ [\%1,$$

$$1, \ \{ \ [\ -1 \quad 0 \quad 1 \quad \%1^2 + \%1 - 1 \quad \%1^3 + \%1^2 - 2 \ \%1 \quad 0$$

$$-\%1^3 - \%1^2 + 2 \ \%1 \quad -\%1^2 - \%1 + 1 \quad -\%1 \quad \%1 \ ] \ \} \ ]$$

$$\%1 := \text{RootOf}(\_Z^4 + \_Z^3 - 3 \_Z^2 - \_Z + 1)$$

$$\%2 := \text{RootOf}($$

$$\_Z^6 - \_Z^5 - 7 \_Z^4 + 5 \_Z^3 + 13 \_Z^2 - 6 \_Z - 4)$$

Let us consider the last element in this sequence.

```
> "[2];
```

$$[\%1, \ 1, \ \{ \ [\ -1 \quad 0 \quad 1 \quad \%1^2 + \%1 - 1 \quad \%1^3 + \%1^2 - 2 \ \%1 \quad 0$$

$$-\%1^3 - \%1^2 + 2 \ \%1 \quad -\%1^2 - \%1 + 1 \quad -\%1 \quad \%1 \ ] \ \} \ ]$$

$$\%1 := \text{RootOf}(\_Z^4 + \_Z^3 - 3 \_Z^2 - \_Z + 1)$$

The first component specifies the eigenvalue associated with the eigenvector. The second component is the multiplicity of the eigenvalue. The third component is the actual eigenvector. In case of a multi-dimensional eigenspace, the third component would be a basis of eigenvectors. You should actually consider the above object as a description of four eigenvectors: %1 can take four values, but you must always choose the same value in one vector. Below is the one that corresponds with the eigenvalue $-\frac{1}{4} + \frac{1}{4}\sqrt{5} + \frac{1}{4}\sqrt{11 - \sqrt{5}}\sqrt{2}$.

```
> allvalues(",´d´)[1];
```

$$\left[\%2, \ 1, \ \left\{ \left[\begin{array}{ccccc} -1 & 0 & 1 & \%2^2 - \frac{5}{4} + \frac{1}{4}\sqrt{5} + \frac{1}{4}\%1 \\ \\ \%2^3 + \%2^2 + \frac{1}{2} - \frac{1}{2}\sqrt{5} - \frac{1}{2}\%1 & 0 \\ \\ -\%2^3 - \%2^2 - \frac{1}{2} + \frac{1}{2}\sqrt{5} + \frac{1}{2}\%1 \\ \\ -\%2^2 + \frac{5}{4} - \frac{1}{4}\sqrt{5} - \frac{1}{4}\%1 & \frac{1}{4} - \frac{1}{4}\sqrt{5} - \frac{1}{4}\%1 & \%2 \end{array} \right] \right\} \right]$$

$$\%1 := \sqrt{11 - \sqrt{5}}\sqrt{2}$$

$$\%2 := -\frac{1}{4} + \frac{1}{4}\sqrt{5} + \frac{1}{4}\%1$$

Singular values of a matrix M, which are defined as the square roots of the eigenvalues of MM^T, can be computed by **singularvals**.

Numerical eigenvalues and eigenvectors can be obtained by **Eigenvals**.

```
> eigenvalues := evalf(
>    Eigenvals( topological_matrix, ´eigenvectors´ ) );
```

$$eigenvalues := [\ -2.095293985 \quad -1.869213984$$

$$-1.579218099 \quad -.7376403029 \quad -.4003923188$$

$$.4772599976 \quad .8869752420 \quad 1.355674293$$

$$1.651572314 \quad 2.310276842\ ]$$

Let us check the first eigenvector.

```
> subvector( eigenvectors, 1..`number of C-atoms`, 1 );

    [ .18 10⁻⁸   .19 10⁻⁸   .5 10⁻⁹   .12 10⁻⁸   .1810 10⁻⁸

        -.4 10⁻⁹   .5 10⁻⁹   .13 10⁻⁸   .29 10⁻⁸   .2 10⁻⁸ ]

> evalm( ( topological_matrix
> - eigenvalues[1] ) &* " );

    [ -.2590786300   .1881 10⁻⁸   .2590786280   .3354972117

        -.1601193962   -.2190 10⁻⁸   .1601194004

        -.3354972138   .5428458950   -.5428458923 ]

> map( fnormal, " ); # floating-point normalization

    [ .18 10⁻⁸   .19 10⁻⁸   .5 10⁻⁹   .12 10⁻⁸   .1810 10⁻⁸

        -.4 10⁻⁹   .5 10⁻⁹   .13 10⁻⁸   .29 10⁻⁸   .2 10⁻⁸ ]
```

We end this example with a numerical description of the π-electron energy and the π-electron density function. When the orthonormalized molecular orbitals ψ_i's are occupied by n_i π-electrons the π-electron density q_j on the Carbon atom labeled j is defined as

$$q_j = \sum_{i=0}^{10} n_i c_{ji}^2.$$

We shall concentrate on the state with lowest π-electron energy.

```
> occupation_numbers := [0,0,0,0,0,2,2,2,2,2,2]:
> pi_electron_energy := sum( `occupation_numbers[i]
>   * ( alpha + eigenvalues[i]*beta )`,
>   `i`=1..`number of C-atoms` );

      pi_electron_energy := 10 α + 13.36351737 β
```

In this case, no eigenvalues with multiplicities greater than one occur, otherwise we would have applied Gram-Schmidt orthogonalization (via the produre **GramSchmidt** in the *lialg* package). Here, we only have to normalize the eigenvectors. This can be done with the **normalize** procedure.

```
> eigenvectors := map( normalize,  [ seq(
>   subvector( eigenvectors, 1..`number of C-atoms`, i ),
>   i=1..`number of C-atoms` ) ] ):
```

We are now ready to compute the π-electron density.

```
> electron_density := seq( sum( `occupation_numbers[i] *
>     (eigenvectors[i][j])^2`, `i`=1..`number of C-atoms` ),
>     j=1..`number of C-atoms` );

   electron_density := 1.172879340, 1.046599708,

          1.172879339, .8549456656, .9864468455,

          .8700013802, .9864468483, .8549456632,

          1.027427606, 1.027427605
```

For the chemists among us, this simple model explains stereospecificity of substitution. Electrophylic substitutions (like substitution of a Chlorine atom) are most likely to take place at positions of highest electron density. In the case of Azulene, this is position 2. Nucleophilic substitution (e.g., of a Methyl group) is most likely to take place at positions of lowest electron density, i.e., on positions 4 and 8.

18.4 Prolate Spheroidal Coordinates

Vector analysis procedures like **grad** (for *gradient*), **diverge** (short for *divergence*), **laplacian**, and **curl** are present in the *linalg* package and work well for Cartesian coordinates.

```
> alias(f=f(x,y,z), g=g(x,y,z), h=h(x,y,z), v=[x,y,z]):
> grad(f,v);
```

$$\left[\begin{array}{ccc} \dfrac{\partial}{\partial x}\, f & \dfrac{\partial}{\partial y}\, f & \dfrac{\partial}{\partial z}\, f \end{array}\right]$$

```
> diverge(",v);
```

$$\left(\dfrac{\partial^2}{\partial x^2}\, f\right) + \left(\dfrac{\partial^2}{\partial y^2}\, f\right) + \left(\dfrac{\partial^2}{\partial z^2}\, f\right)$$

```
> laplacian(f,v);
```

$$\left(\dfrac{\partial^2}{\partial x^2}\, f\right) + \left(\dfrac{\partial^2}{\partial y^2}\, f\right) + \left(\dfrac{\partial^2}{\partial z^2}\, f\right)$$

```
> curl([f,g,h],v);
```

$$\left[\left(\dfrac{\partial}{\partial y}\, h\right) - \left(\dfrac{\partial}{\partial z}\, g\right)\quad \left(\dfrac{\partial}{\partial z}\, f\right) - \left(\dfrac{\partial}{\partial x}\, h\right)\quad \left(\dfrac{\partial}{\partial x}\, g\right) - \left(\dfrac{\partial}{\partial y}\, f\right)\right]$$

```
> diverge(",v);
```

$$0$$

```
> curl( grad(f,v), v );
```

$$[\, 0 \quad 0 \quad 0\,]$$

The last two statements are well-known properties.

But Maple has no built-in facilities to express gradient, divergence, laplacian, and curl in terms of curvilinear coordinates. However, Maple can assist you in deriving the formulae.

We shall study prolate spheroidal coordinates which are used to compute the overlap integrals between Slater-Zener type atomic orbitals (q.v., [11]). These coordinates ξ, η, and ϕ are in this context best defined as

$$x = a\sqrt{(\xi^2 - 1)(1 - \eta^2)}\cos\phi,$$
$$y = a\sqrt{(\xi^2 - 1)(1 - \eta^2)}\sin\phi,$$
$$z = a\,\xi\,\eta,$$

where

$$a > 0,\ 1 \le \xi < \infty,\ -1 \le \eta \le 1,\ 0 \le \phi < 2\pi.$$

We are only interested in how the volume element is described in this new coordinate system.

We start with computing the Jacobian matrix J of the above coordinate transformation (denoted by T).

```
> T := [a*sqrt((xi^2-1)*(1-eta^2))*cos(phi),
>          a*sqrt((xi^2-1)*(1-eta^2))*sin(phi), a*xi*eta ];
```

$$T := \left[\, a\sqrt{\xi^2 - 1}\sqrt{1 - \eta^2}\cos(\phi),\right.$$
$$\left. a\sqrt{\xi^2 - 1}\sqrt{1 - \eta^2}\sin(\phi),\ a\,\xi\,\eta \,\right]$$

```
> J := jacobian(T,[xi,eta,phi]);
```

$$J :=$$

$$\left[\ \frac{a\sqrt{1-\eta^2}\cos(\phi)\,\xi}{\sqrt{\xi^2-1}}\ ,\right.$$

$$-\frac{a\sqrt{\xi^2-1}\cos(\phi)\,\eta}{\sqrt{1-\eta^2}}\ ,$$

$$-a \sqrt{\xi^2 - 1} \sqrt{1 - \eta^2} \sin(\phi) \Bigg]$$

$$\left[\frac{a \sqrt{1 - \eta^2} \sin(\phi) \xi}{\sqrt{\xi^2 - 1}} \ , \right.$$

$$- \frac{a \sqrt{\xi^2 - 1} \sin(\phi) \eta}{\sqrt{1 - \eta^2}} \ ,$$

$$\left. a \sqrt{\xi^2 - 1} \sqrt{1 - \eta^2} \cos(\phi) \right]$$

$$[\, a\,\eta \ , \ a\,\xi \ , \ 0\,]$$

In this case, the *metric tensor* g is equal to $J^T J$.

```
> g := evalm( transpose(J) &* J ):  g := map(simplify,g);
```

$$g := \begin{bmatrix} \dfrac{a^2 \left(-\eta^2 + \xi^2 \right)}{\xi^2 - 1} \ , & 0 \ , & 0 \\[2ex] 0 \ , & -\dfrac{a^2 \left(-\eta^2 + \xi^2 \right)}{-1 + \eta^2} \ , & 0 \\[2ex] 0 \ , & 0 \ , & a^2\,\xi^2 - a^2\,\eta^2\,\xi^2 - a^2 + a^2\,\eta^2 \end{bmatrix}$$

```
> simplify( det(g) );
```

$$\left(-\eta^2 + \xi^2 \right)^2 a^6$$

```
> dV := abs(sqrt("));
```

$$\left| -\eta^2 + \xi^2 \right| \left| a \right|^3$$

Maple does not know yet what to do with the absolute value, but we do: the ranges for ξ and η, and the fact that a is positive imply that the above expression simplifies.

```
> assume(a>0):  assume(xi>1):
> assume( eta, RealRange(-1,1) ):
> dV;
```

$$\left| -eta\tilde{\ }^2 + xi\tilde{\ }^2 \right| a\tilde{\ }^3$$

```
> is( xi^2-eta^2>0 );
```

$$true$$

The last result shows that the **abs** procedure does not take into account the knowledge about the range of the expression $\xi^2 - \eta^2$. We conclude that

$$dV = a^3(\xi^2 - \eta^2)\,d\xi\,d\eta\,d\phi.$$

Knowing the metric tensor and its inverse, the gradient, laplacian, and other notions can easily be computed in the new coordinate system. This is described in any book on differential geometry or vector analysis.

18.5 Moore-Penrose Inverse

In this book, we have not considered Maple as a programming language allowing for extension of the built-in facilities. But, sometimes, programming is a big word. For example, the *Moore-Penrose inverse* A^+ of a matrix A can be computed via a limit-definition [1],

$$A^+ = \lim_{x \to 0}\left((A^T A + x^2 I)^{-1} A^T\right),$$

if the limit exists. With all the tools of the *linalg* package and your knowledge of Maple, you are already able to extend Maple.

```
> MPinv := A -> map( limit, evalm(
>    (transpose(A)&*A+x^2)^(-1) &* transpose(A) ), x=0 );
```

$$MPinv := A \rightarrow \mathrm{map}\left(limit,\ \mathrm{evalm}\left(\frac{1}{(\ transpose(\,A\,)\ \&*\ A\,)\ +\ x^2}\ \&*\ transpose(\,A\,)\right),\ x=0\right)$$

```
> M := randmatrix(3,2);
```

$$M := \begin{bmatrix} -85 & -55 \\ -37 & -35 \\ 97 & 50 \end{bmatrix}$$

```
> MPinv(M);
```

$$\begin{bmatrix} \dfrac{427}{88957} & \dfrac{2579}{88957} & \dfrac{2275}{88957} \\[2mm] \dfrac{-14093}{889570} & \dfrac{-45953}{889570} & \dfrac{-14939}{444785} \end{bmatrix}$$

```
> poly := proc() Randpoly(2,y) mod 2 end:
> M := randmatrix(3,2,entries=poly);
```

$$M := \begin{bmatrix} y^2 & y^2 + y + 1 \\ y^2 + y & y^2 + y + 1 \\ y^2 & y^2 \end{bmatrix}$$

```
> MPinv(M);
```

$$\left[-\frac{2\ y^4 + 3\ y^3 + 3\ y^2 + 2\ y + 1}{y\ \%1}\ , \right.$$

$$\left. \frac{y^4 + y^3 + 3\ y^2 + 2\ y + 1}{y\ \%1}\ , \quad \frac{y^3 + 3\ y^2 + 3\ y + 2}{\%1} \right]$$

$$\left[\frac{2\ y^3 + 3\ y^2 + 2\ y + 1}{\%1}\ , \quad -\frac{y\ (y^2 + 1)}{\%1}\ , \right.$$

$$\left. -\frac{y\ (y^2 + 2\ y + 1)}{\%1} \right]$$

$$\%1 := 2\ y^4 + 4\ y^3 + 5\ y^2 + 2\ y + 1$$

18.6 Exercises

1. In [99] the following Denavit-Hartenberg parameters for a PUMA robot arm can be found.

Joint	α	θ	d	a
1	$-90°$	θ_1	0	0
2	$0°$	θ_2	0	a_2
3	$90°$	θ_3	d_3	a_3
4	$-90°$	θ_4	d_4	0
5	$90°$	θ_5	0	0
6	$0°$	θ_6	0	0

Determine the position and orientation of the tip of this robot arm as a function of the kinematic parameters. Also describe the translational and rotational velocity of the tip.

2. Consider the following 4-compartmental model for cadmium transfer in the human body.

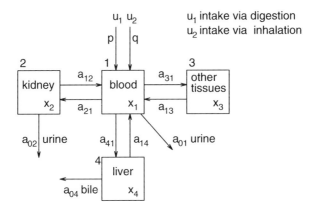

The corresponding mathematical equations are

$$\dot{x}(t) = A\,x(t) + B\,u(t), \qquad x(0) = x_0,$$
$$y(t) = C\,x(t),$$

where

$$A = \begin{pmatrix} a_{11} & a_{12} & a_{13} & a_{14} \\ a_{21} & a_{22} & 0 & 0 \\ a_{31} & 0 & a_{33} & 0 \\ a_{41} & 0 & 0 & a_{44} \end{pmatrix},$$

$$B = \begin{pmatrix} p & q \\ 0 & 0 \\ 0 & 0 \\ 0 & 0 \end{pmatrix},$$

$$C = \begin{pmatrix} c_{11} & c_{12} & 0 & 0 \\ 0 & c_{22} & 0 & 0 \\ 0 & 0 & 0 & c_{44} \end{pmatrix},$$

with $a_{11} = -(a_{01} + a_{21} + a_{31} + a_{41})$, $a_{22} = -(a_{02} + a_{12})$, $a_{33} = -a_{13}$, $a_{44} = -(a_{04} + a_{14})$, $c_{11} = a_{01}$, and $c_{12} = a_{02}$. The parameters p, q, c_{22}, and c_{44} are supposed to be known. Use Maple to prove that this model is structurally globally identifiable.

3. Using the molecular-orbital Hückel theory, compute the π-electron energy levels. Determine also the charge distribution of state with lowest energy.

Bibliography

[1] A.E. Albert, *Regression and the Moore-Penrose Pseudoinverse*, Academic Press, 1972.

[2] C.M. Andersen and J.F. Geer, *Power Series Expansions for the Frequency and Period of the Limit Cycle of the van der Pol Equation*, SIAM J. Appl. Math. **42** (1982), 678–693.

[3] T. Banchoff, *Differential Geometry and Computer Graphics*, In: W. Jäger, J. Moser, R. Remmert (eds.) *Perspectives in Mathematics*, Oberwolfach 1984, Birkhäuser, 1984, pp. 43–60.

[4] D. Barton and J.P. Fitch, *Applications of Algebraic Manipulation Programs in Physics*, Rep. Prog. Phys. **35** (1972), 235–314.

[5] D. Barton and J.P. Fitch, *CAMAL: the Cambridge Algebra System*, SIGSAM Bull. **8**/3 (1974), 17–23.

[6] D. Barton and R. Zippel, *Polynomial Decomposition Akgorithms*, J. Symbolic Computation **1** (1990), 159–168.

[7] C. Batut, D. Bernardi, H. Cohen, and M. Oliver, *User's Guide to PARI-GP, version 1.37*, Université Bordeaux I, 1992.

[8] A.V. Bocharov and M.L. Bronstein, *DELiA User Guide*, Program Systems Institute of the USSR Academy of Science, Pereslavi, 1989.

[9] M. Bronstein, J.H. Davenport, and B.M. Trager, *Symbolic Integration is Algorithmic*, Tutorial, Computers and Mathematics 1989, MIT.

[10] M. Bronstein, *Integration of Elementary Functions*, J. Symbolic Computation **9** (1990), 117–174.

[11] D.A. Brown, *Quantum Chemistry*, Penguin Books, 1972.

[12] P.F. Byrd and M.D. Friedman, *Handbook of Elliptic Integrals for Engineers and Physicists*, Die Grundlagen der Mathematischen Wissenschaften, Band LXVII, Springer, 1971.

[13] J. Carminati, J.S. Devitt, and G.J. Fee, *Isogroup of Differential Equations Using Algebraic Computing*, J. Symbolic Computation **14** (1992), 103–120.

[14] R.M. Corless, G.H. Gonnet, D.E.G. Hare, and D.J. Jeffrey, *On Lambert's W Function*, preprint in Maple Share Library, 1993.

[15] A. Boyle and B.F. Caviness (eds.), *Future Directions for Research in Symbolic Computation*, SIAM Reports on Issues in the Mathematical Sciences, 1990.

[16] C. de Bruijn, *De Structurele Identificeerbaarheid en het schatbaar zijn van de modelparameters van het compartimentele model voor de verspreiding van cadmium in het menselijk lichaam*, (in Dutch), RIVM Report, 1990.

[17] B. Buchberger and R. Loos, *Algebraic Simplification*, In: B. Buchberger, G.E. Collins, and R. Loos (eds.), *Computer Algebra — Symbolic and Algebraic Computation*, Springer, second edition, 1983, pp. 11–44.

[18] B. Buchberger, *Groebner Bases: An Algorithmic Method in Polynomial Ideal Theory*, In: N.K. Bose (ed.), *Progress, Directions and Open Problems in Multidimensional Systems Theory*, Reidel, 1985, pp. 184–232.

[19] B. Buchberger, *Applications of Groebner Bases in Non-Linear Computational Geometry*, In: R. Janssen (ed.), *Trends in Computer Algebra*, Springer, 1988, pp. 52–80.

[20] G. Butler and J. Cannon, *The Design of Cayley - A Language for Modern Algebra*, In: A. Miola (ed.), *Design and Implementation of Symbolic Computation Systems*, Lecture Notes in Computer Science 429, Springer, 1990, pp. 10–19.

[21] J. Calmet and J.A. van Hulzen, *Computer Algebra Applications*, In: B. Buchberger, G.E. Collins, and R. Loos (eds.), *Computer Algebra — Symbolic and Algebraic Computation*, Springer, second edition, 1983, pp. 245–258.

[22] J. Cannon and W. Bosma, *Cayley Quick Reference Guide*, Univ. of Sydney, 1991.

[23] B.W. Char, K.O. Geddes, W.M. Gentleman, and G.H. Gonnet, *The Design of Maple: A Compact, Portable, and Powerful Computer Algebra System*, In: J.A. van Hulzen (ed.), *Computer Algebra — (Proceedings of EUROCAL '83)*, Lecture Notes in Computer Science 162, Springer, 1983, pp. 101–115.

[24] B.W. Char, K.O. Geddes, G.H. Gonnet, B.L. Leong, M.B. Monagan, and S.M. Watt, *Maple V Library Reference Manual*, Springer, first edition, 1991.

[25] B.W. Char, K.O. Geddes, G.H. Gonnet, B.L. Leong, M.B. Monagan, and S.M. Watt, *Maple V Language Reference Manual*, Springer, first edition, 1991.

[26] B.W. Char, K.O. Geddes, G.H. Gonnet, B.L. Leong, M.B. Monagan, and S.M. Watt, *First Leaves: A Tutorial Introduction*, Springer, first edition, 1992.

[27] B.W. Char, K.O. Geddes, and G.H. Gonnet, *GCDHEU: Heuristic GCD Algorithm Based On Integer GCD Computation*, J. Symbolic Computation **7** (1989), 31–48.

[28] P.L. Chebyshev, *Sur l'integration des differentielles qui contienent une racine carrée d'un polynôme du troisième ou du quatrième degré*, In: *Oeuvres de P.L. Tchebychef*, Vol. I, Chelsea, 1957, pp. 171–200.

[29] A.M. Cohen, *Computer Algebra, Theory and Practice*, Nieuw Arch. voor Wisk. IV, Ser. **7** (1989), 215–230.

[30] A.M. Cohen and G.C.M. Ruitenburg, *Generating Functions and Lie Groups*, In: A.M. Cohen (ed.), *Computational Aspects of Lie Group Representations and Related Topics*, CWI Tract 84, CWI, 1991, pp. 19–28.

[31] M.A. van Leeuwen, A.M. Cohen, and B. Lisser, *LiE A Package for Lie Group Computations*, CAN, 1992.

[32] A.M. Cohen, R.L. Griess Jr., and B. Lisser, *The Group L(2,61) embeds in the Lie Group of type E_8*, Comm. Algebra, to appear (1992).

[33] A.M. Cohen, J.H. Davenport, and A.J.P. Heck, *An Overview of Computer Algebra*, In: A.M. Cohen (ed.), *Computer Algebra for Industry: Problem Solving in Practice*, John Wiley & Sons, 1993, pp. 1–52.

[34] A.M. Cohen and G.C.M. Ruitenburg, *Algorithms in Algebra*, Cambridge University Press, 1993, in preparation.

[35] J.W. Cooley and J.W. Tukey, *An Algorithm for the Machine Calculation of Complex Fourier Series*, Math. Computation **19** (1965), 297–301

[36] J.H. Davenport, *On the Integration of Algebraic Functions*, Lecture Notes in Computer Science 102, Springer, 1981.

[37] J.H. Davenport, Y. Siret, and E. Tournier, *Computer algebra: systems and algorithms for algebraic computation*, Academic Press, 1988.

[38] J.H. Davenport and B.M. Trager, *Scratchpad's View of Algebra I: Basic Commutative Algebra*, In: A. Miola (ed.), *Design and Implementation of Symbolic Computation Systems*, Lecture Notes in Computer Science 429, Springer, 1990, pp. 40–54.

[39] J.H. Davenport, *The Axiom System*, In: *Proceedings of NAGUA'91*, NAG Ltd., 1991.

[40] J. Dieudonné, *Treatise on Analysis, Vol. III*, Pure and Applied Mathematics, Vol. 10-III, Academic Press, 1972.

[41] A. v.d. Essen, *Polynomial Maps and the Jacobian Conjecture*, In: A.M. Cohen (ed.), *Computational Aspects of Lie Group Representations and Related Topics*, CWI Tract 84, CWI, 1991, pp. 29–44.

[42] R.J. Fateman, *Advances and Trends in the Design and Construction of Algebraic Manipulation System*, In: S. Watenabe and M. Nagata (eds.), *Proceedings of ISSAC'90*, ACM Press, 1990, pp. 60–67.

[43] R.P. Feynman, R.B. Leighton, and M. Sands, *The Feynman Lectures on Physics*, Vol. II,Addison-Wesley, fourth printing, 1964, p. 22-8.

[44] J. Fitch, *Solving Algebraic Problems with REDUCE*, J. Symbolic Computation **1** (1985), 211–227.

[45] I. Frick, *SHEEP User's Manual*, Univ. of Stockholm, 1977.

[46] F.N. Fritsch, R.E. Shafer, and W.P. Crowley, *Solution of the Transcendental Equation $we^w = \chi$*, Comm. A.C.M. **16** (1973), 123–124.

[47] E. Fehlberg, *Klassische Runge-Kutta Formeln vierter und niedriger Ordnung mit Schrittweiten Kontrolle und ihre Anwendungen Wärmeleitungsprobleme*, Computing **6** (1970), 61–71.

[48] K.O. Geddes, *Numerical Integration in a Symbolic Context*, In: B. Char (ed.), *Proceedings of SYMSAC'86*, ACM Press, 1986, pp. 185–191.

[49] K.O. Geddes and G.H. Gonnet, *A New Algorithm for Computing Symbolic Limits Using Hierarchical Series*, In: P. Gianni (ed.), *Symbolic and Algebraic Computation, Proceedings ISSAC '88*, Lecture Notes in Computer Science, vol. 358, Springer, 1989, pp. 490–495.

[50] K.O. Geddes and T.C. Scott, *Recipes for Classes of Definite Integrals Involving Exponentials and Logarithms*, In: E. Kaltofen and S.M. Watt (eds.), *Computers and Mathematics 1989*, Academic Press, 1989, pp. 192–201.

[51] K.O. Geddes and L.Y. Stefanus, *On the Risch-Norman integration method and its implementation in Maple*, In: G.H. Gonnet (ed.), *Proceedings of ISSAC '89*, ACM Press, New York, 1989, pp. 212–217.

[52] K.O. Geddes, *Numerical Integration using Symbolic Analysis*, The Maple Technical Newsletter **6** (1991), 8–17.

[53] K.O. Geddes, S.R. Czapor and G. Labahn, *Algorithms for Computer Algebra*, Kluwer Academic Publishers, 1992.

[54] A. Giovini and G. Niesi, *CoCoA User's Manual*, Univ. of Genova, 1989.

[55] A. Giovini and G. Niesi, *CoCoA: A User-Friendly System for Commutative Algebra*, In: A. Miola (ed.), *Design and Implementation of Symbolic Computation Systems*, Lecture Notes in Computer Science 429, Springer, 1990, pp. 20–29.

[56] G.H. Gonnet and D.W. Gruntz, *Algebraic Manipulation: Systems*, In: A. Ralston et al (eds.), *Encyclopedia of computer Science & Engineering*, Van Nostrand Reinhold, third edition, 1991.

[57] G.H. Gonnet and D.W. Gruntz, *Limit Computation in Computer Algebra*, submitted to J. Symbolic Computation, 1992.

[58] M.J. González-López and T. Recio, *The ROMIN inverse geometric model and the dynamic evaluation method*, In: A.M. Cohen (ed.), *Computer Algebra for Industry: Problem Solving in Practice*, John Wiley & Sons, 1993, pp. 117–141.

[59] R.W. Gosper, *Decision Procedure for Indefinite Hypergeometric Summation*, Proc. Natl. Acad. Sci. USA **75** (1978), 40–42.

[60] I.S. Gradshteyn and I.M. Ryzhik, *Table of Integrals, Series and Products*, Academic Press, fourth edition, 1965, formula 2.269. The error is corrected in the 4th [sic] edition (1980).

[61] A. Griewank, *On Automatic Differentiation*, In: M. Iri and K. Tanabe (eds.), *Mathematical Programming*, Kluwer, 1989, pp. 83–107.

[62] A. Griewank, *The Chain Rule Revised in Scientific Computing*, SIAM News, May 1991, part I, 20–21, SIAM News July 1991, part II, 8–9, 24.

[63] A. Griewank, G.F. Corliss, *Automatic Differentiation of Algorithms: Theory, Implementation and Application*, In: *Proceedings in Applied Mathematics* **53**, SIAM, Philadelphia, 1991.

[64] J. Gutiérrez, T. Recio, and C. Ruiz de Velasco, *Polynomial decomposition algorithm of almost quadratic complexity*, In: *Proceedings of AAECC-6*, Springer, 1989.

[65] E. Groswald, *Bessel Polynomials*, Lecture Notes in Mathematics 698, Springer, 1980.

[66] D. Harper, C. Wooff, and D. Hodgkinson, *A Guide to Computer Algebra Systems*, John Wiley & Sons, 1991.

[67] B.K. Harrison and F.B. Estabrook, *Geometric Approac to Invariance Groups and Solutions of Partial Differential Equations*, J. Math. Phys. **12** (1971), 653–665.

[68] A.C. Hearn, *REDUCE User's Manual*, The Rand Coorporation, Santa Monica, California, 1987.

[69] A.J.P. Heck, *Transformation between Geocentric and Geodetic Coordinates*, In: A.M. Cohen (ed.), *Computer Algebra for Industry: Problem Solving in Practice*, John Wiley & Sons, 1992, pp. 203–219.

[70] A.J.P. Heck, *Computer Algebra: A Tool in Identifiability Testing* Proceedings SCAFI'92, Amsterdam, 1993 (in preparation).

[71] L. Hornfeldt, *STENSOR Reference Manual*, Univ. of Stockholm, 1988.

[72] E. Horowitz, *Algorithms for Partial Fraction Decomposition and Rational Integration*, In: S.R. Petrick (ed.), *Proceedings of SYMSAM '71*, ACM Press, 1971, pp. 441–457.

[73] J.A. van Hulzen and J. Calmet, *Computer Algebra Systems*, In: B. Buchberger, G.E. Collins, and R. Loos (eds.), *Computer Algebra — Symbolic and Algebraic Computation*, Springer, second edition, 1983, pp. 221–244.

[74] Richard D. Jenks and Robert S. Sutor, *AXIOM, The Scientific Computation System*, Springer, 1992.

[75] Eugene W. Johnson, *Maple and Linear Algebra*, Brooks/Cole, 1993, in preparation.

[76] E. Kaltofen, *Polynomial Factorization*, In: B. Buchberger, G. Collins, and R. Loos (eds.), *Computer Algebra — Symbolic and Algebraic Computation*, Springer, second edition, 1983, pp. 95–114.

[77] E. Kaltofen, *Polynomial Factorization 1982–1986*, In: D.V. Chudnovsky and R.D. Jenks (eds.), *Computers & Mathematics*, Lecture Notes in Pure and Applied Mathematics 125, Marcel Dekker, 1990, pp. 285–309.

[78] W. Kahan, *Branch Cuts for Complex Elementary Functions or Much Ado About Nothing's Sign Bit*, In: A. Iserles and M.J.D. Powell (eds.), *The State of the Art in Numerical Analysis*, Clarendon, 1987, pp. 165–212.

[79] E. Kaltofen, *Polynomial Factorization 1987–1991*, In: *Proceedings of LATIN '92, Sao Paulo, Brazil*, Springer Lecture Notes of Comput. Sci., Springer, to appear.

[80] M. Kleber and F. Grossman, *Error Rates in Tables of Indefinite Integrals*, Industrial Mathematics **18** (1968).

[81] D.E. Knuth, *The Art of Computer Programming, Vol. II, Seminumerical Algorithms*, Addison-Wesley, second edition, 1981.

[82] D.E. Knuth, *Problem E3335*, Amer. Math. Monthly **96** (1989), 525.

[83] J. Kovacic, *An algorithm for solving second order homogeneous differential equations*, J. Symbolic Computation **2** (1986), 3–43.

[84] L. Lamport, *LaTeX, A Document Preparation System*, Addison-Wesley, 11th Print, 1988.

[85] D. Lazard and R. Rioboo, *Integration of Rational Functions: Rational Computation of the Logarithmic Part*, J. Symbolic Computation **9** (1990), 113–116.

[86] Y. Lecourtier and A. Raksanyi, *The Testing of Structural Properties Through Symbolic Computation*, In: E. Walter (ed.), *Identifiabilty of Parametric Models*, Pergamon Press, 1987.

[87] R. Loos, *Computing in Algebraic Extensions*, In: B. Buchberger, G.E. Collins, and R. Loos (eds.), *Computer Algebra — Symbolic and Algebraic Computation*, Springer, second edition, 1983, pp. 173–187.

[88] MACSYMA *User's Guide*, Symbolics, Inc., 1987.

[89] The Mathematica Journal **1**, Issue 3 (1991), 65.

[90] M. Mignotte, *Mathematics for Computer Algebra*, Springer, 1992.

[91] R. Moenck, *On computing closed forms for summation*, In: Proc. MACSYMA User's Conf., 1977, pp. 225–236.

[92] J. Moses, *Symbolic Integration: The Stormy Decade*, Comm. A.C.M. **14** (1971), 548–560.

[93] A.H. Nayfeh and D.T. Mook, *Nonlinear Oscillations*, John Wiley & Sons, 1979.

[94] B. Noble and M.A. Hussain, *Multiple Scaling and a Related Expansion Method, with Applications*, Report BICOM 87/7 (June 1987), Brunel Univ., Uxbridge, England.

[95] V.W. Noonburg, *A neural network modeled by an adaptive Lotka-Volterra system*, SIAM J. Appl. Math. **49** (1989), 1779–1792.

[96] P.J. Olver, *Applications of Lie Groups to Differential Equations*, Springer, 1986.

[97] M.K. Paul, *A Note on Computation of Geodetic Coordinates from Geo-centric (Cartesian) Coordinates* Bull. Géodésique **108** (1973), 135–139.

[98] R.P. Paul, *Robot Manipulators: Mathematics, Programming and Control*, The MIT Press, 1981.

[99] R.P. Paul, *Kinematic Control Equations for Simple Manipulators*, In: C.S.G. Lee et al (eds.), *Tutorial on Robotics*, IEEE Computer Society Press, 1983, pp. 66–72.

[100] R. Pavelle, Problems sent to the USENET sci.math.symbolic bulletin board; archived in the REDUCE network library.

[101] A. Raksanyi, Y. Lecourtier, E. Walter, and A. Venot, *Identifiability and Distinguishability Testing Via Computer Algebra*, Math. Biosciences **77** (1985), 245–266.

[102] R.H. Rand, *Computer Algebra in Applied Mathematics: An Introduction to MACSYMA*, Research Notes in Mathematics 94, Pitman Publishing, 1984.

[103] R.H. Rand and D. Armbruster, *Perturbation Methods, Bifurcation Theory and Computer Algebra*, Applied Mathematical Sciences 65, Springer, 1987.

[104] R.H. Risch, *The problem of integration in finite terms*, Trans. AMS **139** (1969), 167–189.

[105] M. Rothstein, *Aspects of Symbolic Integration and Simplification of Exponential and Primitive Functions* Ph.D. Thesis, Univ. of Wisconsin, Madison, 1976.

[106] M. Schoenert et al, *GAP Groups, Algorithms and Programming*, RWTH Aachen, 1992.

[107] F.W. Schwarz, *Symmetries of Differential Equations: From Sophus Lie to Computer Algebra*, SIAM Review **30** (1988), 450–481.

[108] T.J. Smedley, *Fast Methods for Computation with Algebraic Numbers*, Ph.D. Thesis, University of Waterloo, Waterloo, 1990.

[109] H. Stephani, *Differential Equations: Their Solution Using symmetries*, Cambridge University Press, 1989.

[110] M. Stillman, M. Stillman and D. Bayer, *Macaulay User Manual*, 1989.

[111] J. Stoer, *Einführung in die Numerische Mathematik I*, Springer, third edition, 1983.

[112] D. Stoutemyer, *Derive User Manual*, Soft Warehouse, Inc., Honolulu, Hawaii, fourth edition, 1990.

[113] D. Stoutemyer, *Crimes and Misdemeanors in the Computer Algebra Trade*, Notices of the AMS. **38** (1991), 778–785.

[114] H. Strubbe, *Manual for SCHOONSCHIP*, Comput. Phys. Commun. **8** (1974), 1–30.

[115] R.S. Sutor (ed.), *The Scratchpad II Computer Algebra System Interactive Environment Users Guide*, IBM Thomas J. Watson Research Center, Yorktown Heights, draft 1.3, 1988.

[116] R.G. Tobey, *Algorithms for Antidifferentiation of Rational Functions*, Ph.D. Thesis, Univ. of Wisconsin, Madison, 1967.

[117] B. Trager, *Algebraic Factoring and Rational Function Integration*, In: R.D Jenks (ed.), *Proceedings of SYMSAC '76*, ACM Press, 1976, pp. 219–226.

[118] B. Trager, *Integration of Algebraic Functions*, Ph.D. Thesis, MIT, 1984.

[119] J.A.M. Vermaseren, *Symbolic Manipulation with FORM*, CAN, 1991.

[120] D. Wang, *An Implementation of the Characteristic Set Method in Maple*, RISC-Linz Series **91-25.0**, 1991.

[121] F. Winkler, *Computer Algebra: Problems and Developments*, talk at SCAFI '92 — Amsterdam, 1992.

[122] S. Wolfram, *Mathematica: A System for Doing Mathematics by Computer*, Addison-Wesley, second edition, 1991.

[123] C. Wooff and D. Hodgkinson, *MuMath: A Microcomputer Algebra System*, Academic Press, 1987.

[124] P.E.S. Wormer and F. de Groot, *The Potential Energy Surface of Triplet* H_3^+: *A Representation in Hyperspherical Coordinates*, J. Chem. Phys. **90** (1989), 2344.

[125] R. Zippel, *Rational Function Decomposition*, In: S.M. Watt (ed.), *Proceedings of ISSAC '91*, ACM Press, 1991, pp. 1–6.

Index

In this index, the same notation is used as throughout the book: Maple keywords are typeset in Courier font and references to Maple procedures are in bold type.

B.W. CHAR, Drexel University, Philadelphia, PA; **K.O. GEDDES**, University of Waterloo, Ontario, Canada; **G.H. GONNET**, ETH Zentrum, Zürich, Switzerland; **B.L. LEONG**, University of Waterloo, Ontario, Canada; **M.B. MONAGAN**, ETH Zentrum, Zürich, Switzerland; **S.M. WATT**, IBM Thomas J. Watson Research Center, Yorktown Heights, NY

FIRST LEAVES

A Tutorial Introduction to Maple V

This tutorial shows how to use Maple V both as a calculator with instant access to hundreds of high-level math routines and as a programming language for more demanding or specialized tasks. Topics covered include the basic data types and statements in the Maple V language. It explains the differences between numeric computation and symbolic computation and illustrates how both are used in Maple V. Extensive "how-to" examples are used throughout the tutorial to show how common types of calculations can be expressed easily in Maple V. The book also uses many graphics examples to illustrate the way in which 2D and 3D graphics can aid in understanding the behavior of problems.

1992/253 pp./Hardcover/$24.00/ISBN 0-387-97621-3

MAPLE V LANGUAGE REFERENCE MANUAL

This book describes the Maple Symbolic Computation System and the Maple V language. It describes the numeric and symbolic expressions that can be used in Maple V. All the basic data types, such as names, polynomials, and functions, as well as structured data types, are covered. The book also gives a complete description of the programming language statements that are provided in the Maple V system and shows how a user can extend the functionality of the Maple V system by adding user-defined routines.

The manual also provides a complete description of the Maple V system, including its 2D and 3D graphics. Maple V features a newly designed user interface on many systems. Separate appendices describe how to use Maple V on systems using the X Window System, DOS, and the Macintosh.

1991/267 pp./Hardcover/$24.95/ISBN 0-387-97622-1

MAPLE V LIBRARY REFERENCE MANUAL

Each of Maple V's functions is described in this book with a brief explanation of the function, a description of the parameters that it uses, and additional details about the function. Every description is accompanied by several examples of how the function can be used.

1991/698 pp./Hardcover/$39.50/ISBN 0-387-97592-6

For additional information on Maple V software, please contact Waterloo Maple Software, 160 Columbia Street West, Waterloo, Ontario, Canada, N2L 3L3. Telephone: (519)747-2373. E-mail: wmsi@daisy.uwaterloo.ca.

AVAILABLE IN JULY 1993...

D. REDFERN, Practical Approach, Ontario, Canada

THE MAPLE HANDBOOK

The Maple Handbook is an efficient, well-planned, and comprehensive reference and learning tool for the Maple V Release 2 symbolic computation language. All Maple commands are described in a precise, concise, and consistent manner. Topics include calculus, linear algebra, number theory, programming, etc., each explained in context. This book will be an indispensable tool for all Maple users.

The Maple Handbook begins with a "Getting Started With Maple" tutorial which lays the groundwork for using Maple efficiently and effectively. The following 12 chapters go into the commands and structures for specific disciplines of computation; and each chapter is prefaced by an introductory quick tutorial providing simple explanations and examples.

Entries for individual commands contain information on various aspects, including common parameter sequences, what type of output to expect, additional hints and information, and page references to the standard Maple manual set.

1993/app. 400 pp./Hardcover/$29.00/ISBN 0-387-94054-5

AVAILABLE IN MAY 1994...

E. KAMERICH, Catholic University of Nijmegen, The Netherlands

A GUIDE TO MAPLE

This "hands-on" book is for people who are interested in immediately putting Maple to work. The reader is provided with a compact, fast and surveyable guide that introduces them to the extensive capabilities of the software. The book is sufficient for standard use of Maple and will provide techniques for extending Maple for more specialized work. The author discusses the readability of results systematically and presents ways of testing questionable results. The book allows a reader to become a user almost immediately and helps him or her to grow gradually to a broader and more proficient use. As a consequence, some subjects are dealt with in an introductory manner early in the book, with references to a more detailed discussion later on.

1994/app. 250 pp./Hardcover/$29.00(tent.)
ISBN 0-387-94116-9

Springer-Verlag New York, Inc.